ILYA KATSOV

THE THEORY AND PRACTICE OF
ENTERPRISE AI

Recipes and Reference Implementations for
Marketing, Supply Chain, and Production Operations

This book was set in the LATEX programming language by the author.

Printed in the United States of America.

Katsov, Ilya

The theory and practice of enterprise AI: recipes and reference implementations for marketing, supply chain, and production operations/ Ilya Katsov

Includes bibliographical references and index.

ISBN 978-0-578-32862-1 (hardcover)

Praise for *The Theory and Practice of Enterprise AI*

"A must read primer for any data science leader. Ilya has taken on the Herculean task of systemizing AI-based problem solving in a business setting, and has succeeded spectacularly. This book is of interest to all kinds of analytics practitioners as it comes with real-world examples for the curious, and an abundance of theoretical explanations for the audacious."

—Suman Giri
Head of Data Science, Merck & Co.

"This book is an excellent introduction to machine learning and its applications in enterprise. It is a great resource for data scientists looking for bridging theory and practice – it presents many distinctly different business use cases and clearly shows how state of the art methods in AI can be applied, with complete reference implementations provided in interactive notebooks. In a world where AI is increasingly present in all parts of businesses this is a comprehensive guide with everything you need to know."

—Anna Ukhanova
Research Technical Program Manager, Google AI

"Ilya Katsov's previous book set the standard as the clearest, most complete, and self-contained treatment of modern algorithmic marketing that I'm aware of – I have used and recommended it many times. Now he applies the same level of expert guidance providing a one-stop-shop for deep/reinforcement learning techniques in marketing, supply chain, and operations. This book will sit within arm's reach for years to come."

—Spencer Stirling
Director of Data Science, Activision

"Excellent. I strongly recommend this book for anyone involved in Enterprise AI for a great overview of solutions for key marketing, supply chain & production business processes."

—Joost Bloom
Head of Machine Learning & Foundational AI, H&M Group

"This is a unique book in that it dives into the depths of machine learning theory while still being organized around business applications and use-cases. By presenting a detailed understanding of machine learning algorithms alongside their applications, this text is versatile – applicable to a variety of users from technical students to data scientists and all the way to data and IT leadership. A very valuable addition to our Data Science world."

—Ellie Magnant
Director of Data Science, UnitedHealth Group

"This textbook provides an ultimate guide to data scientists and AI engineers on building best-in-class AI capabilities to solve a wide spectrum of business problems. Furthermore, Ilya did a great job covering the end-to-end development lifecycle of AI solutions with practical case studies. Excellent book, Highly Recommended."

—Fouad Bousetouane
Senior Principal Machine Data Scientist, W.W. Grainger, Inc.,
2020 Timmy-Award, Best-Tech-Manager Chicago Region

"The book is a resource where algorithmic theory, algorithmic system design, and their applications are strongly tied to each other and discussed in depth. It offers a guide to technical leaders on how to make their systems more actionable, technically sound, and applicable at various scales. To business leaders, this book helps connect the dots and offers ideas on how to improve their current processes to have a meaningful communication with AI practitioners."

—Addhyan Pandey
Senior Director of Data Science, Cars.com

"The book by Ilya Katsov equips technical and data/AI professionals working in the Marketing, Supply Chain and Production Operations domains with modern techniques and approaches for solving a broad range of AI problems. The book provides a very systematic overview of methodologies and does a fantastic job in explaining rationale and assumptions for their use. This makes this book suitable not only for entry level but also for expert AI professionals. Finally the book provides multiple case studies which make it even more valuable for practitioners."

—Alexander Statnikov
Head of Go-to-Market Platform and Ecosystem Products, Square,
Previously Professor of Data Science at New York University

"The Theory and Practice of Enterprise AI combines cutting-edge AI modeling concepts, academic rigor, and actionable industry domain knowledge in one concise tome. It is an absolute must on any data science practitioner's book shelf or desk."

—Skander Hannachi
AI/ML Specialist, Google Cloud

"Timely and inspiring! An essential handbook for those seeking a primer on the data science community, from enthusiastic to novice to developers to resident experts interested in scalable enterprise AI and ML for any industry domain. Ilya paints a vision of what's possible and aligns it with the business problem to guide the journey toward solution options & architecture, model architecture, implementation plan, reference code, and modeling prototype. In addition, Ilya has created a very comprehensive framework for organizing and prioritizing the key building blocks of model representation and mapping, customer experience, content intelligence, revenue & inventory management, and production operations. With Ilya's breadth of experience in the field of enterprise AI, this book should be considered the de-facto reference guide for any organization undergoing a digital AI transformation. If you can't work directly with Ilya, this is a close second best! Enjoy, Learn & Apply... and watch what happens..."

—Srikanth Victory
Vice President, Digital Advanced Analytics & Products,
CommonSpirit Health

"This book provides technical depth and reference architecture to solve real-world business problems using AI. The book will resonate with the data science community, and this book is an excellent addition to AI literature. Ilya has done a fantastic job bringing theoretical and practical AI closer with this book."

—Prateek Srivastava
Director of AI Products, Dell Technologies

CONTENTS

PREFACE

The role of data-driven automation and optimization in enterprise operations has been increasing for many decades, and, over the last ten years, the range of use cases that can be efficiently handled by automatic systems has expanded considerably with the advent of deep learning methods. These developments have created a diverse landscape of decision-making and automation methods, including traditional econometric models and optimization algorithms, specialized machine learning methods for computer vision and natural language processing which can, however, often be adopted to other domains, and emerging methods such as deep reinforcement learning that have limited adoption in enterprise practice. In this book, we explore how a wide range of enterprise operations including marketing, supply chain management, and production control, can benefit from the crossover of traditional modeling, optimization, and simulation techniques with deep learning and reinforcement learning methods. We aim to develop an engineering framework, as well as a collection of practical recipes, that help to systematically apply various combinations of these methods in real-world enterprise settings.

INTENDED AUDIENCE

This book is written for data scientists and analytics managers to provide a systematic treatment of how enterprise decision-making and optimization problems can be approached using deep learning, reinforcement learning, and probabilistic programming methods. Our primary goal is to develop a systematic framework for translating various enterprise use cases into quantitative, statistical, and optimization problems and decomposing these problems into machine learning tasks. At the beginning of the book, we give an overview of the generic building blocks. Detailed descriptions of the use of case-specific models and algorithms are covered later, but we do not aim to provide a systematic treatment of machine learning theory and its mathematical underpinnings. The reader is expected to be familiar with the basic concepts of data science and machine learning, as well as having hands-on experience with statistical modeling including both traditional and deep learning methods.

The book may also be useful for data science and machine learning practitioners who have a background in bioinformatics, physics, or other fields unrelated to typical enterprise operations, and who are looking to learn about specialized modeling methods for marketing, supply chain, and manufacturing applications.

STRUCTURE AND SUGGESTED USE

We approach the problem of building enterprise AI solutions from the system engineering perspective, considering machine learning algorithms mainly as off-the-shelf components and focusing on the adaptation of generic methods to specific enterprise use cases. We spend the first three chapters developing a framework that helps to decompose enterprise problems into machine learning and optimization tasks, and reviewing the main categories of machine learning algorithms needed to solve such tasks. Our choice and categorization of algorithms and methods, however, is somewhat different from the canonical categorization used in most machine learning textbooks because we focus exclusively on the enterprise applications. We then develop a number of recipes (Chapters R1 – R11) for specific use cases in marketing, supply chain, and production domains. We use the following three-layer structure in most recipes to cover both the theoretical and practical aspects of the solutions:

DESIGN OPTIONS In each recipe, we define the business problem and discuss several solution options. Some solutions do not require the generic models or algorithms to be modified significantly, and we focus mainly on practical aspects such as integrations and econometric considerations. Other solutions require the development of specialized algorithms, and we describe these in full mathematical detail.

PROTOTYPES In each recipe, we develop one or more basic prototypes to illustrate the approach and main properties of the solution. These reference implementations typically use synthetic data or simulators to avoid the complexities associated with real-world datasets. We normally describe how the prototype works and how the outputs prove the solution to be viable, but we avoid cluttering the book with low-level implementation details; instead, we provide links to the corresponding notebooks in the companion source code repository, so the reader can dive deeply into the implementation if need be.

CASE STUDIES For some recipes, we develop more comprehensive reference implementations using larger data samples created based on the statistics of real-world datasets. These implementations help to highlight the challenges that do not manifest themselves in the smaller-scale prototypes. Similar to the prototypes, we do not discuss these implementations at the level of source codes, but provide links to the repository with complete notebooks.

This book can be read sequentially to study the concepts used in enterprise AI systematically, including its main building blocks, and major categories of solutions. The recipes, however, are mostly independent, and readers familiar with deep learning fundamentals can consider scanning through the first three chapters and reading the recipes in any order according to their needs and priorities.

REFERENCE IMPLEMENTATIONS

The implementations and prototypes referenced in this book, as well as several additional models, are released as an open source project called TensorHouse. This project is available on `https://github.com/ikatsov/tensor-house`. A dedicated git branch `"book-enterprise-ai"` has been created with a version of code compatible with this book.

We use TensorFlow as a primary platform for deep learning models and leverage several other frameworks and libraries for auxiliary operations and specialized functionality.

The recipes provided in this book and its reference implementations complement each other. The recipes provide a comprehensive analysis of business problems and solution options, but only short summaries of the actual implementations. The reference notebooks provide detailed step-by-step tutorials on how certain solutions can be implemented but do not duplicate all the analysis and theoretical details provided in the book.

Part I

BUILDING BLOCKS

In the first part of the book, we aim to establish a framework that helps to convert enterprise decision automation problems into machine learning tasks. In Chapter 1, we start by examining the typical levels of decision-making in enterprise operations and defining the basic concepts that are applicable to a wide range of use cases and applications. In Chapter 2, we develop a toolkit for learning mappings between entities, their attributes, and trajectories, that enables us to infer hidden properties and predict future entity states. Finally, in Chapter 3, we discuss the decision automation and entity control methods.

1

DECISION AUTOMATION IN ENTERPRISE OPERATIONS

We can informally define enterprise artificial intelligence (AI) as a collection of methods for improving enterprise operations using statistical learning and probabilistic reasoning. This collection is very broad and includes methods for improving strategic decisions at the level of the entire enterprise such as demand forecasting, methods for optimizing decisions at the level of individual business processes such as promotion targeting and safety stock management, and methods that help to automate or optimize individual transactions such as object detection models and dialog management systems.

Although the concept of enterprise AI is relatively new, one can argue that it is fundamentally as old as the concept of the enterprise itself. Historically, the first category of problems that was tackled using data-driven methods was strategic decision-making – the idea that the financial health and future trajectory of an economic entity can be assessed using aggregated financial records has been well understood since ancient times. In this sense, accountants were the first enterprise data scientists. By collecting and aggregating financial records, an accountant creates a concise quantitative representation of the enterprise in the space of certain metrics such as profits and revenues, and this space is then used to assess the financial performance of the enterprise, forecast future results, and make managerial decisions. Although it may seem a stretch of the imagination to link accountancy to AI, we will show in the next sections that even the basic quantitative techniques used in accounting, stock trading, and investments can be consistently related to the methods that are commonly deemed as modern AI.

The second level of decision automation, that is optimization of tactical decisions at the level of individual processes within the enterprise, was widely unlocked in the last third of the twentieth century with the widespread availability of affordable computers. These early attempts were mainly focused on solving numerical and combinatorial optimization problems in supply chain management, transportation, and manufacturing. Some of these applications involved statistical analysis of enterprise data as well, but the adoption of data-driven methods was limited by the low level of digitalization of both businesses and consumers.

The next level for intelligent automation was achieved in the mid-2010s, mainly because of three factors. The first of these was the comprehensive digitalization of corporate environments followed by mass adoption of Big Data strategies which made all enterprise processes continuously generate detailed, statistically analyzable data traces. The second factor was the digitalization of consumer environments that enabled real-time personalization and optimization of products, services, and their representations. Finally, the third factor was the revolutionary advancement in statistical methods, particularly deep learning, that enabled comprehension of textual and visual data by software systems which, in turn, unlocked a wide range of new types of automation related to natural language processing (NLP) and computer vision (CV) use cases.

This book is mainly focused on the methods for small-scale decision automation in data-rich environments, which corresponds to the last level in the above categorization. However, before we go more deeply into the details of these methods, let us develop a lightweight framework that helps to properly plan and place analytical and decision automation capabilities within the enterprise, so that we approach the design of individual components more systematically, from the right angle, and in the right context.

1.1 SCENARIO PLANNING FRAMEWORK

It is often said that major enterprise systems and capabilities are created with specific business goals in mind, and the degree of success is typically measured using key performance indicators (KPIs). For instance, a new product recommendation algorithm can be developed with the goal of improving session conversion rates from 3% to 3.5%; a price optimization system can be created to improve profits by $200 million; and a new computer vision system can be installed on an assembly line to reduce defect rate by 20%. This is one of the most basic and well-known paradigms in the enterprise world. However, its practical implementation is not straightforward.

One of the challenges arises from the fact that many improvements and actions impact several KPIs at the same time, and while some metrics can be affected positively, the influence on others can be negative. For example, trade promotions can increase the sales volume but reduce profits, increased safety stock levels can improve product availability and customer experience but increase the storage costs, and profit-optimal prices can destroy the business that needs to grow its market share to become sustainable. The analysis of such tradeoffs and making decisions on them is challenging, and converting them into formal optimization problems is even more so.

The second challenge is the long-term nature of business operations that sometimes makes it difficult to define and measure a single KPI. For example, trade promotions are commonly used by retailers and manufacturers and are known to be an efficient way of boosting sales, but sales acceleration during the promotional period often comes at the expense of future sales. This is particularly true for consumable products such as paper towels where promotions often encourage consumers to buy and stockpile larger amounts of the products and then wait till the next promotion period. This makes short-term sales uplift measurements inaccurate or misleading, while long-term measurements are also challenging because all other parts of the environment change and drift, distorting the observations.

The third challenge is measurability of the KPIs. In the previous example regarding trade promotions, long-term effects are one but not the only factor that can invalidate the measurements. Promotions and price changes can make consumers switch from one product or vendor to another creating cross-products and cross-retailer effects. Most sellers are aware of such effects and know that the sales uplift numbers of individual products can be misleading, but more comprehensive and accurate measurements can be challenging because of their higher data requirement and implementation complexity. In many practical cases, it makes sense to disaggregate a single objective with multiple internal factors into several metrics or KPIs that can be tracked separately, and this brings us back to the first challenge of multiple conflicting KPIs.

Finally, we can call out the evaluation of the solution as another major challenge. Development of a solution that aims to improve certain metrics generally requires some means of evaluating its performance before it gets deployed into production and actual results are collected. This problem inherits all of the previously discussed complexities that essentially belonged to the field of descriptive analytics, and adds predictive and prescriptive elements on top of them.

These considerations suggest that we generally need to account for multiple entities, metrics, their correlations, and joint dynamics in order to convert enterprise problems into optimization and decision automation problems. We can try to put these basic ideas together into a more formal framework grounded on the following concepts:

ENTITY When we automate or optimize some aspect of the enterprise, we usually focus on improving performance of one or several entities that can be the enterprise as a whole, business unit, location, product, or customer.

SCENARIO Scenario specifies an action or sequence of actions that we can potentially execute to achieve certain improvements. We can usually choose between several scenario options including a no-action baseline.

UTILITY SPACE Entities of interest can be described using one or more metrics (KPIs), and we will refer to the space spanned on the metric dimensions as a utility space. For example, it is common to use utility spaces such as Revenue × Margin and Risk × Reward in conventional business analytics. We will also refer to utility spaces with two or more dimensions as *utility maps* or *value maps*.

TRAJECTORY Executing a scenario makes entities move in the space of metrics, ideally in a direction that is beneficial for the business. Consequently, a scenario leaves a trace in the utility space that we will call a trajectory.

PARETO FRONTIER If the metrics used to construct the utility space are in inverse relationship (e.g. cost and quality), we can normally choose between several scenarios that correspond to different trade-offs. In such a situation, however, we cannot improve all metrics simultaneously, so the set of best possible trade-offs will form the *Pareto frontier* that can be visualized as a surface in the utility space. However, we can shift the Pareto frontier if we change some underlying factors that unlock simultaneous improvement of all metrics of the utility space.

These concepts are illustrated in Figure 1.1 where an entity moves in a two-dimensional utility space, and one considers three alternative intervention scenarios that lead to three different outcomes that form the frontier.

At this point, our scenario planning framework is fairly abstract and it might not be clear how to apply this concept to practical problems

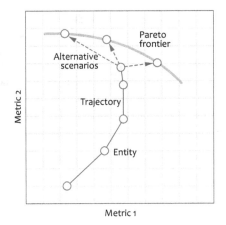

Figure 1.1: The main concepts of the scenario planning framework.

and how to connect it to machine learning (ML) methods. We gradually bridge this gap in the next sections where we discuss more concrete examples for different types of problems, and then what machine
learning methods are needed to implement that approach. Our goal,
however, is only to illustrate how we can think of different use cases
in the scenario planning terms, and we do not aim to build a rigorous
theory around it in this chapter.

1.1.1   Strategy: Enterprise as a Whole

We start with examples of strategic analysis in which one is interested
to study the trajectory of the entire company. This type of analysis
is commonly used by venture capital investors to assess startups and
portfolio managers to assess public companies. This is arguably the
highest possible level at which one can consider applying decision automation methods.

Imagine that we need to assess an early-stage company to make an
investment decision. One of the most basic questions we might ask is
how well the company and its product fit the market – is there an indication that the company is poised to grow or are there signs of headwinds and deceleration [Hsu, 2019]. To a certain extent, this question
can be answered using quantitative methods, and the results would
prescribe further actions for both the investors and the management of
the company.

We can start the assessment with a technique called *growth account-ing* that focuses on the analysis of the revenue components and evolu-tion of these components over time. In terms of the scenario planning framework, we define entities as different categories of revenue, utility space as a single dimension measured in dollars, and trajectories as the evolution of the revenue categories. For the sake of this analysis, let us decompose the revenue at time period t as follows:

$$
\begin{aligned}
\text{Revenue}(t) = \ &\text{Retained}(t) + \\
&\text{New}(t) + \\
&\text{Resurrected}(t) + \\
&\text{Expanded}(t)
\end{aligned}
\tag{1.1}
$$

where the *retained* component corresponds to the revenue from the existing customers carried over from the previous time period, *new* revenue comes from the customers who were acquired in time period t, *resurrected* revenue comes from the customers who churned in the past but came back in period t, and *expanded* revenue is the incremental growth of revenue from the existing customer on top of the retained part. Next, let us decompose the retained revenue as follows:

$$
\begin{aligned}
\text{Retained}(t) = \ &\text{Revenue}(t-1) - \\
&\text{Churned}(t) - \\
&\text{Contracted}(t)
\end{aligned}
\tag{1.2}
$$

where *churned* is the revenue lost due to the customers who were active in period $t-1$ but became inactive in period t, and *contracted* is the revenue shrinkage for the customers who remained active. For example, a company with two customers who spent $100 and $200 in time period $t-1$ and $150 and $180 in period t, respectively, will have retained revenue of $280 ($100 + $180), expanded revenue of $50 ($150 – $100), and contracted revenue of $20 ($200 – $180). We can now combine equations 1.1 and 1.2 into the following identity:

$$
\begin{aligned}
\text{Revenue}(t) - \text{Revenue}(t-1) = \ &\text{New}(t) + \\
&\text{Expanded}(t) + \\
&\text{Resurrected}(t) - \\
&\text{Churned}(t) - \\
&\text{Contracted}(t)
\end{aligned}
\tag{1.3}
$$

Since we use a simple one-dimensional utility space, we can visualize the trajectories of the above revenue components using regular time series plots. Let us examine the examples that correspond to two different companies shown in Figure 1.2.

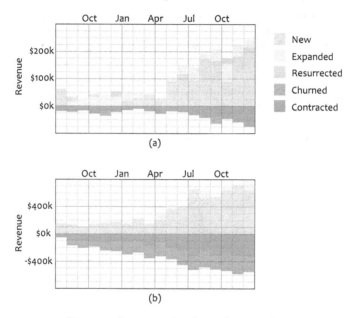

Figure 1.2: Two examples of growth accounting.

Plate (a) shows a company that grows rapidly in terms of revenue having relatively low churn and contraction rates. This pattern is typical of B2B subscription-based businesses that are good at expanding revenue from existing customers and can maintain positive growth even without adding new clients. Plate (b) shows a company that also grows rapidly in terms of revenue, but its churn and contraction components are much more significant compared to the first example. This pattern is typical of companies that sell discretionary B2C products and need a continuous flow of new customers to maintain growth.

The informal analysis and forecasting of the revenue trajectories in the above examples provides investors and executives with guidance on which scenarios they need to plan for. For instance, it appears that the first company will need to scale up its sales and account management teams, whereas the second company may need to work on reducing customer acquisition costs to remain sustainable. These more granular problems that are derived from the top-level analysis can then also be approached using data-driven methods, but more complex models and techniques can be involved due to the smaller scale and scope of the task. For example, the problem of the customer acquisition costs can be addressed using targeting and personalization models that we will develop in the next chapters.

The second question we might ask while assessing the market fit of the company and its products, is what the internal structure of the customer base looks like, and what the dynamics of individual components are. We choose the cohorts of customers acquired at different time periods to be the entities, and cumulative lifetime value (LTV) to be the one-dimensional utility space. This design is illustrated in Figure 1.3: we group the customers into monthly cohorts based on their acquisition dates, and plot how the cumulative revenue evolves over time for each cohort as a function of the cohort age.

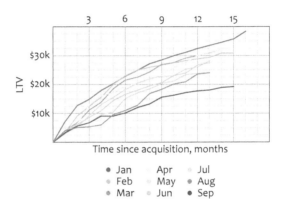

Figure 1.3: An example of cohort analysis.

This technique, called the *cohort analysis*, helps to profile the dynamics of individual cohorts, as well as the trajectory of the company with regard to the quality of the customer base. The example in Figure 1.3 exhibits a strong degradation trend in the sense that the newest cohorts (e.g. ones acquired in August and September) have much worse trajectories in the LTV space compared to the older cohorts (e.g. ones acquired in January and February). We can also see that the trajectories of the oldest cohorts rise steeply at the beginning, which suggests that newly acquired customers tended to increase product usage after the acquisition, maybe due to upgrades or cross-sells. The newest cohorts, however, do not exhibit this behavior and accumulate the LTV in a more linear way. In practice, such dynamics can be caused by an excessively aggressive customer acquisition strategy that pursues quantity at the expense of quality and long-term sustainability.

We can extend the analysis of cohorts with other useful metrics that characterize the dynamics of the customer base. An example is shown in Figure 1.4 where we added the retention rate dimension to visualize and quantify how well the company retains the previously acquired clients which is the key metric for subscription-based businesses. Similar to the growth accounting, the cohort analysis points us to the scenarios that need to be evaluated such as the optimization of the acquisition costs.

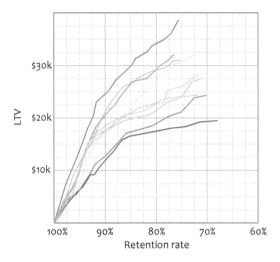

Figure 1.4: An example of cohort analysis in the utility space that includes LTV and retention rate. These are the same cohorts as in Figure 1.3

Both growth accounting and cohort analysis are just business analytics (BI) techniques. However, one can apply more advanced methods such as regression analysis to understand the factors that drive the entities along their trajectories, time series forecasting to accurately estimate future positions of the entities in the utility spaces, anomaly detection to identify abnormal developments, and clustering to discover useful entity groupings. In practice, however, it is not always possible to benefit from advanced methods at this level of analysis because the processes that we study are influenced by a large number of complex factors ranging from macroeconomics to management biases, and the scenario planning itself typically requires deep domain knowledge and human judgment. On the other hand, we should not underestimate the importance of quantitative top-level analysis in the overall enterprise AI strategy based on the relative simplicity of its statistical underpinning: establishing the right entities, metrics, and perspectives on the market fit, revenue streams, and customer base helps to ensure that the development of more sophisticated components will drive valuable business outcomes.

1.1.2   Tactics: Departments, Services, and Products

In the previous section we have reviewed several examples of how enterprise-level entities can be examined though the optics of the scenario planning framework. We now turn to smaller entities such as individual business processes, locations, and products. Smaller scale generally enables a higher degree of decision automation, so we can define more formal and self-contained optimization problems and engage more advanced statistical methods for solving them.

First, let us take the concept of the market fit to the next level of details and consider the case of a company with a relatively large product portfolio, such as a large manufacturer or retailer. In order to manage the portfolio, the company needs to analyze how the positions and trajectories of individual products align with the overall financial trajectory of the company, and then develop proper strategies for these products and other related entities such as product lines, categories, locations, and business units. We can start with constructing a utility map that shows how products are moving on the market and what their significance is to the company. We choose the total product revenue to gauge the product performance on the market and gross profit margin to measure its value to the company. There are, of course, many alternative metrics. For instance, one can choose the market share or sales volume as the measure of market performance. For each product, we can then visualize its past trajectory starting from the product's launch date and predict its future trajectory using some forecasting model. An example of such a utility map is shown in the top chart of Figure 1.5.

Although the above analysis is fairly straightforward, it can help to define pricing and promotion strategies for the product which, in turn, will be the inputs to the downstream models for optimizing prices, promotions, and inventory levels. More specifically, we can choose between the following strategies depicted in Figure 1.5:

(a) In the most favorable situations, it is possible to pursue improvements in both volume and margin. For instance, this can be the case for a new innovative product that rapidly acquires the market share, facing little competition. Trajectory analysis helps to identify such products and adjust their price setting models accordingly.

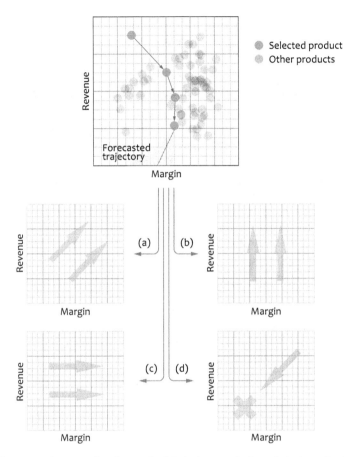

Figure 1.5: An example of a product trajectory analysis and strategy development.

(b) Some products' trajectories can indicate a potential for increasing the market share. This is typically the case for products that are in the early stages of their life cycle. The guideline to optimize for volume can then be passed to the downstream price optimization models and processes.

(c) Some products may not have enough potential for increasing their volume, and the company can focus on maximizing the margins that it derives from them. This is typically the case for products that are approaching the end of their life cycle. Consequently, the downstream price management components can be configured to maximize the profits. This will normally involve demand forecasting and price-response modeling.

Margins can also be improved through the reduction of costs which can be a starting point for involving stock level optimization and other inventory management models into the process.

(d) Finally, the products that are moving towards the zone where both the volumes and profits are low might need to be retired or upgraded. This can trigger the assortment optimization and product feature management processes.

We can perform similar analyses not only for products but for larger entities such as categories and locations. Overall, this analysis aims to decompose the top-level financial targets usually defined in terms of revenue and profitability into granular action plans which can, in turn, be executed by the next tier of decision-automation components.

We turn next to the second example of process-level scenario planning, this time focusing on an inventory management use case. Consider a retailer that runs a brick-and-mortar store and also sells products online, servicing online orders directly from the store shelves. (This capability is commonly referred to as *buy online ship from store*.) Let us assume that the store associates take items directly from shelves, thus competing with regular customers for the available inventory, orders are processed with some latency, and the online store receives inventory availability updates every morning. Consequently, the retailer faces fulfillment exceptions when a certain product is available at the beginning of the day, but gets sold out before an online order is placed and processed. The retailer can attempt to reduce such exceptions by forecasting in-store demand for each product, reserving the corresponding number of units for in-store customers, and making only the remaining inventory available for online ordering. This approach creates a trade-off between the availability rate (percentage of the inventory exposed to the online customers) and fulfillment rate (percentage of successfully fulfilled orders). Ideally, the retailer wants to maximize both rates, but these two objectives are in conflict with one another. This means that all practically possible solutions will be located within a bounded area on the utility map spanned on these two metrics, and the boundaries of this area correspond to the Pareto frontier.

An example of the utility map for the above use case is shown in Figure 1.6. Assuming that the total inventory capacity is fixed, each value of the fulfillment rate has the maximum achievable availability rate, and the set of such rate pairs forms the Pareto frontier. The retailer is free to choose any point on or under the frontier based on the business considerations. For instance, the retailer may choose to maintain the high level of customer experience and pick the point based on the minimum acceptable fulfillment rate, or may choose to pursue revenues and pick the point based on the availability rate. The frontier, however, can be lifted by increasing the total inventory capacity (as shown in the figure) or developing more accurate forecasting or reservation algorithms.

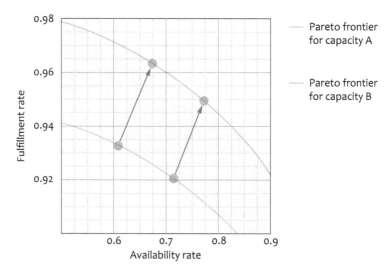

Figure 1.6: An example of Pareto frontiers for the Buy Online Ship From Store use case.

The examples considered in this section illustrate that the variety and complexity of the decision automation methods generally increases as we move from enterprise-level to process-level problems and focus on smaller-scale entities. In the above two examples, forecasting and optimization models are not the optional extension of descriptive analytics, but the core solution components. Our next step is to examine even lower levels of granularity.

1.1.3 Execution: Customers, Transactions, and Equipment

Although all levels of decision-making in the enterprise can benefit from statistical and optimization methods, the making of automatic decisions becomes a necessity at the level of individual customers and transactions. At the relatively high levels of aggregations which we discussed in previous sections, one has a certain freedom to choose between traditional business analytics, decision support models, and decision automation, but at the lower levels there are no alternatives to automation. In this section, we review several examples of scenario planning at the level of individual customers and transactions and contrast them with examples from the previous sections.

Let us start with an example from the customer intelligence domain. For many subscription-based businesses such as telecom and insurance, customer attrition (churn) is a major concern because both customer acquisition costs and lifetime values are high in these markets which makes customer retention much more preferable to losing old clients and acquiring new ones. Marketing teams usually create retention offers that can be presented to customers to prevent them from churning, but efficient usage of these packages is a complex problem. One needs to identify customers who are at the risk of churning, determine the optimal offer for each customer based on the factors that presumably drive this particular customer toward account cancellation, balance the potential loss with the cost of the offer, determine optimal time to send the offer, and so on. These decisions are depicted in Figure 1.7 where, using the scenario planning terms, each customer is a separate entity, probability of churn is the utility metric, and different offers and intervention times are considered scenarios.

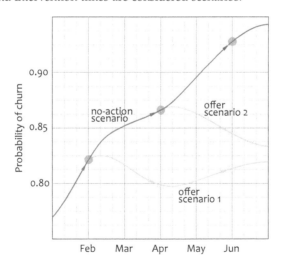

Figure 1.7: An example of a customer trajectory in the context of the churn prevention problem. Alternative utility measures for this problem include survival probability (inverse of the churn probability) and expected LTV.

In practice, most of these tasks can be efficiently solved using statistical models, so that each customer gets personalized treatment. Moreover, it is often possible to build highly automated systems that make many of these decisions autonomously and in near real time which is hardly achievable for the more-strategic use cases we discussed in the previous sections.

Another example that illustrates the capabilities of automated decision-making for low-level entities is anomaly detection. Many quality and safety-control tasks, including the monitoring of system metrics in data centers, the monitoring of telemetry data collected from industrial equipment, and the surveillance of financial transactions, boil down to differentiating between normal and abnormal trajectories in various metric spaces. For example, a bank can monitor the number or percentage of charge-back transactions and detect outliers that fall out of the regular daily patterns, as illustrated in Figure 1.8. In practice, the detection of such outliers can often be done automatically with high precision given that it is possible to build a reasonably accurate model of the process that approximates the observed patterns, and then use this model to forecast the expected behavior deviations which will be deemed to be anomalies.

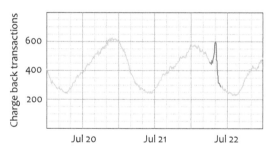

Figure 1.8: An example of anomaly in transactional metrics.

The two examples above illustrate that the development of decision automation components for entities of a smaller scale is often facilitated by the ability to build reasonably accurate and self-contained mathematical models of the process, which is more challenging for larger scale entities. Unlike large entities, smaller entities such as online users and payment transactions tend to be numerous, so we often observe millions or billions of instances, which also facilitates and, in fact, commands the usage of statistical methods. The spectrum of entities is very wide, ranging from entire markets and companies to consumers and transactions, so enterprises usually need to build a hierarchy of quantitative decision-support and decision-automation components. The top-level components in this hierarchy are usually decision-support tools focused on decomposition of a complex problem into smaller ones and determining the right objectives and parameters for the downstream components. The lower-level components are usually autonomous models that optimize actions and controls based on the objectives passed from the upper levels.

1.2   MODELING CAPABILITIES

In the previous sections, we reviewed several basic examples that illustrate how quantitative methods can help with decision automation at various levels of granularity and in various enterprise domains. The implementation of these approaches requires a comprehensive toolkit of statistical and optimization methods that can collectively address several categories of problems. The first category is related to the incorporation of various signals and data sources into the analysis and extracting semantically meaningful representations that can be used in decision-making:

ENTITY REPRESENTATIONS Many entities have complex digital footprints that include numerical, textual, image, and graph data. For example, a customer can be represented by account settings, transaction and browsing histories, social connection graphs, and text messages; a product can be represented by numerical and categorical attributes, textual descriptions, images, and customer reviews. Consequently, one needs tools to extract semantic meaning out of these data and create compact representations of entities that can be used in downstream models and analytical processes. For instance, textual messages can be represented as collections of topic and sentiment tags, product images can be annotated with style tags, and so on. We refer to such compact semantic-preserving representations of entities as *entity embeddings* in the sense that a high-dimensional entity representation is mapped into a low-dimensional semantic space. Such representations can be constructed manually, and this process is referred to as *feature engineering*, or learned using statistical techniques which is known as *representation learning*.

ENTITY ALGEBRA The problem of computing entity embeddings is closely related to the problem of computing distances between entities. Many enterprise AI problems, especially in marketing and information management applications, can be reduced to estimating distances or, alternatively, similarities between entities in an appropriate semantic space. Examples include product recommendation systems where one needs to measure similarities between products and users, text and image search problems where one needs to find items similar to a search query or reference image, and price and assortment management problems where a distance metric between products is often required. Embedding vectors provide a generic and convenient way for computing distances and performing other algebraic operations on entities.

ENTITY MANIFOLDS In many applications, we need to distinguish between different classes of entities or predict unobserved entity attributes. For example, we might need to categorize customer accounts based on the expected revenue over the next year, or categorize images from a surveillance camera as normal situations, crowds, street fights, and unauthorized vehicles. Each such category can be thought of as a geometric region in the space of all possible entities, and we refer to such semantically meaningful regions as *manifolds*. For example, we can have manifolds of normal situations, crowds, and street fights in the case of surveillance video analytics.

We often want to learn models of manifolds from the observed samples, and then use these models to predict which manifolds a given entity belongs to. In some cases, the manifold model can be simply a rule that specifies a region in the space of metrics and attributes the entity originally represented. In many other cases, this approach is not feasible because the geometry of the region is extremely complex, and we need to learn an appropriate embedding space where the manifolds of interest are more distinguishable.

The second category of problems is related to models that help to understand the internal structure of entity trajectories and forecast future moves. If we use the branches of physics as an analogy, this category can be thought of as a discipline that studies the *dynamics* of entities, whereas the previous category can be viewed as *statics*. The problems we need to address in this area are as follows:

TRAJECTORY DECOMPOSITION A trajectory can be shaped by many different forces which may or may not be directly observable. For example, a retailer can straightforwardly track weekly sales numbers for a given product, but this series represents a complex mix of components such as seasonality, responses to price changes and marketing campaigns, cannibalization effects related to similar products or competitor price changes. Most of these effects cannot be measured explicitly, and one needs to estimate them using statistical analysis. This process of trajectory decomposition into elementary components enables deeper manual analysis as well as automatic optimization. For example, a price management system that does not account for cannibalization effects is prone to making suboptimal decisions that boost sales of one product, but harm the overall category profitability.

The trajectory decomposition problem can be viewed as a dynamic counterpart of entity representation learning. While the main purpose of representation learning is to describe the static state of an entity using semantically meaningful components (dimensions), the main goal of trajectory decomposition is to describe the dynamics of an entity in terms of forces that have clear semantic meanings.

TRAJECTORY PREDICTION The trajectory analysis and decomposition can typically be extended into prediction. In our previous example regarding price management, a model that allows for decomposition of the sales numbers into seasonal and price-related components can be used to forecast future sales. Decomposition and forecasting can often be viewed as two different modes (descriptive and predictive) of using the same or similar models.

TRAJECTORY MANIFOLDS The predicted trajectory can be viewed as a manifold of the normal (expected) entity behaviors. Consequently, one can use trajectory prediction models to detect unexpected deviations from normal behavior by comparing the predicted values that the values are expected to be (or the range they are expected to be within), with the actual observations. We refer to such deviations as *outliers*. The ability to detect outliers has many important applications including system monitoring and IoT analytics. This problem is a dynamic counterpart of the entity manifold learning problem.

Finally, the ultimate goal of enterprise AI systems and tools is to improve specific actions and decisions in terms of optimality or degree of automation, so we define the third category of tasks that are related to the optimal entity control:

ENTITY CONTROL Predictive models enable *what-if analysis* of possible actions, so that an optimization algorithm can evaluate multiple scenarios and determine the optimal one. This creates a foundation for the development of prescriptive tools and autonomous decision-making components for entity control. The design of optimization models that capture all important economic factors and that are capable of finding strategically optimal multistep scenarios are the central problems in entity control.

In theory, the main goal of entity control algorithms is to produce optimal or near-optimal action policies or prescriptions. In practice, we often need to answer additional questions about the solution and the structure of the solution space. One important example is *sensitivity analysis* that aims to measure how the quality of the solution degrades when the action parameters are shifted away from the optimal values or if modeling assumptions are violated. For instance, an inventory planner might be interested to know the difference between the theoretically optimal replenishment cycles of 6.53 days and the practically meaningful cycle of 7 days (once a week).

DYNAMIC CONTROL The problems we discussed above, starting from representation learning to action planning, are traditionally approached from the angle of statistical analysis of historical data. This generally includes many manual steps related to data preparation, model development, and production integrations. This approach is not always feasible in complex or dynamic environments where representative historical data might not be available or might be getting obsolete quickly due to continuous changes in the statistical properties of the processes. For example, a personalization system that relies on customers' behavioral profiles might not work satisfactorily in the environment with a continuous stream of new customers. This leads to the problem of dynamic control where the system is required to continuously explore the environment, learn instantly from the ongoing feedback, and continuously adjust decision-making and exploration policies.

In practice, one does not necessarily build a complete pipeline with distinct stages for embedding computing, prediction, and control optimization. For example, some merchandising processes such as product image tagging can be automated using only computer vision models that create and classify image embeddings. The complete framework, however, can be useful for planning of more complex solutions that automate complex operations and include multiple models and components.

The implementation of the above capabilities can involve a broad range of statistical and optimization methods. The deep learning and reinforcement learning methods, however, provide the most comprehensive platform for implementing enterprise AI applications that cover most of the required capabilities including semantic analysis, forecasting, and action optimization. We spend the next two chapters lining up the necessary building blocks and discussing the above modeling capabilities in more detail.

1.3 SUMMARY

- Data-driven methods can be applied at different levels of granularity: strategic decisions and large economic entities such as companies, tactical decisions and optimization of individual processes, and micro-decisions at the level of individual customers, transactions, and operations.

- Many enterprise decision-making and optimization problems can be conveniently represented in terms of entities, utility spaces, trajectories, and intervention scenarios.

- Analysis of entities and scenarios requires learning semantically meaningful entity representations, explaining and forecasting trajectories, and evaluating potential interventions.

- Deep learning and reinforcement learning methods provide a solid platform for entity and scenario modeling. This platform has certain limitations that can be addressed using alternative machine learning methods.

2

LEARNING REPRESENTATIONS AND MAPPINGS

A developer of enterprise AI solutions has an extremely wide range of statistical and optimization methods at their disposal. The availability of such an extensive toolkit is certainly beneficial, but it imposes challenges as well. First, statistical and machine learning methods are being developed in many different contexts including computer vision, natural language processing, life sciences, and video game playing. This complicates the selection of the right tools for a specific enterprise problem because it can sometimes be difficult to recognize that an algorithm originally developed for playing video games can be applied in supply chain management or to adapt a text classification model to clickstream analytics. Second, different branches of statistics and machine learning such as causal inference, econometrics, deep learning, and reinforcement learning tend to be studied and used separately, and practitioners often have challenges embracing and combining various methods in an optimal way.

In this chapter, we outline the most important categories of modeling techniques focusing on the principal capabilities they provide in the context of enterprise operations. These methods will then be used throughout the book as generic building blocks. We describe machine learning methods mainly from the system engineering standpoint, considering them as components with certain functionality, inputs, and outputs, and explaining how multiple components can be wired together. We provide basic details about statistical and algorithmic underpinning of these methods, but we do not aim to provide a comprehensive and rigorous introduction into machine learning theory. The latter would, of course, be a completely intractable problem considering the broadness and complexity of methods used in enterprise AI applications. Finally, we choose to use deep learning as the core framework that enables us to explain and implement a very broad range of solutions in a unified way. We will discuss the advantages and limitations of this approach as well as alternatives, in the next chapters, in the context of specific use cases.

2.1 SYSTEM ENGINEERING PERSPECTIVE ON ENTERPRISE AI

All methods and solutions described in this book rely on the ability to build a model of a certain entity or process, such as an individual customer or a large group of customers who are collectively considered as a market. Although we always have an option to specify the model manually, the complexity of doing this is prohibitively high for the absolute majority of use cases, and we have to use statistical methods to learn models from past observations or ongoing interactions with the environment.

In many cases, it is convenient to view a statistical model as a component that provides certain functionality and integration points. We usually build a model of an entity or process to approximate or reconstruct hidden parts of their current state or to predict future states based on the incomplete or noisy information available to us. For example, a model can output the products that a customer is likely to purchase based on their demographic profile, the names of the objects shown in the image based on the image bitmap, the word in a certain position in a sentence based on the surrounding words, and the expected time to machine failure based on the current sensor metrics. The information that can be used to create a model usually includes *prior knowledge* about the structure of the entity or process and *samples* of the observed parts of the state. The prior knowledge is typically used to design the model structure, or to set some of its fixed parameters (hyperparameters), and initialize the values of its learnable parameters. The samples are used to learn the actual values of the parameters that maximize the accuracy of the approximation. Consequently, the main integration points of the model component include inputs x, outputs y, and prior information, as shown in Figure 2.1. We also assume that all learnings gained from the observed samples are incorporated into model parameters θ.

The dependency between the input (observed) and output (hidden or future) parts can be extremely complex. This complexity often stems from the high level of redundancy and noise in the original representation of the input samples. For example, we can observe items produced by some manufacturing process in the form of images captured

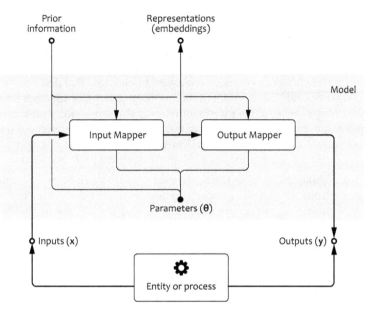

Figure 2.1: The conceptual architecture of a statistical model.

by a camera, and develop a model that estimates the probability of a given item being defective. In this case, the items are initially represented by matrices of pixels, and it is very difficult to specify a rule of function that delineates the subset of matrices that corresponds to defective items in the space of all possible matrices. We call this subset a manifold of defective images, and, more generally, we use term *manifold* to refer to a subset of inputs that corresponds to a specific output value or range of such values. The problem can, however, be drastically simplified if we manage to find a transformation that maps the original representation to a smaller, less noisy, and less redundant representation that is aligned with the semantics of the desired output. In the above example regarding defect detection, the desirable representation should include signals related to edges, contrast, and other image features that can potentially highlight the presence of anomalies such as scratches or holes. Consequently, the model design often includes, explicitly or implicitly, an input mapper that learns to produce a condensed representation of the input. Dimensions of such a representation can correspond to semantically meaningful features of the modeled entity or process, so the space of such representations is often referred to as a *semantic space*. The dimensionality of the semantic space is typically smaller than the dimensionality of the input space, and thus it is common to say that the inputs are getting *embedded* into the semantic space, and refer to representations of individual input samples as *embeddings*. A properly constructed semantic space enables us to describe the manifolds of interest using much simpler, often trivial, rules or functions compared to functions that describe the same manifolds based on the initial representation. The function that transforms embeddings into the final output corresponds to the output mapper block in Figure 2.1. In our example of defect detection, we would first map input images to low-dimensional embedding vectors and then map these embeddings to the final defect probability values.

The ability to learn semantically meaningful embeddings for complex entities or processes, especially ones that are observed as noisy multidimensional structures such as images or texts, is one of the key tasks in modern statistical modeling. Such embeddings can be used to reconstruct hidden parts or properties of the entities, predict future states of processes, assess similarities between entities, and much more. In some cases, models that are built for the sake of producing certain outcomes can compute useful representations internally as a side effect, and these embeddings can be captured and used for other purposes. In other cases, models are designed specifically to learn high-quality embeddings that are used as inputs for downstream models and processes.

In the framework defined above, the principal question is how the manifolds of interest can be outlined using reference input and output samples, so that the model can learn the general shape of the manifolds based on these points. Our strategy for specifying inputs and outputs also dictates how the model is integrated with the environment and determines the complexity of this integration. The first option is to explicitly mark the boundaries of the manifolds, so that each sample consists of an input and the corresponding target output, as illustrated in Figure 2.2. In this scenario, known as *supervised learning*, the output values need to be generated using some supervising process. For example, a retailer might be interested to predict the revenue for a particular customer in the next six months based on their activity over the past six months. In this case, the training samples can be generated by a process that consumes customer profiles, each of which includes transactions and other attributes for a time period of twelve months, creates the input values (features) that describe customer state based on the first six months, and computes the output labels as the revenue over the last six months. The model then attempts to learn the manifolds of customer states x that correspond to different levels of the numerical revenue label y. This situation corresponds to the sketch in Figure 2.2 (a) where we assume that the customer state is repre-

sented by a two-dimensional vector and, consequently, the manifold
of the revenue values spans over a two-dimensional plane. The same
approach can be used to learn manifolds specified using categorical
labels and more complex structures such as vectors and matrices. For
example, a retailer that aims to predict whether a customer will make
a purchase or not, instead of predicting the revenue, would build a
model for learning the manifolds of purchasers and nonpurchasers using a binary output label, which corresponds to the situation depicted
in Figure 2.2 (b).

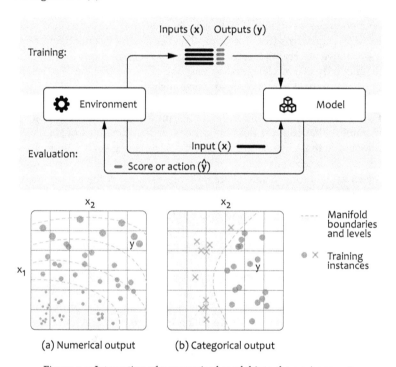

Figure 2.2: Integration of a supervised model into the environment.

The integration strategy outlined above does not prescribe either
how exactly the training samples are collected, nor how the model
outputs are converted into actions and interventions that change the
trajectory of the entities and processes. The most typical approach is to
collect a sufficiently large batch of input samples, train the model, and
use it to estimate the outputs for new input instances that arrive from
the environment. The estimated outputs are then operationalized, that
is converted into actions, using some heuristic process. This approach
generally assumes the stationarity of the process we are modeling, so

that the historical data remain representative during the time needed to build or retrain the model, and the model remains valid for the time needed to produce and operationalize its outputs. These assumptions are never perfectly true in real-world enterprise environments, but many important problems can be solved practically using methods that rely on such assumptions and relatively basic modifications such as frequent model retraining. In some scenarios, however, it can be challenging to adapt methods that assume stationarity because of the highly dynamic nature of the environment and other factors. For example, a newsfeed personalization service that aims to find and recommend the most relevant articles to its users may have a limited ability to learn patterns from historical data because new content and new users arrive at very high rates. This type of problem requires methods that not only fit a model based on past observations, but combine learning, environment exploration, and action control in one seamless algorithm. This strategy, known as reinforcement learning, is illustrated in Figure 2.3. Internally, reinforcement learning algorithms usually learn manifolds that connect possible actions in specific states of the environment with the value (utility) derived from taking such actions. This concept is sketched in the lower part of Figure 2.3 where the model estimates value y for a potential scenario represented by the environment state feature x_1 and action feature x_2.

The concepts of supervised and reinforcement learning models require the manifolds of interest to be explicitly marked out using output labels, so that the model parameters can be optimized to learn this outline. In many applications, however, we might not have an explicit delineation between the observed (features) and hidden (labels) parts of the process we are trying to model, but we can define a rule that extracts the input-output pairs directly from the raw data captured from the entity or process that we are trying to approximate. As an illustration, consider an anomaly detection system that monitors the number of active sessions on a website and raises an alert if this number suddenly jumps or drops. A typical solution for this problem is a model that forecasts the number of sessions for the next time interval based on the patterns observed during the previous intervals, and flags significant deviations from the forecast as anomalies. In this case, the time series that describes how the number of active sessions changes over time is both the input and output of the model, and the model can learn to predict the future segments of the series based on the past segments. Once the model captures the manifold of normal patterns, it can evaluate the distance between the newly observed samples and this manifold. A similar strategy is commonly used in language models that are trained to predict the next word in a sentence based on

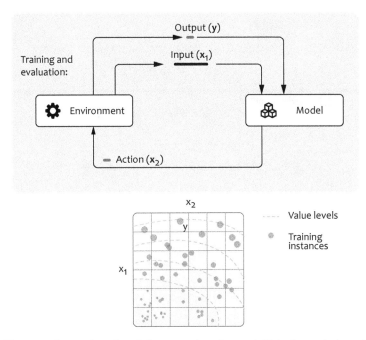

Figure 2.3: Integration of a reinforcement learning model into the environment.

the previous words by capturing the manifold of meaningful phrases and sentences. In both cases, the inputs and outputs of the model are automatically generated from the raw unlabeled data using the prior knowledge about the problem and structure of the data, that are temporal and spatial relationships between the segments of a time series or words in a text. This strategy, known as unsupervised learning, is outlined in Figure 2.4.

The designs presented in Figures 2.2 – 2.4 can be combined in various ways to capture signals from multiple sources. One common pattern is to chain multiple models together in a way that upstream models extract useful features (embeddings) from various types of input data including numerical vectors, event sequences, images, texts, and graphs; and downstream models produce the final outputs by applying additional transformations on top of the extracted representations. In such architectures, the feature extraction step is often done using generic off-the-shelf models, and the final transformation is learned based on a custom domain-specific dataset. This scenario is illustrated in Figure 2.5 where we assume that a model of a complex environment E_2 needs to be built based on a limited number of training in-

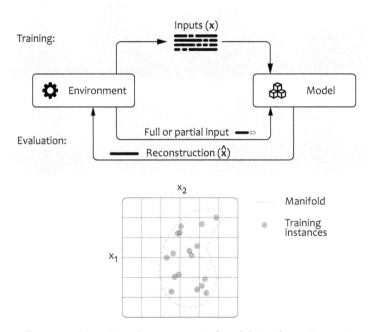

Figure 2.4: Integration of an unsupervised model into the environment.

stances. Since the environment is complex, the available training instances might not be sufficient to mark out all the details of the manifold curvature, making the problem intractable. We can, however, work
around this limitation provided that we have enough instances for a
similar or related environment E_1 and build an auxiliary model M_1
that extracts useful features from the samples generated by this environment. This model can then be used to extract features from samples generated by environment E_2, and the second model M_2 can be
trained to map these embeddings to the final outputs using a limited
number of samples available for E_2. This approach works if embeddings x' produced by the first model represent the entities in E_2 better
than the initial inputs x, making it easier for the second model to learn
E_2-specific representations x'' which, are in turn, used to compute the
final output. This process, generally referred to as *transfer learning*, is
illustrated in the lower part of Figure 2.5.

In this and the next chapters, we will define a more rigorous mathematical framework for the concepts we introduced informally above,
develop more specialized models for various types of inputs and outputs, and build complete solutions for specific business use cases. More

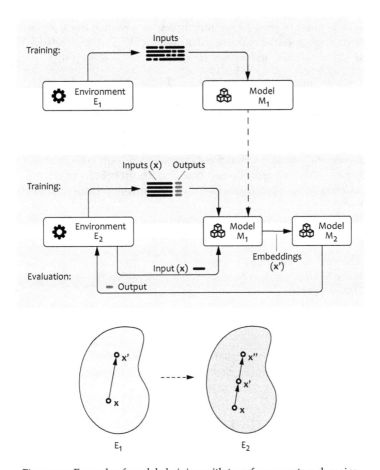

Figure 2.5: Example of model chaining with transfer across two domains.

concretely, we spend the rest of this chapter discussing methods and algorithms for learning useful representations, manifolds, and mapping functions based on input and output samples. We defer the discussion of control policies and decision-making algorithms till the next chapter where we review the reinforcement learning methods.

2.2 MAXIMUM LIKELIHOOD METHOD

Generally speaking, models are created to approximate real-world stochastic processes based on observed data samples. Each sample can represent an entity generated by a process or a state of the process at a certain point of time. Consequently, we assume that the samples are drawn from a data-generating distribution $p_{data}(x)$ that reflects the real-world process, and a finite set of n samples is observed:

$$X = \{x_1, \ldots, x_n\} \tag{2.1}$$

We can approach the problem of building a model for this process by defining a family of parametric distributions $p_{model}(x \mid \theta)$ where θ is a vector of model parameters, and finding the value of θ that provides the best approximation of the available data. The goodness of approximation can be evaluated based on the probability of generating the observed data given specific model parameters which is known as the *likelihood*:

$$\mathcal{L}(\theta) = p_{model}(X \mid \theta) \tag{2.2}$$

The optimal values of parameters that correspond to the *maximum likelihood (ML)* can then be determined by solving the following optimization problem:

$$\theta_{ML} = \underset{\theta}{argmax}\ \mathcal{L}(\theta) \tag{2.3}$$

We can further assume that the observed samples are drawn independently from the data-generating distribution which allows for the following probability decomposition[1]:

$$
\begin{aligned}
\theta_{ML} &= \underset{\theta}{argmax}\ \prod_{i=1}^{n} p_{model}(x_i \mid \theta) \\
&= \underset{\theta}{argmax}\ \sum_{i=1}^{n} \log p_{model}(x_i \mid \theta) \\
&= \underset{\theta}{argmax}\ \mathbb{E}_{x \sim \hat{p}_{data}}\left[\log p_{model}(x \mid \theta)\right]
\end{aligned}
\tag{2.4}
$$

The last transition is valid because the argmax operation is invariant to rescaling of its argument, so we can divide the sum over the observed samples by n and, consequently, express the right-hand side as the expected value over the empirical distribution of the data. Solving this optimization problem with regard to θ, we obtain a fully specified

---

1 The assumption about independently drawn samples is appropriate for many practically important problems. For example, user profiles used in personalization applications are typically viewed as independent samples. However, many problems exist where observations are by nature interdependent. For instance, a series of daily sales numbers clearly cannot be viewed as a collection of independent values. Such problems can be cast to the standard formulation with independent samples by a proper design of vectors x, and we discuss this problem further in Section 2.4.2.

model that can be used to draw new samples and study properties of the data-generating process.

In the case of supervised learning, we are interested to learn a model that approximates the mapping (dependency) between input and output values rather than learning a model that approximates the distribution of some input values. Consequently, the model learns from a set of samples where each instance is a pair of input features and output values (labels):

$$X = \{(x_1, y_1), \ldots, (x_n, y_n)\} \tag{2.5}$$

In this formulation, the goal is to learn a model that allows drawing of output labels y using feature vectors x as input arguments. The framework developed above can be adapted to this problem by replacing unconditional data distribution by conditional distribution $p_{data}(y \mid x)$ where x is the input feature vector and y is the output label. The model also changes to $p_{model}(y \mid x, \theta)$, so that both θ and x are needed to evaluate y. Finally, the maximum likelihood expression 2.4 transforms into the following:

$$\theta_{ML} = \underset{\theta}{argmax} \sum_{i=1}^{n} \log p_{model}(y_i \mid x_i, \theta)$$
$$= \underset{\theta}{argmax} \; \mathbb{E}_{x,y \sim \hat{p}_{data}} [\log p_{model}(y \mid x, \theta)] \tag{2.6}$$

The actual optimization problem can be derived from the above framework by approximating the likelihood by an evaluable loss function. In the case of supervised learning, it is convenient to introduce a per-sample loss function and define it as an approximation of the negative log-likelihood for one observation:

$$L(x_i, y_i, \theta) = -\log p_{model}(y_i \mid x_i, \theta) \tag{2.7}$$

The loss of zero is achieved when the model assigns the probability of one to the observed ground truth label y_i. The actual loss function, however, is not necessarily identical to the log-likelihood – it can be specified using various approximation techniques, and include special terms that prevent overfitting and computational stability issues. In certain cases, the design of the loss function can also include business considerations. For example, the right-hand side of expression 2.7 can be rescaled using a nonlinear function to penalize deviations from the ideal fit based on the business impact of the error.

Assuming that we specified an evaluable per-sample loss function, the total loss that corresponds to the negative log-likelihood over the observed dataset can be evaluated as

$$J(\theta) = \frac{1}{n} \sum_{i=1}^{n} L(x_i, y_i, \theta) \tag{2.8}$$

The minimization of this loss is equivalent to solving problem 2.6. The loss can be minimized by performing gradient descent in the space of parameters θ. The gradient descent can be implemented as an iterative process that estimates the gradient of the loss function

$$\nabla_\theta J(\theta) = \frac{1}{n} \sum_{i=1}^{n} \nabla_\theta L(x_i, y_i, \theta) \tag{2.9}$$

and shifts the parameters in the direction of the minimal loss as follows

$$\theta \leftarrow \theta - \alpha \cdot \nabla_\theta J(\theta) \tag{2.10}$$

where α is a hyperparameter that controls the update rate. This process produces the loss-minimizing value of θ that approximates θ_{ML} and thus allows us to specify the model.

The methodology outlined above can be viewed as a high-level framework for building models of stochastic processes, but its practical implementation requires the solving of several challenging problems:

- First, we need to define the model architecture in a way that provides enough capacity and flexibility for approximating complex data-generating distributions, but allows for stable and efficient parameter learning. This is a very challenging task that requires developing a comprehensive collection of composable methods that can be used to design custom solutions for various problems and use cases.

- Second, we need to specify a meaningful and computationally tractable loss function. The design of such a function generally depends on the type and structure of the outputs, and also requires the incorporation of various considerations related to computational stability.

- Finally, the optimization of model parameters is also much more challenging than the basic gradient descent procedure outlined above. It requires the solving of numerous issues related to computational complexity and stability associated with fitting a model on real-world datasets.

It is beyond the scope of this book to discuss the computational aspects of the optimization process, but the first two problems (model design and loss function design) need to be discussed at some length in order to create a toolkit for the development of an appropriate method for real-world enterprise use cases. We spend the next several sections laying this foundation.

2.3   MODELS WITH VECTOR INPUTS

 The complete reference implementation for this section is available at https://bit.ly/3j7SBh9

We start by reviewing supervised models that are capable of learning the relationship between a one-dimensional input vector and one or several output values. The input vector is usually a concatenation of several features, each of which describes a certain property or attribute of the modeled entity or process. These features may or may not have semantic relationships, but the model design does not make any specific assumptions about temporal, causal, or spatial dependencies between the features or their order in the input vector. A wide range of practical enterprise problems can be cast to such plain-input formulation, making this design extremely versatile.

2.3.1   *Linear Layer*

Our first step is to examine a basic model design that uses a linear transformation to map the input vector to the output values. In this section, we discuss how the parameters of such a linear mapper can be learned and how it can be combined with several different output mappers to estimate the output values of different types. We refer to this basic unit as a *linear layer* because, as we discuss in the next sections, it can be viewed as one of the building blocks that can be composed together to obtain higher-capacity models.

The maximum likelihood framework requires specifying a parametric model and loss function as inputs for the learning process. The model and loss can be designed to learn the full distribution $p(y \mid \mathbf{x}, \theta)$, but in most practical applications we are interested only in estimating the expected value of y given the known input x, that is learning a function that computes the estimate of the output value based on the input vector:

$$\hat{y}_i = \mathbb{E}\left[p_{model}(y_i \mid x_i, \theta)\right] = f_{model}(x_i, \theta) \tag{2.11}$$

In this case, we can interpret the loss function as the distance between the true value y_i and its estimate $\hat{y}_i$:

$$
\begin{aligned}
L(x_i, y_i, \theta) &= L(y_i, \hat{y}_i) \\
&= L(y_i, f_{model}(x_i, \theta)) \\
&= \text{distance}(y_i, f_{model}(x_i, \theta))
\end{aligned}
\tag{2.12}
$$

The distance function should be designed to match the negative log-likelihood defined in expression 2.7, and thus its design depends on the assumed distribution $p(y \mid x)$. This distribution, in turn, needs to be chosen based on the type of the output label y. For example, we can use continuous distributions for real-valued labels and discrete distributions for categorical labels. Let us examine these cases separately starting with real-valued labels.

2.3.1.1 *Regression*

Models that produce real-valued outputs are collectively referred to as *regression models*. The basic regression model can be built under an assumption that label y is a normally distributed variable, that is

$$p(y \mid x, \theta) = N(y; f_{model}(x, \theta), I) \tag{2.13}$$

It can be shown that for the normally distributed label the maximum likelihood maximization is equivalent to minimization of the mean squared error (MSE), and thus we can reduce the loss function in expression 2.12 to Euclidean distance:

$$L(x_i, y_i, \theta) = (y_i - f_{model}(x_i, \theta))^2 \tag{2.14}$$

This loss function can be straightforwardly evaluated, plugged into the gradient expression 2.9, and used to find the optimal model parameters.

The remaining piece is to specify the model. The most basic option we can start with is a linear function specified by a vector of slope coefficients $\mathbf{w}$ and scalar intercept b:

$$f_{model}(x, \theta) = f(x, w, b) = w^T x + b \tag{2.15}$$

This model approximates the dependency between the input and output points as a hyperplane averaging out any nonlinearities (curvatures). The structure of the model and its training process are illustrated in Figure 2.6 where the input vector **x** is assumed to be one-dimensional and the linear unit is specified by equation 2.15.

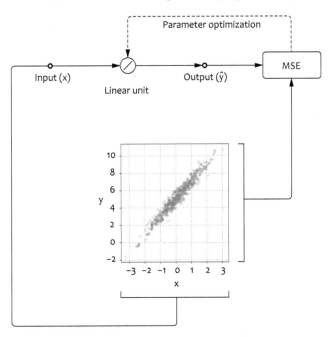

Figure 2.6: Training pipeline for a linear regression model.

The training process optimizes parameters w and b with respect to MSE using gradient descent, and produces an evaluable linear model. We can use this model, for instance, to estimate output value $\hat{y}$ for each input point x as shown in Figure 2.7. This figure illustrates how the linear regression model approximates the dependency between inputs and outputs by a straight line (one-dimensional hyperplane) averaging out all noises and deviations.

2.3.1.2   Single-label Classification

Let us now turn to the case where label y is drawn from a discrete set of k classes $c_1, \ldots, c_k$. This category of problems is referred to as *single-label classification problems*. In this scenario, we can design a model to

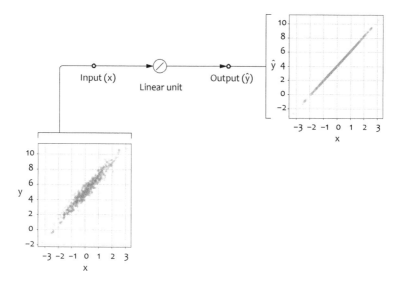

Figure 2.7: Inference pipeline for a linear regression model.

output a k-dimensional vector where each element corresponds to the probability of class c_k, so that

$$\hat{\mathbf{y}}_i = (\hat{y}_{i1}, \ldots, \hat{y}_{ik}) = f_{\text{model}}(\mathbf{x}_i, \theta) \tag{2.16}$$

and

$$\hat{y}_{ij} = p(y_i = c_j \mid \mathbf{x}_i, \theta) \tag{2.17}$$

The final classification decision can then be made by choosing the class that corresponds to the maximum probability value. Since we are assuming that the model explicitly outputs class probabilities, the per-sample loss function can be evaluated straightforwardly based on the definition of the likelihood 2.7 as

$$L(\mathbf{x}_i, y_i, \theta) = -\log p_{\text{model}}(y_i \mid \mathbf{x}_i, \theta)$$
$$= -\sum_{j=1}^{k} \mathbb{I}(y_i = c_j) \log \hat{y}_{ij} \tag{2.18}$$

where $\mathbb{I}$ is an indicator function that takes value 1 when its argument is true and value 0 otherwise. This loss function is known as a *categorical cross-entropy loss*.

The second part of the solution is to specify the model that produces the vector of class probabilities. Similar to the regression case, we can consider assigning a basic linear model to each class, so that the following k values are computed:

$$z_j = \mathbf{w}_j^T \mathbf{x} + b_j, \qquad j = 1, \ldots, k \tag{2.19}$$

We can stack weight vectors $\mathbf{w}_j$ into a matrix $\mathbf{W}$ and rewrite the above expression in matrix notation:

$$\mathbf{z} = \mathbf{W}\mathbf{x} + \mathbf{b} \tag{2.20}$$

so that $\mathbf{z}$ is a k-dimensional vector. The elements of $\mathbf{z}$ cannot be directly interpreted as probabilities because they are not normalized, but we can rescale them to produce a vector of valid probability values. This can be done using a softmax function that is defined as follows:

$$\text{softmax}(\mathbf{z})_j = \frac{\exp(z_j)}{\sum_{c=1}^{k} \exp(z_c)}, \qquad j = 1, \ldots, k \tag{2.21}$$

The softmax function takes a k-dimensional vector $\mathbf{z}$ as an input and produces a vector of k normalized values that can be used to assemble the final output vector $\hat{\mathbf{y}}$:

$$\hat{\mathbf{y}} = (\text{softmax}(\mathbf{z})_1, \ldots, \text{softmax}(\mathbf{z})_k) \tag{2.22}$$

It is easy to check that this vector satisfies the following criteria and thus it represents a valid vector of class probabilities:

$$\hat{y}_j \in [0, 1] \quad \text{and} \quad \sum_{j=1}^{k} \hat{y}_j = 1 \tag{2.23}$$

We can illustrate the overall model architecture with an example shown in Figure 2.8. In this example, the input is a two-dimensional real vector, and the output is a categorical label with three possible values (classes). The model is trained using gradient descent on a dataset that includes three relatively well-separated clusters presented in the lower part of the figure.

The logic learned by the model can be examined through visualization of individual layers as shown in Figure 2.9. The upper part of the figure is created by evaluating and visualizing values of z at various points of the input two-dimensional space, and the data points of the corresponding classes are overlaid on top of it. As expected, the values of z represent linear gradients that are aligned with the locations of the corresponding clusters. The second row depicts the outputs of the softmax function – the linear gradients are blended into the curved

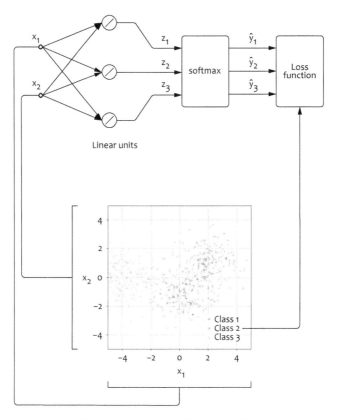

Figure 2.8: Training pipeline for a linear classification model.

areas. The final decision boundaries between the classes, however, are linear as confirmed by the chart below the figure. This chart is obtained by color coding the points of the input space based on which class has the maximum estimated probability at a given point.

2.3.1.3   Multi-label Classification

The third common category of problems we have to consider is that of *multi-label classification*. Similar to the single-label classification discussed in the previous section, the labels are also drawn from a discrete set, but multiple labels may be assigned to each instance. In other words, the classes are not mutually exclusive and each instance can belong to more than one class.

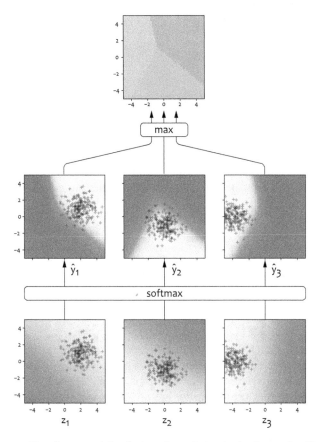

Figure 2.9: Visualization of the decision boundaries in the linear classification model.

The output of the multi-label classification model is a vector of class probabilities, so the expressions 2.16 and 2.17 we used to define the single-label classification model, are also valid for the multi-label case without any modifications. We can also reuse the categorical cross-entropy loss specified by expression 2.18, as well as the linear part of the model specified by equation 2.20. The only part that we need to modify is the mapping between the outputs of the linear transformation and class probabilities. Since the classes are not mutually exclusive, we need to independently normalize each probability value in the output vector rather than jointly normalize all values using the softmax function. Consequently, we can replace the mapping 2.22 with the following:

$$\hat{\mathbf{y}} = (\sigma(z_1), \ldots, \sigma(z_k)) \tag{2.24}$$

where z_i are the elements of the vector produced by the linear transformation and σ is the sigmoid function specified as

$$\sigma(x) = \frac{1}{1 + e^{-x}} \tag{2.25}$$

The sigmoid function maps an arbitrary real value to the range from 0 to 1, so that each element of the output vector is guaranteed to be a valid probability value:

$$\hat{y}_j \in [0, 1] \tag{2.26}$$

Unlike the softmax mapping, however, there is no guarantee that all elements sum up to one.

2.3.2 Nonlinear Layers

The linear models discussed in the previous section are very useful in practical enterprise problems that require quantifying the average correlation between inputs and outputs. By fitting such models, we can establish that a certain factor has positive or negative impact on the output and estimate how sensitive this dependency is using the slope coefficients. The linear models, however, are not able to capture the exact shape of the dependency between inputs and outputs unless it is strictly linear, and neither can complex interactions between the input features be captured. These limitations can be addressed by adding nonlinear transformations to the model.

Many different approaches exist for adding nonlinearities. One of the most versatile strategies that logically extends the framework developed in the previous sections is to stack multiple layers of linear units, interleaving them with nonlinear transformations. We can implement this approach by extending the linear classification model specified by expression 2.20 so that the output of the linear unit is transformed using a nonlinear element-wise function g:

$$\mathbf{h}^{(1)} = g\left(\mathbf{W}^{(1)}\mathbf{x} + \mathbf{b}^{(1)}\right) \tag{2.27}$$

where $\mathbf{x}$ is assumed to be m-dimensional input vector, $\mathbf{W}^{(1)}$ is $m \times k_1$ matrix of parameters, $\mathbf{b}^{(1)}$ is k_1-dimensional vector of parameters, and

$h^{(1)}$ is k_1-dimensional intermediate output. Parameter k_1 basically controls the capacity of the layer. The second layer then can be stacked on top of the first as follows:

$$h^{(2)} = g\left(W^{(2)}h^{(1)} + b^{(2)}\right) \tag{2.28}$$

where $W^{(2)}$ is $k_1 \times k_2$ matrix of parameters and $h^{(2)}$ is k_2-dimensional output. Just like for the first layer, the capacity of the second layer is controlled by parameter k_2. We can continue this process and stack more layers on top of each other.

This architecture is known as a *fully connected neural network* because each element of $(i + 1)$-th layer is computed as a linear combination of all output elements of i-th layer. Individual layers that perform the transformation specified by the above expressions for $h^{(i)}$ are commonly referred to as *fully connected layers* or *dense layers* – we further use these two terms interchangeably. The intermediate layers, that are all layers except the input layer and output layers, are commonly referred to as *hidden layers*. As we will discuss shortly, the fully connected design is an extremely versatile building block for complex models, and it is often combined with more specialized designs to assemble problem-specific neural networks.

The design of the nonlinear transformation g, commonly referred to as an *activation function*, is usually quite basic. The network learns complex distributions through optimizing the coordination between multiple basic units, not through applying complex transformations to individual units. One of the most common and universal choices for g is a rectified linear unit (ReLu):

$$g(x) = ReLu(x) = \max(0, x) \tag{2.29}$$

The second option, which we will use in some architectures, is a sigmoid function. We used it earlier as a tool for mapping arbitrary real values to probabilities, but it is widely used as a generic nonlinear transformation as well:

$$g(x) = \sigma(x) = \frac{1}{1 + e^{-x}} \tag{2.30}$$

Several other alternatives exist as well. Each activation function has its own advantages and disadvantages, but ReLu is widely used in complex architectures due to its computational efficiency and other properties required by the gradient-based training processes.

The fully connected design is illustrated by an example in Figure 2.10. We consider a classification problem that cannot be solved using a model with linear decision boundaries – the two-dimensional input dataset includes two clusters of points twisted in a spiral. This problem, however, can be solved using a three-layer neural network. The first two layers are eight-dimensional, that is $k_1 = k_2 = 8$. The third layer is chosen to be two-dimensional, that is $k_3 = 2$, to make its output easily visualizable. The final output is obtained using a softmax layer, and the model is trained using categorical cross-entropy loss, just like we did for the linear classification model. For the sake of convenience, we denote the output of the top layer $\mathbf{h}^{(3)}$ as $\mathbf{z}$.

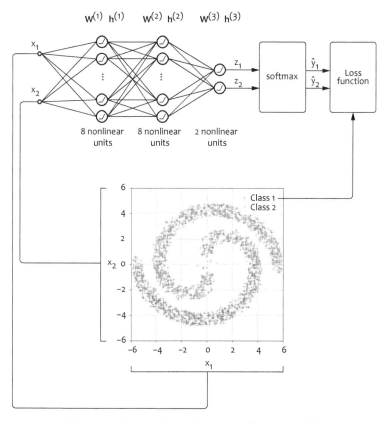

Figure 2.10: Design of a nonlinear classification model.

Once the model is fitted, we can analyze the transformations it performs and the resulting decision boundaries. One crucial insight can be obtained by visualizing the output of the top layer of the network, $\mathbf{z}$. The space spanned on $\mathbf{z}$ can be viewed as a nonlinearly skewed version of the space spanned on $\mathbf{x}$ or, alternatively, vectors $\mathbf{z}$ can be

viewed as embeddings of the input vectors **x**. The space **z** is of interest
to us because vectors **z** are mapped to the final class labels using a
standard softmax unit that has linear decision boundaries. This means
that the model can work if and only if the classes are linearly separable
in space **z**, so the training process is forced to find a representation of
the input space that makes it possible, and this representation captures
the curvature of the clusters in the training dataset. The visualization
presented in Figure 2.11 confirms this statement. The training process
optimizes the parameters of the intermediate network layers in a way
that the linearly inseparable clusters in space **x** are mapped to the linearly separable clusters in the embedding space **z**. This ability of neural
networks to find useful representations is remarkable, and we will discuss various aspects and applications of this capability throughout the
book.

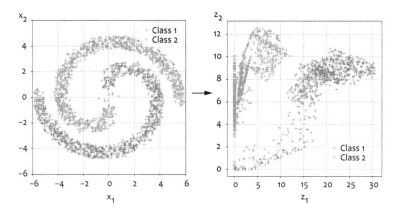

Figure 2.11: Embedding space of the nonlinear classification model.

We can further visualize the overall decision boundaries by computing class probabilities $\hat{y}$ at different points of the input space **x**,
as shown in Figure 2.12. This chart corresponds to the charts in the
middle row of Figure 2.9, but we need only one map instead of three
because the target label is binary (we have only two classes in this
example). This visualization clearly demonstrates sharp nonlinear decision boundaries created by ReLu units, and the ability of the model
to accurately capture the spiral pattern.

We can change the capacity of the model by increasing or decreasing
the number of units at each layer or by changing the number of layers.
The number of units at individual layers is commonly referred to as
the network width, and the number of layers is referred to as the network depth. In most applications, the best performance is achieved by

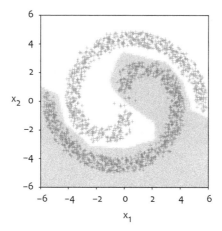

Figure 2.12: Decision boundaries of the nonlinear classification model.

using relatively deep networks with limited width. As we will discuss later, it is also usual to start with relatively wide layers on the input end and gradually decrease the width towards the output end, so that the representations produced by the network layers become more and more dense.

2.3.3 *Embedding Lookup Layer*

The model architecture discussed in the previous section assumes that the input is a real-valued vector that can be interpreted as a single entity such as a point in a multidimensional space. In many applications, however, we have to deal with categorical variables that represent discrete entities such as cities, colors, or product categories. These entities can be encoded as integer numbers (for example, black color can be encoded as 1, red as 2, and so on), but such a representation is generally not appropriate for models with continuous transformations because the numerical distances between the entities are meaningless (for example, the distance between black and red can be 1, whereas the distance between white and blue can be 5). The better representation can be obtained by mapping a categorical feature with cardinality m to an m-dimensional vector so that i-th entity is represented as a vector where i-th position is 1 and other elements are zeros. This approach is known as *one-hot encoding* and commonly used in practice. The challenge is that the dimensionality of the model's input grows proportionally to the cardinality of the categorical features. This increases the number of model parameters and negatively impacts the efficiency of the training process.

The issues with one-hot encoding, as well as some other issues related to the sparsity of the input data, can be mitigated using a technique known as *lookup embeddings*. The main idea is to maintain a lookup table where each entry represents a low-dimensional embedding vector that can be randomly initialized and then iteratively updated using gradient descent as a part of the model training process. Assuming a categorical input feature of cardinality m, we need to maintain a table with m entries, and embedding dimensionality k can be chosen arbitrarily. The input values, that can be represented as category labels or high-dimensional one-hot vectors, can then be transformed into dense k-dimensional embeddings that are consumed by the downstream network, as shown in Figure 2.13. The value of k is usually chosen to be much smaller than m, so that the resulting embeddings are dense real-valued vectors.

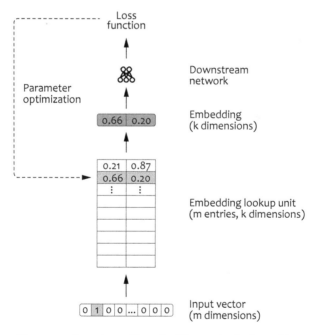

Figure 2.13: Learning entity embeddings using lookup tables.

This technique helps to reduce the dimensionality of the network input from m to k, and also to learn useful semantic representations of the input entities. We illustrate this process by an example shown in

Figure 2.14. In this example, the goal is to model interactions between a pair of entities of two different types x_1 and x_2. There are 10 discrete entities of type x_1 and 10 entities of type x_2, and each interaction is represented by a real number. Consequently, the input data can include up to 100 samples, each of which is a tuple that includes the entity of the first type, entity of the second type, and the interaction value. However, we do not require the dataset to be complete, and some entries can be missed. Our goal is to learn meaningful two-dimensional embeddings for each of 20 entities that capture the semantics of interactions. One real-world use case that closely follows this model is personalized product recommendations – two types of entities correspond to users and products, interactions correspond to user feedback, and the goal is to learn user and product embeddings that allow one to predict the feedback.

 We continue to discuss how lookup embeddings can be used in recommendation engines in recipe R6 (Product Recommendations).

We use a very basic model design where the input entity indexes are mapped to embeddings using the lookup units, then the dot product of two embeddings is computed, and passed through a linear unit to obtain the interaction value. Consequently, interaction value v for a pair of entities x_1 and x_2 can be expressed as

$$v(x_1, x_2) = w \cdot z_1(x_1)^\mathsf{T} \cdot z_2(x_2) + b \qquad (2.31)$$

where z_1 and z_2 are embedding lookup functions which produce two-dimensional embedding vectors $\mathbf{z}_1$ and $\mathbf{z}_2$, respectively, and w and b are the linear unit parameters. This model is basically a regression model, so we train it using the MSE loss function.

Once the model is trained, we can predict the interaction value for any pair of entities by looking up the corresponding embeddings, computing their dot product, and rescaling the result using the linear transformation with the parameters learned by the model. The values predicted this way are shown in Figure 2.15. We can notice that the original dataset has a distinct pattern. There are two blocks of entities with relatively high interaction values (the first one consists of the points such that $x_1 \leqslant 5$ and $x_2 \leqslant 5$, and the second one consists of the points with $x_1 \geqslant 6$ and $x_2 \geqslant 6$); whereas the other two blocks have relatively

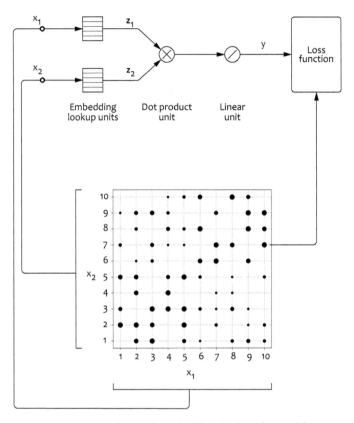

Figure 2.14: Training pipeline with embedding lookup for modeling interactions between two entities.

low values. The predicted values in Figure 2.15 are mainly consistent with this pattern indicating that the semantics of interactions was correctly captured by the embedding vectors. This can also be confirmed by direct visualization of the embedding vectors. For example, the embeddings for all 10 entities of type x_1 are plotted in Figure 2.16, and two distinct clusters of entities that correspond to the left and right halves of the input matrix are clearly visible.

2.3.4 Interaction Layers

The example in the previous section demonstrates how the interaction outcome for two entities can be predicted using the dot product op-

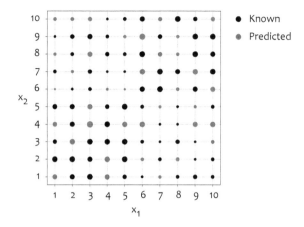

Figure 2.15: Values predicted using the embedding-based model.

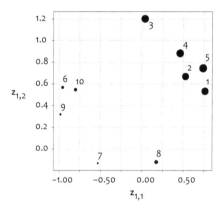

Figure 2.16: Embedding space for the entities of type x_1. The dot sizes correspond to the average interaction value.

eration. We used the dot product as a heuristic solution and did not discuss either its theoretical justification or alternative options. At the same time, the ability to model interactions between entities is essential from the scenario planning perspective because we often need to evaluate multiple possible interaction options and choose the optimal action based on the expected outcome. The personalized recommendations problem that requires evaluating of possible interactions between users and items is a classic example, but many other enterprise problems can be reduced to this formulation as well. In this section, we discuss the interaction modeling problem more thoroughly and, in particular, put the dot product operation into a more comprehensive context.

Let us assume that we want to model the interaction between two entities p and q which are represented as k-dimensional embedding vectors **p** and **q**, respectively. These embeddings can be obtained using either embedding lookup units or deep networks, as shown in Figure 2.17. Our goal is to design a layer that produces value $y(\mathbf{p}, \mathbf{q})$ that can be interpreted as the strength of association between the entities or as an estimation of the interaction outcome.

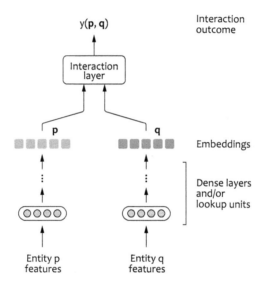

Figure 2.17: Generic architecture of an interaction network.

Let us first assume that both entities belong to the same class. For example, p and q can represent consumer products, and we might be wanting to evaluate the strength of association between them. In this case, it is logical to use the Euclidean distance as a measure of similarity:

$$y_{euclidean}(\mathbf{p}, \mathbf{q}) = \|\mathbf{p} - \mathbf{q}\|^2 \tag{2.32}$$

If the two entities belong to different classes (e.g. p represents a user and q represents an item), we can still assume that they are both mapped to the same semantic space, and the Euclidean distance can approximate the strength of the interaction. This is a fair assumption because the interaction outcome is estimated based on the Euclidean distance, and the network parameters are then optimized to produce embeddings that minimize the estimation error.

We can further recognize that the Euclidean distance and dot product can be used interchangeably provided that the embedding vectors are normalized. Indeed, the following relationship is true for any pair of vectors such that $\mathbf{p}^\mathsf{T}\mathbf{p} = \mathbf{q}^\mathsf{T}\mathbf{q} = 1$:

$$\frac{1}{2}\|\mathbf{p} - \mathbf{q}\|^2 = \frac{1}{2}\left(\mathbf{p}^\mathsf{T}\mathbf{p} + \mathbf{q}^\mathsf{T}\mathbf{q} - 2\mathbf{p}^\mathsf{T}\mathbf{q}\right) = 1 - \mathbf{p}^\mathsf{T}\mathbf{q} \qquad (2.33)$$

Consequently, the dot product layer can be used as a universal component for interaction and similarity modeling purposes:

$$y_{\text{dot}}(\mathbf{p},\ \mathbf{q}) = \mathbf{p}^\mathsf{T}\mathbf{q} = \sum_{i=1}^{k} p_i q_i \qquad (2.34)$$

The dot product, however, is not always the optimal choice because it captures the pairwise interactions between the elements of the input vectors, but not the cross-element interactions. We can address this limitation using the *bilinear layer* that is defined as follows:

$$y_{\text{bilinear}}(\mathbf{p},\ \mathbf{q}) = \mathbf{p}^\mathsf{T}\mathbf{W}\mathbf{q} = \sum_{i=1}^{k}\sum_{j=1}^{k} w_{ij} p_i q_j \qquad (2.35)$$

where $\mathbf{W}$ is a $k \times k$ matrix of learnable parameters. The bilinear layer is less commonly used in the network design than the regular dot product layer, but we will leverage it in some solutions.

2.3.5 *Multi-head and Multi-tower Architectures*

In the previous sections, we have discussed several building blocks including linear units, softmax mappers, nonlinear units, and dense layers. We have also demonstrated how these blocks can be wired together into deep neural networks, and how these networks can be used to solve basic regression and classification problems. Real-world enterprise problems, however, can require far more complex architectures that combine multiple building blocks of different types, including generic and specialized, into one network. In this section, we examine several common design patterns for building such networks using a customer behavior prediction model developed by Google and Pinterest as an example [Wang et al., 2017; Wang, 2020].

The overall architecture is summarized in Figure 2.18. The network is designed to predict customer response metrics such as a click-through rate (CTR) based on the customer features and real-time context such as the type of currently browsed webpage. The inputs of the network are initially processed by the representation layer that maps sparse features to dense embeddings using embedding lookup tables, and concatenates the embeddings, as well as other features that do not require mappings, in one vector. This vector is then transformed by two parallel subnetworks, often referred to as *towers*. One of these networks is a regular fully connected network with k layers denoted as $\mathbf{h}_i$. The second network, called the cross network, has a more specialized design to capture cross-feature interactions. Each layer of this network is specified as

$$\mathbf{x}_{i+1} = \mathbf{x}_0 \mathbf{x}_i^\top \mathbf{w}_i + \mathbf{b}_i + \mathbf{x}_i \tag{2.36}$$

where i is the index of the cross layer, $\mathbf{x}_i$ is the output of i-th layer, $\mathbf{w}_i$ and $\mathbf{b}_i$ are the layer parameters. Assuming that the output of the representation layer $\mathbf{x}_0$ has dimensionality d, each layer of the cross network also produces a d-dimensional output $\mathbf{x}_i$.

The cross network design can be viewed as a generalization of the basic network specified by expression 2.31. Meanwhile, this basic network captures only the pairwise interactions between the embedding elements using a dot product, it can be shown that the cross network with m layers comprises all the cross terms $x_1^{\alpha_1} x_2^{\alpha_2} \cdots x_d^{\alpha_d}$ where x_i are the elements of the input vector and α_i's enumerate all possible combinations of degrees from 1 to $m + 1$.

The outputs of the cross network and deep network are then concatenated and transformed by several dense layers. The top of the network can include several *heads*, that estimate different customer response and engagement metrics $y_i^{(j)}$. Examples of such metrics include the click-through rate, probability of high-value clicks followed by a long page browsing time, and probability of scroll ups. Since these objectives are related, although not equivalent, it is generally beneficial to use a shared bottom network that produces a good representation of the customer and context, and then to use multiple independent heads to map this representation to several specific target labels. This type of learning is known as *multi-task learning* (MLT) [Caruana, 1997]. Finally, the network is trained using a loss function that combines all objectives, that is

$$L(\mathbf{x}_i, y_i^{(1)}, \ldots, y_i^{(q)}) = \sum_{j=1}^{q} L(\mathbf{x}_i, y_i^{(j)}) \tag{2.37}$$

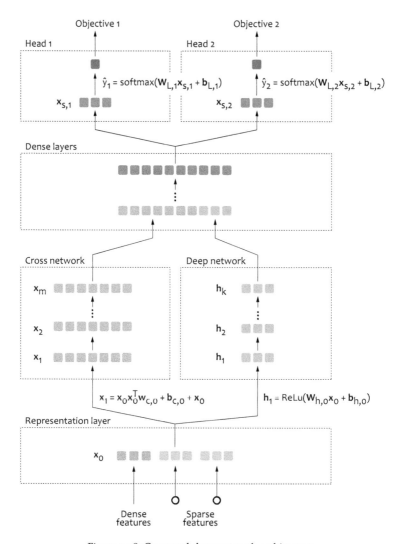

Figure 2.18: Cross and deep network architecture.

where q is the number of objectives, $y_i^{(j)}$ is the target label for j-th objective, and the loss function on the right-hand side is a standard single-objective loss such as categorical cross-entropy or MSE.

The above example illustrates three common patterns used to build complex networks: multiple towers, multiple heads, and multiple objectives. In general, multiple towers are often used in networks with multiple inputs that require different transformations, so that each input is processed by its own tower and then outputs of all towers are merged. In the above example, we have only one input, but apply two different transformations to increase the expressiveness of the network. Multiple heads are typically used to produce multiple outputs that can be used separately or combined into one objective function.

2.4   MODELS WITH SEQUENTIAL INPUTS

 The complete reference implementation for this section is available at https://bit.ly/37kGv1l

Many important classes of enterprise data are conveniently represented as ordered sequences of elements. For example, sales data are sequences of real values, customer interaction histories are sequences of transactions, and texts are sequences of words and characters. Sequences of elements are complex structures that, in a general case, cannot be efficiently represented as plain feature vectors, and thus the modeling methods discussed in the previous sections are not sufficient for solving all types of problems associated with sequential data. The goal of this section is to develop a specialized toolkit for sequence modeling.

2.4.1   *Sequence Modeling Problems*

Sequences or elements are versatile data structures that are used in many different enterprise applications, so we briefly review the main types of sequences and problems associated with sequence modeling before we delve into the mathematical details.

The elements of a sequence are assumed to be ordered. In many applications, the elements are indexed in time order, and such sequences are referred to as *time series*. Each element of the sequence can be associated with a timestamp, or it can just be assumed that elements are observed at successive equally spaced points in time. In time series generated by enterprise processes, each element typically represents the state of the process at a certain moment of time.

The elements of a sequence can be real-valued scalars, discrete tokens, vectors, or other structures. Examples of sequences where elements are real-valued scalars or vectors include weekly sales data, measurements from a sensor installed at a manufacturing machine, and website traffic data. Sequences of discrete tokens can be produced by digital commerce systems that generate sequences of customer events such as logins and checkouts, financial systems that generate sequences of transactions, and web applications that write sequences of words and characters to the logs.

In some applications, we might treat sequences as atomic entities and learn distributions over the entire sequences. In particular, we can build *sequence regression* and *sequence classification* models that map sequences to numerical and categorical labels, respectively. For example, a telecom company might be interested to build a classification model that estimates customers' probability of churn based on their event history. In many other applications, we are interested in learning the distributions of individual elements, and building *element prediction* models. For example, we might be looking to predict future sales figures based on a sequence of historical values. Finally, we might be interested in generating a new sequence based on the input sequence. For example, an online retailer might want to build a recommendation engine that generates an ordered sequence of items the customer is likely to buy based on the items they purchased previously. We refer to this category of problems as *sequence-to-sequence learning*. The semantic relationship between the input and generated sequences can be very different depending on the application. In many applications, the generated sequence is a continuation of the input sequence, so that the sequence-to-sequence learning essentially represents a generalization of the element prediction. In other applications, the generated sequence can be an alternative representation of the input or a completely new object. For instance, a translation model can map a sentence (sequence of words) written in one language to a sentence with the same meaning in a different language.

In the next section, we discuss the fundamental building blocks that can be applied to all of the above scenarios. We use these blocks to develop use case-specific solutions in the next chapters.

2.4.2   *Basic Techniques for Sequence Modeling*

We assume that sequences are generated by stochastic processes, so that a sequence can be viewed as an ordered collection of random variables. This collection may be indexed according to the order the values are obtained in time or according to some other principle. For example, a process can be represented as a sequence x_1, x_2, ..., where x_t is a scalar or vector random variable that denotes the state of the process at time period t. In a general case, we assume that each element of the sequence is dependent on all other elements, and thus the model of the sequence is a specification of the joint distribution $p(x_1, \ldots, x_T)$ where T is the sequence length.

In enterprise applications, we are usually interested in learning more specialized distributions. For example, the sequence classification task requires learning the distribution of the sequence classes c conditioned on the sequence elements:

$$p(c \mid x_1, \ldots, x_T) \tag{2.38}$$

In a similar vein, prediction of the individual sequence elements requires estimating the distributions or expected values of specific elements x_t conditioned on all other elements:

$$p(x_t \mid x_1, \ldots, x_{t-1}, x_{t+1}, \ldots, x_T) \tag{2.39}$$

In principle, these problems can be solved using regression and classification models with vector inputs discussed in the previous section. For example, the classification model defined above can be solved using a model that maps a feature vector $(x_1, \ldots, x_T)$ to the class label. This approach can be feasible in certain applications, but it has several major shortcomings that sharply limit its applicability.

The main disadvantage of the naïve design is that the model parameters are not shared across the input positions – each position is considered unique, and its contribution to the model output is controlled by a dedicated set of parameters. This generally makes the model sample-inefficient – the number of samples needed to train the model grows exponentially with the input length to ensure that the entire space of possible input sequences is covered. This can be illustrated with the following example. Let us assume a training set that consists of binary sequences of length T, that are sequences of zeros and ones. All sequences that include exactly two consecutive ones are labeled as positives, and all other sequences are labeled as negatives. A model that considers each input position as a unique feature cannot recognize that sequence (1, 1, 0, ...) is positive because other sequences that include a pair of ones such as (0, 1, 1, 0, ...) and (..., 0, 1, 1) are positive. Consequently, it requires at least T samples with pairs of ones appearing on each of T positions to generalize properly. In the element prediction problem, the uniqueness of input feature requires the building of a separate model for each position t. Finally, the model needs to be built for the specific length of the sequence, which complicates the processing of variable-length sequences.

Fortunately, most real-world applications do not require us to estimate the complete distribution over the entire sequence because some or all of the following assumptions do hold:

SHORT MEMORY Each element x_t generated by the stochastic process is dependent on context $x_{t-h}, \ldots, x_{t-1}, x_{t+1}, \ldots, x_{t+h}$ where context size h is finite, and independent of the elements outside of the context. The limited memory assumption is crucial because it enables us to constrain the capacity of the model.

STATIONARITY Assuming a stochastic process with limited memory, the joint probability distribution over the context does not change when shifted along the index, so that

$$p(x_{t-h+\tau}, \ldots, x_{t+h+\tau}) = p(x_{t-h}, \ldots, x_{t+h}) \qquad (2.40)$$

for an arbitrary shift τ and all positions t. The stationarity property is extremely important because it implies that the model parameters can be shared across the input positions.

CAUSALITY Each element x_t of the sequence is dependent on the preceding elements $x_{t-1}, x_{t-2}, \ldots$ and independent of the subsequent elements $x_{t+1}, x_{t+2}, \ldots$.

Assuming a stochastic process that complies with the first two properties, the problem reduces to learning distribution $p(x_{t-h}, \ldots, x_{t+h})$. In particular, the previously defined problem of predicting unknown elements based on the known context reduced to learning the following distribution:

$$p(x_t \mid x_{t-h}, \ldots, x_{t-1}, x_{t+1}, \ldots, x_{t+h}) \qquad (2.41)$$

This can be accomplished by building a supervised model with vector inputs and training it using samples generated from the original sequence using a sliding window as shown in Figure 2.19 (a). In this approach, the input features' vectors are assembled from the context elements, and the central elements become the target labels. This allows the reduction of the sequence modeling problem to the vector-input formulation and reuse all the regression and classification methods developed in the previous sections.

Assuming that the causality property holds, the problem of predicting an element based on its context transforms into a problem of predicting the subsequent elements based on the preceding elements. In

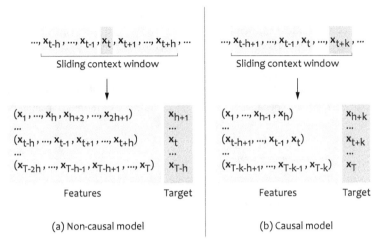

Figure 2.19: Creating vectors from sequences using the sliding window approach.

the context of time series problems, it is common to say that the future (subsequent) elements need to be *forecasted* based on past (preceding) elements, and the terms prediction and forecasting are used interchangeably. It is also common to refer to the elements of the context as *lags*. The forecasting problem requires the estimation of the distribution

$$p(x_{t+k} \mid x_t, \ldots, x_{t-h+1}) \tag{2.42}$$

where $k \geq 1$ is the *forecasting horizon*. This layout is shown in Figure 2.19 (b). The causality assumption is often made in applications where the subsequent elements are not available at the time of the model evaluation (e.g. time series forecasting), but we do not necessarily need to make this assumption when the bidirectional context is available. For example, we can assume that the words in a text are generated one by one by a causal process, and build a word prediction model based on this assumption. However, we can also assume that each word depends on both preceding and subsequent words, and build a model that leverages such a bidirectional context, and this approach generally produces better results.

The feature vectors generated from the original sequence do not necessarily need to include all context elements, that is $2h$ elements in total. In some applications, memory effects can span hundreds or thousands of elements, but these elements can be highly correlated, and only a small subset of them may be sufficient to capture the contribution of the context to the given element. For example, the input vector of a daily sales forecasting model can include lags for several previous days, and then one-week-ago, one-month-ago, and one-year-ago lags that could be sufficient for capturing the seasonal patterns. In such an application, including all 365 daily lags is typically redundant or possibly even harmful because it increases the number of model parameters unnecessarily.

2.4.2.1 *Internal and External Features*

We previously assumed that the element prediction problem requires estimation of the distribution of a specific element x_t based on the context elements $x_{t+\tau}$, and the elements are vectors. Consequently, we assumed that element x_t is completely unobserved, and the i-th feature $x_{t,i}$ of the predicted element is estimated as a function of values of the same feature $x_{t+\tau,\ i}$ in the context vectors, as well as other features $x_{t+\tau,\ j}$ where $j \neq i$. We call models that follow this assumption *autoregressive* models because the t-th state of the element generating process is predicted exclusively based on its preceding and subsequent states.

In many cases, however, we can collect external signals that carry useful information about the state x_t at the moment this state needs to be predicted. For example, we can incorporate the weather forecast into a model that predicts daily sales at a retail store in addition to the past sales values. This requires us to estimate the distribution that is conditioned on both autoregressive and external features:

$$p(x_t \mid x_{t-h}, \ \ldots, \ x_{t-1}, \ x_{t+1}, \ \ldots, \ x_{t+h}, \ q_t) \qquad (2.43)$$

where q_t is the vector of the observed external factors. This extension is relatively straightforward for all model designs we discuss in the next sections, so we mainly focus on the autoregressive formulation without the loss of generality.

2.4.2.2 *Design Options*

The vector-based approach introduced in the previous sections can be implemented in several different ways depending on a specific task. Let us review the most common designs:

CLASSIFICATION AND REGRESSION Sequence classification and regression problems require us to use a whole-sequence window, as shown in Figure 2.20 (a). If sequences of variable lengths need to be handled, this is usually done by implementing a model f for a certain fixed length, and then truncating longer sequences and padding shorter ones with dummy elements such as zeros. The limited ability to handle variable-length sequences and issues with parameter sharing sharply limit the applicability of the vector-input design to this category of problems.

ELEMENT PREDICTION The element prediction tasks are usually solved by building a model that predicts one element based on the input context, as shown in Figure 2.20 (b). In many time series forecasting tasks, we need to produce predictions for multiple horizons, and this can be done by training multiple independent models for different values of k or iterative application of one model. In the latter case, we can use a one-step-ahead model to estimate $\hat{x}_{t+1}$ based on the window $(x_t, \ldots, x_{t-h+1})$, then estimate $\hat{x}_{t+2}$ based on $(\hat{x}_{t+1}, \ldots, x_{t-h+2})$, and so on. The alternative solution is to build a vector-output model that predicts multiple elements of a sequence, as shown in Figure 2.20 (c).

SEQUENCE-TO-SEQUENCE The third design option, shown in Figure 2.20 (d), solves the more general problem of sequence-to-sequence learning. The model is built to predict the elements of arbitrary target sequence y_t based on the input sequence x_t. In a general case, each output element can be predicted based on any subset of input elements, both preceding and succeeding. Sequence-to-sequence learning can also be implemented using single-output or multiple-output approaches.

We illustrate the above designs with two basic examples of time series forecasting models presented in Figures 2.21 and 2.22. In both examples, we use only one instance of a time series which we separate it into the training and test segments. Each of these segments is then transformed into a set of labeled samples using a short sliding window and single-output labels. Finally, we train a linear and two-layer nonlinear models, and evaluate them, producing the forecasts for both training and test datasets.

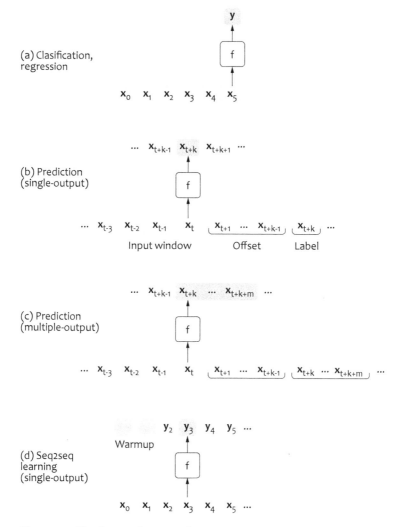

Figure 2.20: The design of input and output vectors for classification, element prediction, and sequence-to-sequence learning tasks.

 We use the sliding window design for demand forecasting and price optimization problems in recipe R7 (Price and Promotion Optimization).

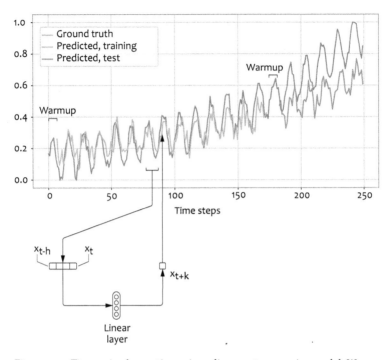

Figure 2.21: Time series forecasting using a linear autoregressive model. We use the input window of size $h = 5$ and forecasting horizon $k = 3$.

The limitations of the approach using the sliding window and vector-input models can be overcome using specialized architectures that make more assumptions that are specific for sequential data. The choice between vector-input models and more specialized models is generally a trade-off between the expressiveness and number of learnable model parameters – more specialized models make more assumptions about the input structure that may or may not be adequate for a given applicable problem. For instance, a demand forecast can be heavily influenced by various external factors such as advertising, weather, and macroeconomic metrics, so that the autocorrelations can play a secondary role. A model with a vector input may be the right solution in such a case. This can be contrasted with certain financial applications where autocorrelations may be the primary factor, and the number of learnable model parameters can be reduced by using time series models that make strong explicit assumptions about the autocorrelation dependencies.

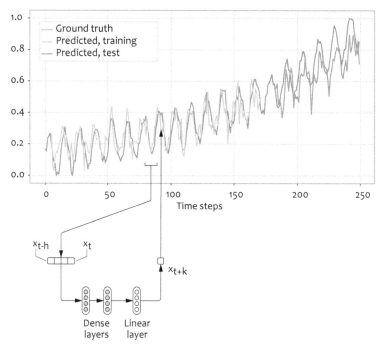

Figure 2.22: Time series forecasting using a nonlinear autoregressive model. We use the input window of size $h = 5$ and forecasting horizon $k = 3$.

2.4.3 Convolution Layer

In the previous section, we introduced the concept of the sliding window and provided a couple of basic examples that illustrate how it can be implemented, but we did not develop any framework for designing models that use the sliding window as an input. This framework should address a number of questions including the following:

- How to construct the input vector given that the elements of the input sequence may be scalar real values, vectors of real values, or embeddings of discrete tokens?

- What model architectures should be used for forecasting, sequence-to-sequence learning, and classification tasks?

- How to summarize a sequence of an arbitrary length into a fixed-length representation which is needed, for example, to perform sequence classification?

These questions cannot be fully addressed using arbitrary vector-input models that operate on a sliding window, and we need to develop more specialized architectures. We can start by defining a basic operation that performs a sequence-to-sequence mapping using a linear transformation over a fixed-width window:

$$y_t = \sum_{i=1}^{h} w_i x_{t-i+1} + b \tag{2.44}$$

where x_t are the elements of the input sequence which are assumed to be scalar real values, y_t are the output elements, w_i are the weights, b is the intercept parameter, and h is the window size. This operation is known as *discrete convolution*, and the vector of weights $\mathbf{w}$ is referred to as a *kernel*. It is usual to say that the input x is *convolved* with kernel $\mathbf{w}$ of size h, and denote this operation as $y = \mathbf{w} * x$.

Most practical problems, however, require the processing of sequences of vectors, not scalars. For example, sequences of discrete tokens are usually converted to sequences of embedding vectors, and many forecasting problems involve multiple time series so that each time step is represented by a vector of metrics. We can extend the basic convolution operation to support sequences of vectors by replacing scalar weights with weight vectors:

$$y_t = \sum_{i=1}^{h} \mathbf{w}_i^T \mathbf{x}_{t-i+1} + b \tag{2.45}$$

In the above expression, $\mathbf{w}_i$ and $\mathbf{x}_t$ are assumed to be k-dimensional vectors, but the output elements y_t are still scalars. The kernel of such a convolution is a $k \times h$ matrix obtained by stacking weight vectors $\mathbf{w}_i$. This operation can also be viewed as a *filter* that transforms the input multivariate signal into the output.

We can develop a sequence-to-sequence transformation component with a higher capacity by stacking multiple filters, so that the input sequence is independently convolved with several kernels, and the results are stacked into output vectors $\mathbf{y}_t$. More specifically, each element of the output vector is computed as

$$y_{t,q} = \sum_{i=1}^{h_q} \mathbf{w}_{qi}^T \mathbf{x}_{t-i+1} + b_q \tag{2.46}$$

where q is the index that iterates all filters, $\mathbf{w}_{qi}$ is the i-th weight vector in the kernel of the q-th filter, and kernel sizes h_q can vary across the filters.

Finally, we add an element-wise nonlinear transformation on top of the linear convolution operation to create a basic block for sequence-to-sequence mapping. For instance, we can use the ReLu operation:

$$y_{t,q} = \text{ReLu} \left(\sum_{i=1}^{h_q} w_{qi}^T x_{t-i+1} + b_q \right) \tag{2.47}$$

This design is known as a *convolution layer*, and its usage for sequence-to-sequence mapping is illustrated in Figure 2.23. Just as the dense layer is an elementary component that performs a nonlinear vector-to-vector transformation, and multiple dense layers can be composed to create complex models, the convolution layer is the elementary component for mapping one sequence of vectors to another.

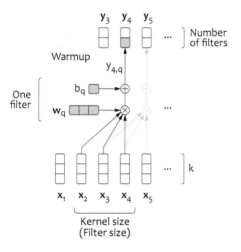

Figure 2.23: The design of a convolution layer.

The convolution layer alone, however, does not address all the questions that we posed in the beginning of this section. It performs only one nonlinear transformation which is not enough to build complex high-capacity models, and can only map the input sequence to a sequence of the same length[1]. The first limitation can be addressed by stacking multiple convolution layers on top of one another, so that the output sequence produced by the first layer is used as an input to the

---

1 Technically speaking, the output of the convolution layer can be shorter than the input by the size of the kernel because of the warmup positions, as shown in Figure 2.23. However, the input sequence can be padded with additional elements before the convolution is performed to produce the output of exactly the same length.

second layer, and so on. This enables us to build deep networks that perform multiple nonlinear transformations of the input sequence.

The second limitation requires us to develop an extension that maps a sequence of one length to a sequence of a different length. In principle, such a mapping can be done by dense layers inserted in between the convolution layers. In a dense layer, however, each output element depends on an input element, and the number of parameters is proportional to the product of the input and output sequence lengths. This design is not optimal for sequences with limited memory effects where we should focus on a local neighborhood of the element rather than on global sequence-wide dependencies.

The alternative approach that overcomes this issue is known as *pooling*. The main idea of pooling is to divide the output of the convolution layer into regions and then map each region to a summary statistic using a *pooling function*. The most common choices for the pooling function are maximum and average, that are simple operations without learnable parameters. Replacing a region, that is a group of elements, with its maximum or average, generally aims to detect the presence of a certain feature and propagate this information to the upper layer. Meanwhile, the information about exactly where this feature is located is discarded. This is indeed a logical approach to sequence summarization which also helps to make the model insensitive to small shifts in the input. The pooling operations are usually implemented using a sliding window, which is similar to the convolution operation, but the window parameters can be adjusted to produce a shorter output sequence. We illustrate this with an example presented in Figure 2.24. The pooling operation is performed by processing the input sequence with a sliding window of three elements (pool size), the window is shifted by two positions (stride), and each step produces one output element such as the maximum over the window. Consequently, the output sequence is half the length of the input sequence. The ratio between the pool size and stride controls the sequence contraction. It is also important that the pooling operation reduces the sensitivity of the model to local changes in the input even when the input and output sequences are the same length because the elements are replaced by the region level aggregates such as averages or maximums.

The convolution and pooling layers provide the necessary toolkit for building complex models for sequence processing and analysis. Such models, typically created by stacking multiple convolution and pooling layers, are known as deep *convolutional neural networks* (CNNs) [Le-Cun et al., 1989]. A typical architecture of a convolutional model for sequence classification is presented in Figure 2.25. In this example, we

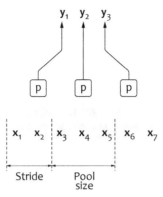

Figure 2.24: The design of the pooling layer. The pooling function is denoted as p.

assume that the model consumes a sequence of k-dimensional vectors, and the length of the sequence is t. The first convolution layer has q_1 filters, and produces a sequence of q_1-dimensional vectors, also of length t. This sequence is then contracted by the first pooling layer. The pooling operation is applied element-wise, so that each input dimension is mapped by the pooling function independently of other dimensions, and thus the output of the pooling layer is also a sequence of q_1-dimensional vectors, but its length t_1 is controlled by the parameters of the pooling layer. This sequence is then processed by the second convolution layer that consists of q_2 filters and produces a sequence of q_2-dimensional vectors. Finally, we use a pooling layer with the pool size equal to the length of the input sequence (so-called *global pooling*) to summarize the sequence produced by the second convolution layer into a single embedding vector. The model output is then computed by some standard output mapper such a dense layer with softmax.

We use one-dimensional convolutions in recipe R10 (Anomaly Detection) to predict the remaining useful life of equipment based on the time series collected from IoT sensors.

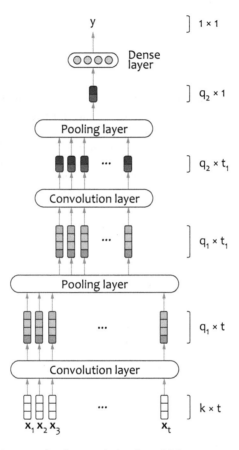

Figure 2.25: An example of a convolutional model for sequence classification.

2.4.4 Recurrent Layers

The convolutional architecture presented in the previous section is only one of several commonly used designs for sequence modeling. In this section, we discuss an alternative architecture that solves the problem of parameter sharing across the sequence positions by creating a stateful unit that consumes the input sequence element by element.

Let us assume function f specified by a vector of parameters θ that takes two vector arguments, x_t and c_t, and produces two output vectors which we denote as y_t and c_{t+1}:

$$(y_t, c_{t+1}) = f(x_t, c_t, \theta) \tag{2.48}$$

We interpret x_t as the primary input, y_t as the primary output, and c_t as a state that is updated using x_t at every invocation of the function and can be carried over between the invocations. We can then create a chain of units that implements function f, and feeds a sequence of elements $(x_1, \ldots, x_t)$ into it as shown in Figure 2.26. Note that all units are assumed to be identical, so that there is only one vector of parameters θ shared across all units. Since all units are identical, this chain is equivalent to a single unit that processes the sequence elements one by one, updating the state vector at every iteration, as illustrated in the right-hand side of Figure 2.26. Assuming that function f is implemented as a neural network, this design is known as a *recurrent neural network* (RNN) and its units are commonly referred to as *cells* [Rumelhart et al., 1986].

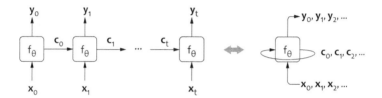

Figure 2.26: The conceptual design of a recurrent neural network.

The design presented in Figure 2.26 is essentially a sequence-to-sequence model: it consumes sequence $(x_1, \ldots, x_t)$ and produces a sequence of the same length $(y_1, \ldots, y_t)$. This layout can be used, for instance, to create a model that consumes a text word by word and produces sentiment scores for each position. However, the RNN approach can be straightforwardly adapted to other standard tasks including element prediction, sequence classification, and sequence-to-sequence generation as illustrated in Figure 2.27:

PREDICTION In the case of element prediction, the network can process the available sequence $(x_1, \ldots, x_t)$ and predict the next element x_{t+1}. If a new element arrives, it is processed using the latest state vector as another input, and a new prediction, as well as an updated state vector, are produced.

CLASSIFICATION In the case of classification, we are interested only in the final output that is obtained by summarizing the entire sequence into one vector and mapping this vector to the output label. The intermediate outputs can be discarded.

SEQUENCE-TO-SEQUENCE The third case is a more generic design for sequence-to-sequence learning which is known as the encoder-decoder architecture. The limitation of the basic design presented in Figure 2.26 is that the input and output sequences must be of the same length. This approach is not feasible for learning complex sequence-to-sequence mappings where the length of the output sequence is determined by the content of the input sequence, not its length. A typical example of this is a translation model that consumes a sentence in one language and produces a sentence in another language.

This type of problem can be solved by learning a sequence embedding (state vector) using one network and then generating the output sequence using the second network. These two parts are known respectively as the encoder and decoder. The sequence-to-sequence architecture shown in Figure 2.27 highlights several typical design patterns. First, the flow is controlled using special tokens – the *end of sequence* element is appended to the input sequence, and generation of the output sequence is initiated with the *beginning of sequence* token. The network is supposed to learn appropriate embeddings for these tokens that help to finalize the state vector and initialize the generation, respectively. Second, the output sequence is generated element by element so that the output of one step is used as the input to the next step.

In order to implement the RNN architecture, we have to specify the design of an individual cell. One of the most basic options is presented in Figure 2.28. In this design, the input and state vector are concatenated, or transformed using a dense layer to produce a new state, and the output is computed using another dense layer that maps the state vector to the required output format. For example, we can specify the design of a classification model using this layout as follows:

$$
\begin{aligned}
c_t &= \mathrm{ReLu}(\mathbf{W}_c(c_{t-1}, \mathbf{x}_t) + \mathbf{b}_c) \\
\mathbf{y}_t &= \mathrm{softmax}(\mathbf{W}_y c_t + \mathbf{b}_y)
\end{aligned}
\tag{2.49}
$$

where matrices $\mathbf{W}$ and vectors $\mathbf{b}$ are the model parameters that specify the transformations performed by the two layers. The model then can be trained using categorical cross-entropy or another standard loss function to minimize the discrepancy between output $\mathbf{y}$ and ground truth labels.

The design presented in Figure 2.28 is simple and easy to understand, but, unfortunately, it is not feasible for many practical problems. The main idea behind the RNN architecture is to continuously admix new elements of the input sequence into the state vector, so that the state vector at each step represents a condensed summary (embedding) of all elements encountered before that step. This summary is used as

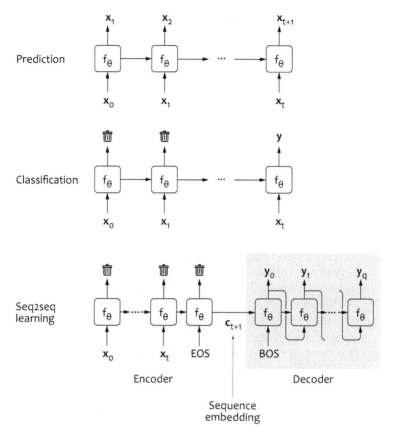

Figure 2.27: Design variants for forecasting, classification, and sequence generation problems. In the latter case, the flow is controlled using special tokens EOS and BOS which stand for *end of sequence* and *beginning of sequence*, respectively.

a context for predicting the output value of the cell. From that perspective, the crucial question is for how long the traits of a specific input sample x_t stay in the state vector before they are washed out and displaced by subsequent samples x_{t+1}, x_{t+2}, ... If this process is misbalanced, and old samples are becoming forgotten relatively quickly, the network might not be able to learn long-term dependencies between the elements of the sequence. It turns out that the basic designs such as the one presented in Figure 2.28 are prone to this problem, and special enhancements need to be made in order to control the forgetting dynamics [Bengio et al., 1994]. These enhancements can substantially improve the ability of the network to memorize the long-term depen

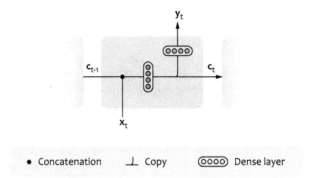

Figure 2.28: An example of a basic RNN cell.

dencies and improve the overall performance of the model. We discuss one of the most common and well-known solutions in the next section.

2.4.5   *Long Short-Term Memory Layer*

The performance of recurrent neural networks on problems that require learning long-term dependencies can be improved through advanced state management. The *long short-term memory* (LSTM) cell architecture implements this idea by extending the basic RNN cell with special signal amplifying and de-amplifying units called *gates* that are controlled by learnable parameters [Hochreiter and Schmidhuber, 1995, 1997].

The LSTM cell includes several components, each of which has a clearly defined function, so we describe the LSTM design component by component. First, the LSTM design assumes that the state vector c_t is modified using only two operations which are element-wise multiplication and element-wise addition, as shown in Figure 2.29. The purpose of the multiplication operation is to modulate the old state, that is to control how much of the old state will be preserved in the new state. Thus, this operation is known as the *forget gate*. The purpose of the addition operation, on the contrary, is to add new information to the state. This operation is referred to as the *input gate*. Each of these operations, of course, requires the second operand, and these operands are computed by other components of the cell.

The weight vector for the forget gate is computed using a dense layer with a sigmoid activation function based on the concatenation of the

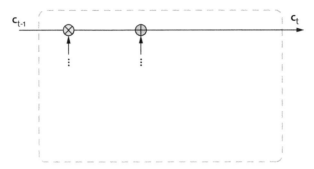

Figure 2.29: The cell state path in LSTM.

previous cell output $\mathbf{y}_{t-1}$ and current sequence element $\mathbf{x}_t$. We denote this weight vector as $\mathbf{f}_t$, and specify it as follows:

$$\mathbf{f}_t = \sigma\left(\mathbf{W}_f \cdot (\mathbf{y}_{t-1}, \ \mathbf{x}_t) + \mathbf{b}_f\right) \tag{2.50}$$

where $\mathbf{W}_f$ and $\mathbf{b}_f$ are the layer parameters that are fine-tuned during the learning process to achieve the optimal forgetting dynamics. The sigmoid activation function is applied element-wise, and thus ensures that elements of $\mathbf{f}_t$ are normalized into the range between zero and one. The value of zero means that the corresponding element of $\mathbf{c}_{t-1}$ will be completely removed, and the value of one means that the element will pass through without modifications. The complete design of the forget gate is presented in Figure 2.30.

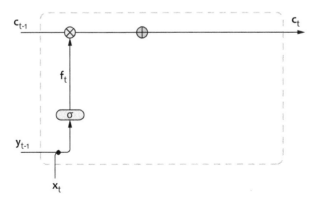

Figure 2.30: The design of the forget gate in LSTM. Block σ denotes a dense layer with a sigmoid activation function.

The input vector for the input gate is computed using two parallel dense layers. These layers initially produce the following two vectors based on the concatenated cell input:

$$\tilde{c}_t = \tanh\left(\mathbf{W}_c \cdot (\mathbf{y}_{t-1},\, \mathbf{x}_t) + \mathbf{b}_c\right)$$
$$\mathbf{i}_t = \text{softmax}\left(\mathbf{W}_i \cdot (\mathbf{y}_{t-1},\, \mathbf{x}_t) + \mathbf{b}_i\right)$$

(2.51)

We can view vector $\tilde{c}_t$ as a candidate state and $\mathbf{i}_t$ as its modulating vector similar to $\mathbf{f}_t$. Vector $\tilde{c}_t$ is computed using tanh activation function which is an alternative to ReLu, and vector $\mathbf{i}_t$ is computed using a sigmoid function. These two vectors are then multiplied element-wise and added to the state vector, so that the final expression for the state vector update is as follows:

$$\mathbf{c}_t = \mathbf{f}_t \odot \mathbf{c}_{t-1} + \mathbf{i}_t \odot \tilde{c}_t$$

(2.52)

where $\odot$ denotes the element-wise multiplication. The complete design of the input gate is shown in Figure 2.31.

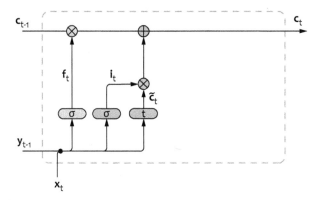

Figure 2.31: The design of the input gate in LSTM. Blocks σ and t denote dense layers with σ and tanh activation functions, respectively.

Finally, we need to specify how the output vector $\mathbf{y}_t$ is computed. This part of the LSTM cell is referred to as the *output gate*. Similar to the input gate, the output gate consists of two parts. The first part computes the candidate output vector by normalizing the updated state $\mathbf{c}_t$ using element-wise tanh transformation, and the second is a dense layer that computes the modulating vector based on the concatenated cell input, while the final output is obtained as an element-wise multiplication of these two components:

$$\mathbf{o}_t = \sigma\left(\mathbf{W}_o \cdot (\mathbf{y}_{t-1},\, \mathbf{x}_t) + \mathbf{b}_o\right)$$
$$\mathbf{y}_t = \mathbf{o}_t \odot \tanh(\mathbf{c}_t)$$

(2.53)

The complete LSTM design that includes the forget, input, and output gates is presented in Figure 2.32. The full model can also include an output mapper that post-processes the output vector $\mathbf{y}_t$ produced by the cell. For example, a sequence classification model can map the final output obtained at the end of the sequence using a softmax layer to produce the class label.

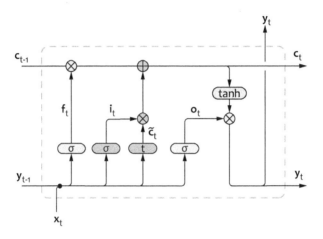

Figure 2.32: The complete design of the LSTM cell.

As discussed in the previous section, some problems require the use of the full sequence of outputs $(\mathbf{y}_1, \ldots, \mathbf{y}_t)$ produced by the cell, and some other problems, such as sequence classification, can be solved by using only the final output value $\mathbf{y}_t$. In the latter case, intermediate values $(\mathbf{y}_1, \ldots, \mathbf{y}_{t-1})$ are computed internally, similar to the cell state vectors $\mathbf{c}$, but not outputted. These intermediate values are commonly referred to as *hidden state vectors* of LSTM.

The main concepts of LSTM are used in a number of alternative architectures that differ in the number and structure of the gates. These variants can outperform LSTM or reduce computational complexity on certain tasks, but the standard LSTM design is known to provide an efficient trade-off for many applications [Greff et al., 2017].

LSTM can be used to analyze customer journeys and build personalization models, optimize marketing spend, and forecast the demand. We discuss these applications in recipes R1 (Propensity Modeling) and R7 (Price and Promotion Optimization). LSTM is also used in reinforcement learning solutions that require keeping track of the environment history. We discuss this topic in the context of supply chain optimization in recipe R9 (Inventory Optimization).

We illustrate the capabilities of LSTM using the time series forecasting example presented in Figure 2.33. In this example, we develop a model for one-step-ahead forecasting of a univariate time series. We train and evaluate the model using a single time series that is visualized in the figure. The series is cut into short segments of length k, and the LSTM model is trained using a subset of segments that corresponds to the beginning of the series. The model is designed as a regression model, so that it predicts value x_{t+1} based on input segment $(x_t, \ldots, x_{t-k})$ where x_t are scalar values taken from the original series. This approach requires the use of an additional linear layer that maps the output vector of the LSTM cell $\mathbf{y}_t$ to scalar value x_{t+1}. Model validation is done using the samples from the end of the series.

2.4.6 *Attention Mechanism*

The standard LSTM model for classification or regression starts with a random output vector $\mathbf{y}_0$, sequentially updates it with the elements of the input sequence, and estimates the output value based on the final value of the output vector. This approach is not always optimal because the final value does not necessarily provide a complete representation of the input sequence, and better results can be obtained by using a weighted average of intermediate values as outlined in Figure 2.34.

This extension of the basic LSTM architecture is known as an *attention mechanism*. It was originally developed for natural language processing applications in which the intuition was that the weights associated with the intermediate states essentially model the attention that a

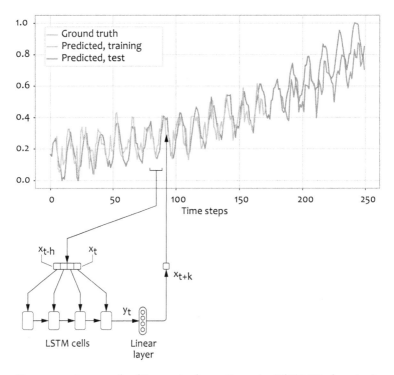

Figure 2.33: An example of time series forecasting using LSTM. Window size h is 5, forecasting horizon k is 3. We use a two-dimensional output space ($\dim(\mathbf{y}) = 2$).

human reader pays to different words in a sentence [Bahdanau et al., 2014].

The attention mechanism requires the learning of weights for combining the intermediate output vectors $\mathbf{y}_t$ together into the final output. These weights, known as attention weights, can be viewed as modulators that control the contribution of individual output vectors to the *history vector* $\mathbf{s}$ which is used to compute the final output. A typical implementation of the attention mechanism includes the following operations:

- First, a dense layer with tanh activation function is used to squash each output vector $\mathbf{y}_t$ into an attention vector $\mathbf{u}_t$:

$$\mathbf{u}_t = \tanh\left(\mathbf{W}\mathbf{y}_t + \mathbf{b}\right) \tag{2.54}$$

where $\mathbf{W}$ and $\mathbf{b}$ are the learnable parameters.

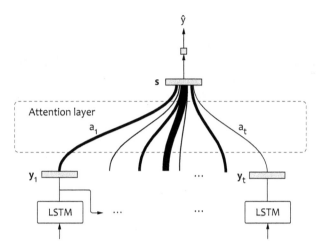

Figure 2.34: The conceptual design of the attention mechanism.

- Second, the importance of each step, that is the *attention weight*, is estimated as the normalized similarity between $\mathbf{u}_t$ and so-called context vector $\mathbf{c}$:

$$a_t = \text{softmax}\left(\mathbf{u}_t^\mathsf{T} \mathbf{c}\right) \tag{2.55}$$

The context vector is a vector of model parameters that is learned jointly during the training process, similar to $\mathbf{W}$ and $\mathbf{b}$.

- Finally, the history vector $\mathbf{s}$ is obtained as an attention-weighted sum of the intermediate outputs:

$$\mathbf{s} = \sum_t a_t \mathbf{y}_t \tag{2.56}$$

It is easy to see that the design of attention weights is structurally similar to the design of gates inside the LSTM cell. The final output of the model is created based on the history vector $\mathbf{s}$ using additional layers such as linear or softmax.

The attention layer helps to improve the performance of LSTM on certain classes of tasks, but it also provides a way of estimating the contribution of individual elements of the input sequence into the final output. Since the intermediate outputs $\mathbf{y}_t$ are modulated by the attention weights, we can interpret each weight a_t as a measure of contribution of the corresponding LSTM input $\mathbf{x}_t$. This is an important feature that turns LSTM with attention mechanism into a powerful tool for the analysis of sequential patterns.

We use the attention mechanism in recipe R1 (Propensity Modeling) for customer journey analytics.

2.4.7 *Transformer Layer*

The LSTM with attention architecture presented in the previous section has two layers. The first one is LSTM that transforms the input sequence into another sequence of the same length. The second layer is the attention mechanism that mixes the outputs of LSTM into the final output. This layer is relatively simple and lightweight because it aims only to refine the representations produced by the LSTM layer. A logical question that can be asked is whether we can extend the attention layer and make it sufficiently expressive to model the entire sequence, so that the LSTM layer can be removed completely. This, in particular, can eliminate the disadvantages associated with LSTM such as computational inefficiency due to sequential processing of the input elements.

In this section, we analyze the concept of attention in greater detail, develop a more advanced design that can capture complex patterns, and discuss how classification and forecasting models can be created by stacking multiple attention layers.

2.4.7.1 *Self-attention*

We aim to develop a component that, similar to LSTM, implements a sequence-to-sequence operation: it should consume a sequence of vectors $(\mathbf{x}_1, \ldots, \mathbf{x}_t)$ and produce another sequence of vectors $(\mathbf{y}_1, \ldots, \mathbf{y}_t)$. For the sake of specificity, let us also assume that both input and output vectors are embedding some entities. For example, the input vectors can be created from discrete tokens using embedding lookups, and output vectors can be mapped to labels using softmax. One of the most basic implementations of a sequence-to-sequence operation would be a linear model that estimates each output element as a linear combination of all input elements:

$$\mathbf{y}_i = \sum_{j=1}^{t} w_{ij}\mathbf{x}_j \qquad (2.57)$$

where w_{ij} are the weights optimized during the training process. This simple model is not particularly useful because it captures only linear dependencies and its weights are position-specific which, as we discussed earlier, is not feasible for sequence modeling. However, we can extend this design by replacing constant weights with functions that are evaluated based on the input values:

$$w_{ij} = f(\mathbf{x}_1, \ldots, \mathbf{x}_t) \tag{2.58}$$

Expressions 2.57 and 2.58 define a generic framework, known as *self-attention*, that can be used to create specific models by supplying specific functions f. For example, we can create a basic self-attention model by computing weights as dot products between the input vectors:

$$w_{ij} = \mathbf{x}_i^T \mathbf{x}_j \tag{2.59}$$

This design is illustrated in Figure 2.35. To understand why this design works, we can compare it with the model that we developed earlier to illustrate the concept of the lookup embeddings (see Figure 2.14). In that model, the idea was to express the interactions between two entities as a dot product between the corresponding embedding vectors. This approach worked because the training process optimized the embeddings with the goal of making the dot product in the created embedding space a good approximation of the actually observed interaction labels. The same principle works for the self-attention model specified in expression 2.59 – we fix the weight function, and then train the model to find the optimal embeddings $\mathbf{x}$ for the input elements. In this simple example, input embeddings are the only learnable model parameters because the self-attention weights are computed as plain dot products which do not require any additional parameters. In a general case, the training process jointly learns both the embeddings and parameters of function f which, as we discuss next, can be much more complex than a dot product.

The dot product–based design is not a feasible solution for most real-world sequence modeling problems. Instead, it is common to use the following architecture of the self-attention layer to provide enough capacity for building complex models:

1. For each input element $\mathbf{x}_i$, we compute three additional embeddings using three separate linear transformations:

$$\begin{aligned} \mathbf{k}_i &= \mathbf{W}_k \mathbf{x}_i \\ \mathbf{v}_i &= \mathbf{W}_v \mathbf{x}_i \\ \mathbf{q}_i &= \mathbf{W}_q \mathbf{x}_i \end{aligned} \tag{2.60}$$

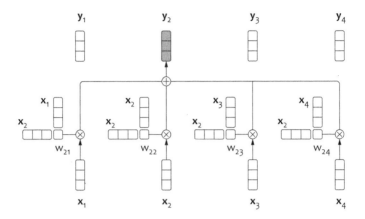

Figure 2.35: A basic example of a self-attention model.

These embeddings are referred to as *key*, *value*, and *query*, respectively. Matrices $\mathbf{W}_k$, $\mathbf{W}_v$, and $\mathbf{W}_q$ are the learnable parameters of the model.

2. Next, we compute the matrix of attention weights. For each pair of input and output positions $\mathbf{x}_i$ and $\mathbf{y}_j$, the attention weight is computed as a softmax-normalized product between the corresponding query and key embeddings:

$$w_{ij} = \underset{j}{\text{softmax}} \left(\mathbf{q}_i^\top \mathbf{k}_j \right) \tag{2.61}$$

3. Finally, the output values are computed as a weighted sum of the value embeddings:

$$\mathbf{y}_i = \sum_j w_{ij} \mathbf{v}_j \tag{2.62}$$

This design is illustrated in Figure 2.36. The key-value-query terminology is borrowed from the information retrieval field. For each output value, we query the input sequence, evaluate the relevance of each input element as a dot product between the *query* and element's *key*, and compute the final output using *values* of the input elements.

Finally, it is common to have multiple parallel self-attention layers to increase the model capacity even further. This is usually implemented as follows:

1. First, we choose the total number of self-attention layers R. It is a fixed model hyperparameter.

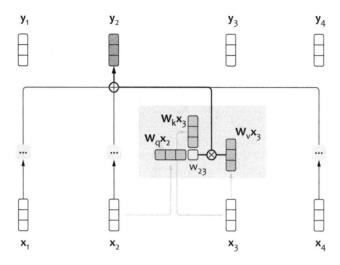

Figure 2.36: The self-attention with key, value, and query transformations.

2. For each self-attention layer, we use a separate set of transformation matrices $\mathbf{W}_k^r$, $\mathbf{W}_v^r$, and $\mathbf{W}_q^r$ where $1 \leqslant r \leqslant R$ is the index of the layer. These matrices are then used to compute multiple sets of embeddings, multiple attention weight matrices, and finally multiple outputs $\mathbf{y}_i^r$.

3. The final output is computed using a linear transformation of the concatenated layer outputs:

$$\mathbf{y}_i = \mathbf{W}_r \cdot \left(\mathbf{y}_i^1, \, \ldots, \, \mathbf{y}_i^R \right) + \mathbf{b}_r \tag{2.63}$$

where $\mathbf{W}_r$ and $\mathbf{b}_r$ are the learnable parameters. Assuming that output vectors $\mathbf{y}_i^r$ are k-dimensional, their concatenation is a kR-dimensional vector, and $\mathbf{W}_r$ is usually chosen to be $k \times kR$ matrix so that the final output $\mathbf{y}_i$ is also k-dimensional.

In the above design, layers are commonly referred to as heads, and the design as a whole is referred to as *multi-head self-attention* [Vaswani et al., 2017]. This architecture was originally developed as a component for high-capacity NLP models, and it proved itself to be very efficient for a wide range of NLP problems, as well as other applications including time series forecasting and event sequence analysis.

2.4.7.2   *Causal Attention*

The design of the self-attention layer presented in the previous section assumes that each output value y_i depends on (attends to) all input values x_j. This is a valid assumption for classification models that use output values to label the entire sequence, but this design is not suitable for forecasting problems where each output value y_t must be estimated using only the preceding input elements $x_t, \ldots, x_1$. In other words, the relationship between inputs and output sequences in forecasting problems must be *causal*. We can adapt the self-attention architecture to this type of problems by masking the attention weights in a way that the model does not have access to the elements that follow x_t to estimate y_t. This can be implemented by inserting a special masking term into expression 2.61 so that the attention weights are computed as follows:

$$w_{ij} = \underset{j}{\mathrm{softmax}} \left(\mathbf{q}_i^T \mathbf{k}_j + m_{ij} \right) \tag{2.64}$$

where m_{ij} are the elements of a triangular matrix in which entries on the main diagonal and below it are zeros, and all entries above the main diagonal are set to $-\infty$, as shown in Figure 2.37. The softmax operation then turns all elements of the weights matrix above the main diagonal into zeros which, in turn, disables all non-causal dependencies between inputs and outputs, as illustrated in the lower part of Figure 2.37. This version of the self-attention layer is known as *causal attention*.

2.4.7.3   *From Self-attention to Transformer*

The self-attention layer is a generic component that performs a sequence-to-sequence mapping. A model that consists of a single self-attention layer, however, has relatively limited capacity, and we need to develop a method for composing multiple self-attention layers together in order to build practically useful models.

It turns out that the basic self-attention layers do not provide enough computational stability to be easily composable, so the first step towards creating a multilayer architecture is to combine self-attention with additional components that improve the learning efficiency and stability. The result of such a combination is also a generic sequence-to-sequence layer known as a *transformer block* or *transformer layer*. A typical design of the transformer block is presented in Figure 2.38. This design includes a self-attention layer, skip connections, layer normalization operations, and shared dense layers. The skip connections are

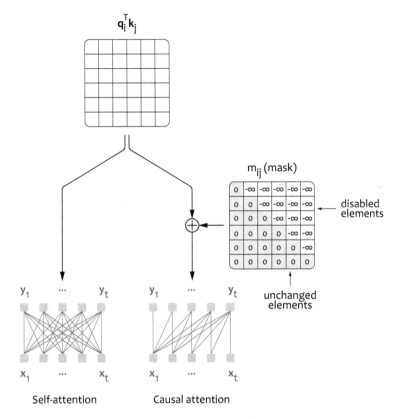

Figure 2.37: Attention weights masking for causal attention.

the shortcuts that jump over layers, helping to train a deep network. The normalization layer rescales each training sample to zero mean and unit variance which is also a technique for improving the training efficiency. Finally, the outputs of the first normalization layer are further transformed with a shared dense layer which is independently applied to each output vector. There is only one instance of this layer, so exactly the same transformation is applied to all sequence elements.

A composable transformer block enables us to build high-capacity models for various tasks that require the learning of complex distributions. Such models are typically constructed by stacking multiple transformer blocks as shown in Figure 2.39 where two typical architectures are presented. The first model is a classification model, and its final output is computed by averaging the output vectors of the topmost transformer. The second model is an autoregressive model that

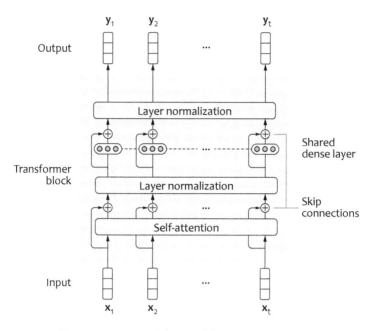

Figure 2.38: A typical design of the transformer block.

is trained to predict the next element of a sequence, and thus it uses a stack of transformer blocks with causal attention layers.

In both models, the input to the first transformer block is created by adding special vectors, denoted as $\mathbf{p}_t$ in Figure 2.39, to the regular inputs. These special vectors, known as *position embeddings*, are an essential component for building fully functional transformer models. The position embeddings are needed because the self-attention layer is permutation invariant: if we change the order of the elements in the input sequence, the elements of the output sequence will remain the same but will also be shuffled. Consequently, a stack of transformer blocks is also permutation invariant. In causal attention, a partial order is established, but each output element is still invariant to permutations of its inputs. However, we need a complete model to be fully aware of the order of the input elements. For example, a language model that predicts the next word in a sentence should account for the order of the previous words. Position embeddings are a standard technique for addressing this limitation – we create an embedding lookup table where entries are indexed by positions rather than by input tokens, and optimize these embeddings just like regular lookup embeddings during the training process. The shortcoming of this design is that the

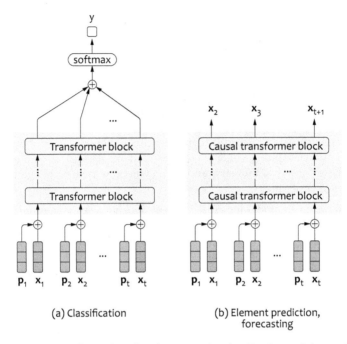

(a) Classification

(b) Element prediction, forecasting

Figure 2.39: Transformer-based architectures for classification and forecasting problems.

lookup table has to have as many entries as the maximum sequence length, and, if the model is trained on sequences of various lengths, some embeddings might be undertrained. An alternative solution is to use *position encodings* – a fixed set of vectors generated using some deterministic function such as a sinusoid. Unlike position embeddings, position encodings are non-learnable parameters of the model. Both of these techniques, as well as their variations, are used in common transformer architectures [Wang and Chen, 2020].

2.5   MODELS WITH MULTIDIMENSIONAL INPUTS

We spent the previous section developing models for sequences, that is one-dimensional arrays, of elements. In case the elements of the sequence are vectors, the sequence can be viewed as a two-dimensional matrix where columns correspond to the elements, and rows correspond to the elements' dimensions. The models that we have developed, however, would account only for the order of columns in such a matrix and consider all rows to be independent. At the same time, many enterprise applications require the processing of matrices or tensors of elements that have interdependencies along two or more axes. The most prominent example is computer vision applications that deal with images represented as two-dimensional arrays of pixels. In photographic images, the probabilistic distribution of each pixel is, of course, conditioned on its neighbors along both horizontal and vertical dimensions, and the sequence modeling framework is insufficient for capturing such two-dimensional dependencies. Other examples of multidimensional inputs include 2D geospatial data, 3D seismic data used in the oil and gas industry, and 3D magnetic resonance imaging in medical applications.

The need to model the cross-element dependencies along multiple dimensions is a distinctive challenge for multidimensional data, but it also inherits all the challenges associated with sequence modeling including parameter sharing and sample efficiency problems. In principle, all models that we have developed for one-dimensional sequences can be generalized to process multidimensional inputs. In practice, convolutional networks is a default platform for building this type of model, and we devote this section to developing several variants of the convolution layer for two-dimensional inputs. The same approach can be used to process inputs with three or more dimensions.

2.5.1   2D Convolution Operation

The one-dimensional convolution operation introduced in Section 2.4.3 can be simply generalized for the case of two dimensions. This can be done by allowing the input, filter (kernel), and output, which are all vectors in the one-dimensional case, to be matrices. Assuming that the filter is a square matrix of size $(2s + 1) \times (2s + 1)$ where s is a nonnegative integer, we can express the basic 2D convolution operation as follows:

$$y_{ij} = \sum_{u=-s}^{s} \sum_{v=-s}^{s} w_{u+s+1,\, v+s+1} \cdot x_{i+u,\, j+v} + b \qquad (2.65)$$

where x_{ij} and y_{ij} are the elements of the input and output matrices, respectively, w_{ij} are the elements of the filter matrix, and b is the intercept term which is also a parameter of the operation. This expression is illustrated by means of an example in Figure 2.40 where we assume a 3×3 filter, so that the corresponding value of s in expression 2.65 is equal to one.

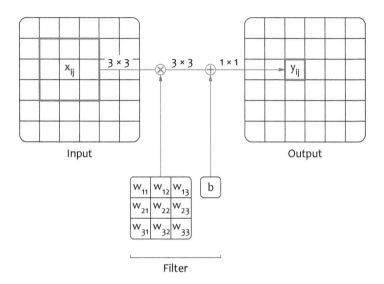

Figure 2.40: An example of a two-dimensional convolution operation for a single-channel input.

The example in Figure 2.40 suggests that the convolution expression cannot be fully evaluated for the edge elements of the input matrix for filters larger than 1×1 because some parts of the filter would protrude outside of the matrix and refer to non-existing elements. There are two common ways of handling this problem. The first is to compute the output only for the positions where the filter can be fully evaluated, so that the convolution between an $n \times m$ input matrix and $(2s + 1) \times (2s + 1)$ filter produces a $(n - 2s) \times (n - 2s)$ output matrix. This basically corresponds to the warmup zones we discussed in the section dedicated to one-dimensional convolution. The second option is to substitute the non-existing elements with the copies of the nearest edge elements, so that an output matrix exactly the same size as the input is produced.

2.5.2 2D Convolution Layer

The convolution operation specified in the previous section is the core concept for processing multidimensional inputs, but we need to extend it in several ways to create a generic component that can be used for building complex models.

First, the convolution operation specified by expression 2.65 is a linear transformation, and the complete convolution layer generally includes a nonlinear activation function such as ReLu that is applied to the result of the convolution.

Second, the basic convolution produces an output the same size as the input, but we often need to produce an output of a smaller size to create denser embeddings. One possible way to achieve this is to shift the filter window by more than one position at a time. The number of positions by which the filter window is shifted is referred to as a *stride*, and the stride values can be specified independently for each dimension. An example of the contracting convolution with a stride of two positions is illustrated in Figure 2.41.

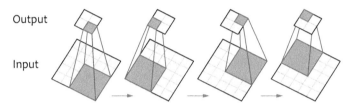

Figure 2.41: Controlling the contraction ratio using the stride parameter. In this example, we assume a 3 × 3 filter and a stride of two positions for both dimensions.

Third, we often need to process matrices with vector-valued elements, that are three-dimensional tensors. For example, color images are matrices of pixels where each pixel is represented by three components (red, green, and blue). We refer to each dimension of the elements as a *channel*. In addition, we often need to apply multiple convolution filters in parallel to increase the model capacity. These filters produce a stack of new representations that can be consumed as a multichannel input by the downstream layers of the model. We already discussed both these problems in the context of one-dimensional convolution in Section 2.4.3, and the design that we developed for the one-dimensional case can simply be generalized to the case of two dimensions. More specifically, the output element at the position (i, j) for a filter with index q can be computed as

$$y_{ijq} = \sum_{k=1}^{c} \sum_{u=-s}^{s} \sum_{v=-s}^{s} w^{q}_{k,\, u+s+1,\, v+s+1} \cdot x_{k,\, i+u,\, j+v} + b_q \quad (2.66)$$

where c is the dimensionality of the elements in the input matrix (number of channels), w^q are the weights of the q-th filter, and all filters are assumed to be of the same size. In other words, the input, output, and each filter are specified as three-dimensional tensors, and each output element is computed as the element-wise multiplication of the filter and the corresponding block of the input tensor. This operation is illustrated in Figure 2.42.

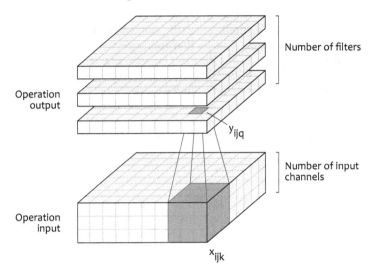

Figure 2.42: The two-dimensional convolution operation with multiple input channels and multiple filters. In this example, we assume 3×3 filter, three input channels, and three output filters.

We can summarize that the standard 2D convolution layer with c channels and n filters is a component that consumes a three-dimensional input (a stack of c channels), computes n linear convolutions with variable contraction ratios, applies an element-wise nonlinear function such as ReLu to the results of the convolutions, and produces a three-dimensional output (a stack of n matrices).

 We use convolution layers in recipe R5 (Visual Search) to build visual search models and recipe R11 (Visual Quality Control) to build a visual quality control system.

2.5.3   2D Upconvolution Layer

The convolution layer described above produces the output that is either smaller than the input, or of the same size. This functionality is sufficient for building models that condense the input into a low-dimensional output which is the case, for example, with classification models. On the other hand, models with high-dimensional outputs, such as tensor-to-tensor models, often require layers that *upscale* the input, that is, produce output larger than the input. Fortunately, we can build such a layer using the same convolution operation as we used earlier in the contracting convolution layer. The upscaling convolution is commonly referred to as a *transposed convolution, upconvolution,* or *deconvolution,* although this operation is not an inverse transformation for the convolution operation in the mathematical sense.

The upconvolution operation is illustrated in Figure 2.43. Similar to the regular convolution, the upconvolution operation is specified by a filter which is a matrix of weights. This filter is independently multiplied by each element of the input matrix; the resulting matrices are shifted according to the positions of the corresponding input elements and superimposed, and finally summed into the final output. The expansion ratio can be further increased using the concept of *strides*, so that the intermediate matrices are shifted by two or more positions before they are summed up.

The complete upconvolution layer can then be specified by adding all the capabilities we developed for the convolution layer (nonlinear activation, multiple channels, and multiple filters) on top of the upconvolution operation. The convolution and upconvolution layer differ only in how the filtering windows are applied and composed; other parts of the designs are virtually identical.

 We use upconvolution layers in recipes R5 (Visual Search) and R11 (Visual Quality Control) for semantic image segmentation.

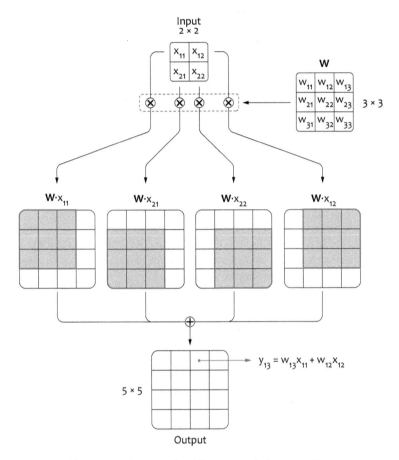

Figure 2.43: An example of the upconvolution operation.

2.5.4 *Deep 2D Convolutional Networks*

In Section 2.4.3, we discussed that multiple one-dimensional convolution layers can be stacked and interleaved with pooling layers to create a deep high-capacity network. We also discussed that such a network can be used to solve several types of sequence modeling problems including classification, forecasting, and sequence-to-sequence mapping. The principles apply to the multidimensional case. The most common problems that are solved using models with multidimensional inputs include the following (for the sake of specificity, we assume a two-dimensional case):

CLASSIFICATION Classification is one of the most common problems solved using convolutional networks. Most classification networks represent a stack of convolutional and pooling layers that consume an input with one or several channels and relatively large height and width, and then progressively reduce height and width but increase the number of channels using the increasing number of filters, as shown in Figure 2.44 (a). The output of the top convolution layer is then processed by a network head that performs the final mapping to the class label using dense and softmax layers.

FEATURE EXTRACTION The outputs of the intermediate layers in the model architecture described above can be viewed as embeddings of the input matrix. These embeddings, often referred to as *feature maps*, can enable new types of analysis that are not possible to be performed directly on the original input. For example, we analyze and qualitatively compare artistic styles of images using such embeddings in recipe R5 (Visual Search).

MATRIX-TO-MATRIX Some problems require the input matrix to be mapped to another matrix. For example, we might need to assign a class to each pixel of the input image, so that the output is a matrix of elements, each of which represents a class label. Similar to sequence-to-sequence mapping problems, this task is often accomplished using the encoder-decoder approach, so that the input matrix is first mapped to a dense embedding using a stack of convolution and pooling layers, and then the embedding is mapped back to a flat matrix using a stack of convolution and upconvolution layers, as shown in Figure 2.44 (b).

MATRIX-TO-TUPLES Finally, some problems require the production of outputs with a complex or variable structure. For example, we might need to detect objects such as people or cars in a photographic image. In this case, the model might produce a set of tuples, each of which includes the coordinates of an individual object, its height, width, and class label.

The examples presented in Figure 2.44 aim only to outline some of the design principles used for building deep convolutional networks, and we discuss specific model architectures in greater detail in the corresponding recipes.

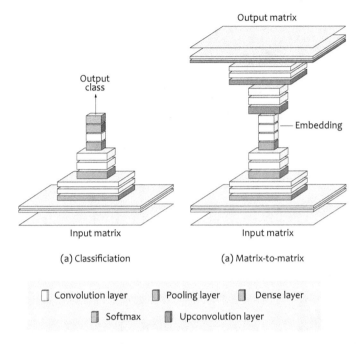

Figure 2.44: Examples of deep convolutional architectures. The thickness of the layer is proportional to the number of channels.

2.5.5   2D Transformer Layer

The transformer models introduced in Section 2.4.7 outperform both convolutional and recurrent networks in many sequence modeling applications, so it is logical to explore how the transformer architecture can be extended to multiple dimensions. In principle, regular self-attention layers and transformer blocks can straightforwardly consume any multidimensional tensor provided that it is flattened into a sequence of elements, and that the spatial relationship between the elements will be captured in position embeddings. This naïve approach, however, requires each element to attend to every other element, so the computational complexity is quadratic in the number of elements in the input. This problem can be mitigated using various partition strategies that limit the number of attention links.

One of the most basic strategies is to group the input elements into fixed-size patches as illustrated in Figure 2.45. We assume that the input is an $h \times w$ matrix of k-dimensional elements. These elements are grouped into square $p \times p$ patches, so that there are $n = hw/p^2$ patches in total.

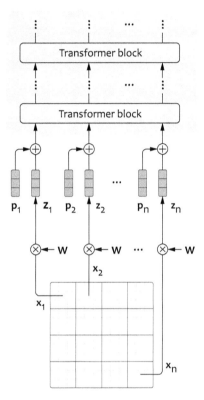

Figure 2.45: Adapting a one-dimensional transformer to process a two-dimensional input.

Each patch is then flattened into a $p^2 k$-dimensional vector, so that the entire input is represented as a sequence of vectors $x_1, \ldots, x_n$. Finally, these vectors are mapped to embeddings using a linear projection:

$$z_i = x_i W, \qquad i = 1, \ldots, n \tag{2.67}$$

where embeddings z are d-dimensional, and W is the $p^2 k \times d$ parameter matrix shared across all patches.

This design, originally developed for computer vision applications and known as the *vision transformer* (ViT), enables one to control the computational complexity of the transformer blocks by varying the patch size parameter [Dosovitskiy et al., 2020]. This architecture represents a generic platform which can be used for solving all standard tasks introduced previously such as classification and matrix-to-matrix learning.

The transformer architecture makes weaker prior assumptions about the structure of input than the convolutional networks. In particular, it does not assume the locality of the element interactions and equivariance to translations which are the main priors of the convolutional design. This can make the transformer approach less sample-efficient than the convolutional one in applications such as computer vision, that strongly comply with these priors [Liu et al., 2022]. This limitation can be addressed using more advanced partitioning schemas with hierarchical and sliding windows that both impose some of the convolutional priors and reduce the computational complexity to near-linear [Liu et al., 2021]. The alternative approach is hybrid architectures where convolution layers are used to extract feature maps from the original input, and transformer layers are used to further process these maps. In this context, the feature-extracting convolutional network is often referred to as a *backbone network*.

2.6   REPRESENTATION LEARNING MODELS

The main focus of the previous sections was on learning functions that perform mapping between input and output values. We have seen that such mapping is usually performed in stages, where each stage produces a new *representation* of the input data, and the training process is designed to iteratively align these representations with the distribution we want to approximate. For example, we demonstrated that embedding lookup units can map discrete entities to low-dimensional representations that are aligned with the entity target labels, or, more generally, deep networks can produce low-dimensional embeddings and feature maps where the input classes are linearly separable. Consequently, the ability of the network to accomplish a certain learning task is usually equivalent to the ability to produce high-quality representations. The ability to produce semantically meaningful embeddings can also help to accomplish various additional tasks such as entity similarity analysis.

Unfortunately, the methods discussed in the previous sections do not provide much control over the structure and properties of the embedding space. We can be certain that the training process will attempt to align the feature maps produced by the top layers of the network with the target labels (otherwise the network would fail to predict the target label based on these maps), but no other guarantees are provided. In practice, this is not necessarily an obstruction because the representations captured at different layers of supervised networks as byproducts are often useful enough and exhibit good properties. Nevertheless, it is logical to pose the following questions:

- How can we influence the properties of the semantic spaces that are learned using supervised models? How can we measure the quality of the embeddings and improve it?

- Is it always necessary to guide the embedding learning process using target labels? Are there alternative ways to specify the desirable structure of the semantic space?

The goal of this section is to answer the above questions, and develop a framework for learning high-quality embeddings in various settings. These methods are very important in many practical applications because they enable algebraic operations over various entities which, as we discussed in Section 1.2, is one of the fundamental problems in the field of enterprise machine learning.

2.6.1   *Loss Functions for Representation Learning*

Let us consider a classification model that first maps input $\mathbf{x}$ to a low-dimensional representation $\mathbf{z}$, and then maps this representation to class label y. We do not make any specific assumptions about the architecture of this model, so it could be a single embedding lookup unit, or a recurrent, convolutional, or transformer network. We would normally train this model using the categorical cross-entropy loss function to minimize the classification error. As we discussed in Section 2.3.2, the cross-entropy loss guides the training process towards the construction of the embedding space where the samples of the same class are clustered together and linearly separable. This also means that the features of the embedding vectors $\mathbf{z}$ are optimized to be discriminative with regard to the class labels. The cross-entropy loss, however, does not provide any specific guarantees regarding the separability of the classes or parameters that control the embedding properties. We can attempt to design a loss function that explicitly accounts for separability, and guides the training process towards creating tightly clustered embeddings.

Let us assume a training set X that consists of samples $(\mathbf{x}_i,\ y_i)$. We can set the goal of constructing an embedding space where the samples of the same class are clustered together and separated from samples of other classes by a certain margin $\alpha > 0$. To express this goal in strict mathematical terms, let us define a set of all possible triplets $(\mathbf{x}^a, \mathbf{x}^p, \mathbf{x}^n)$ that meet the following conditions:

1. Samples $\mathbf{x}^a$ and $\mathbf{x}^p$ have the same class label y^a.

2. Sample $\mathbf{x}^n$ has a different class label $y^n \neq y^a$.

3. All three samples are distinct, that is $\mathbf{x}^a \neq \mathbf{x}^p \neq \mathbf{x}^n$.

We refer to the first element of the triplet as an *anchor*, the second element as *positive*, and the last one as *negative*. The desirable embedding space should then satisfy the following property:

$$d\left(\mathbf{z}_j^a,\, \mathbf{z}_j^p\right) + \alpha < d\left(\mathbf{z}_j^a,\, \mathbf{z}_j^n\right) \tag{2.68}$$

where index j iterates over all triples that satisfy the above conditions, d is the distance function in the embedding space, and vectors $\mathbf{z}_j^a$, $\mathbf{z}_j^p$, and $\mathbf{z}_j^n$ are the embeddings of the anchor, positive, and negative samples, respectively. An example of the perfect separation by margin α is shown in Figure 2.46.

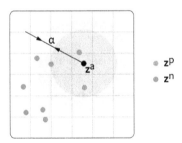

Figure 2.46: Desirable separation of the embedding clusters.

The loss function that penalizes the violations of the separation condition 2.68 can then be defined as follows:

$$L(X) = \sum_{j=1}^{n_b} \max\left(d(\mathbf{z}_j^a,\, \mathbf{z}_j^p) - d(\mathbf{z}_j^a,\, \mathbf{z}_j^n) + \alpha,\, 0\right) \tag{2.69}$$

where n_b is the total number of triplets in the dataset. This loss is known as *triplet loss* [Schultz and Joachims, 2004; Weinberger et al., 2006; Schroff et al., 2015].

The direct evaluation of expression 2.69, however, requires us to enumerate all valid triplets for the training dataset which is infeasible in most real-world applications. This approach is also highly redundant because most triplets would satisfy constraint 2.68 and, consequently, would not contribute towards the optimization of the network parameters. These issues can be mitigated by selecting only the triplets that are most likely to violate constraint 2.68. For example, we can generate only one triplet for each anchor sample by selecting the most distant positive and nearest negative samples, as illustrated in Figure 2.47. This leads to the following training procedure:

1. Randomly choose n_c classes from the set of all classes, and sample n_k instances of each class from the training dataset. This creates a minibatch of $n_b = n_c \cdot n_k$ samples.

2. For each sample x^a in the minibatch, determine the most distant positive (hard positive) and nearest negative (hard negative) in the space of the corresponding embeddings:

$$
\begin{aligned}
x^p_{hard} &= \underset{x^p}{\mathrm{argmax}}\ d\left(z^a,\ z^p\right) \\
x^n_{hard} &= \underset{x^n}{\mathrm{argmin}}\ d\left(z^a,\ z^n\right)
\end{aligned}
\tag{2.70}
$$

and add triplet $(x^a,\ x^p_{hard},\ x^n_{hard})$ to the minibatch of triplets. The total number of triplets per minibatch is the same as the number of samples, that is n_b.

3. Evaluate the loss function and train the model using the generated minibatch of triplets.

4. Sample the next minibatch and repeat the process until the convergence.

The above procedure can be modified in several ways to improve stability and convergence in specific applications. For example, it may be beneficial to include all anchor-positive pairs for each anchor instead of selecting only one hard positive, or apply additional constraints to exclude outliers from hard negatives [Schroff et al., 2015].

The triplet loss belongs to a relatively large group of loss functions that were designed specifically to improve the separability of embeddings [Deng et al., 2019; Wang et al., 2018]. These loss functions are particularly important in applications with an extremely large number of classes that need to be distinguished. For example, a face recognition system might need to reliably distinguish between the faces of thousands or even millions of individuals. In practice, the embedding-shaping losses are widely used to compute high-quality embeddings even in applications with a relatively small number of classes.

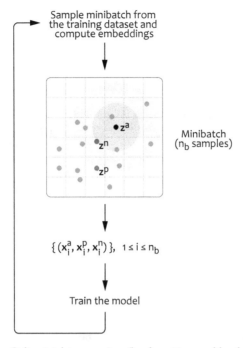

Sample minibatch from
the training dataset and
compute embeddings

Minibatch
(n_b samples)

$\{(x_i^a, x_i^p, x_i^n)\}$, $1 \le i \le n_b$

Train the model

Figure 2.47: Online triplet generation (hard positives and hard negatives).

 Custom loss functions are important in visual search applications that require high-quality image embeddings. We continue to discuss this topic in recipe R5 (Visual Search).

Specialized loss functions and regularization terms are extremely powerful tools that help to align embeddings with the supervision signals, enhance the discriminative power of the embedding features, and control other embedding properties such as feature sparsity. We will discuss more techniques for altering the embedding properties in the next section.

2.6.2 Autoencoders

The supervised methods can learn new entity representations so that entities with the same or similar target labels are collocated. This approach is well-suited for applications that require the embeddings and their features to be discriminative with regard to the target labels. At the same time, applications exist where the target labels are unnecessary or unknown, and we want to learn representations that capture the most characteristic features of the input entities and describe the manifold the entities live on. This generally requires specifying a loss measure that can guide the feature selection process based on the input samples rather than target labels. One possible solution is to guide the feature selection process by the ability to accurately reconstruct the input based on a limited number of features. The models that implement this approach are collectively known as *autoencoders*, and we make use of this section to discuss the basic principles used in the autoencoder design.

2.6.2.1 Linear Autoencoder

The basic idea of autoencoding can be illustrated by a simple model presented in Figure 2.48. This is a linear model that takes a k-dimensional vector $\mathbf{x}$ as an input, maps it to a d-dimensional embedding $\mathbf{z}$ using a linear layer, and then maps the embedding to a k-dimensional output vector using another linear transformation. These two operations are referred to as *encoding* and *decoding*, respectively, and we can express them using the following notation:

$$\mathbf{z} = \mathbf{W}_e \mathbf{x}$$
$$\hat{\mathbf{x}} = \mathbf{W}_d \mathbf{z}$$
(2.71)

where $\mathbf{W}_e$ and $\mathbf{W}_d$ are d × k and k × d matrices, respectively, and d is assumed to be smaller than k. The latter assumption, often referred to as the *information bottleneck*, is a crucial one because it prevents the model from learning trivial embeddings such as direct copying of the inputs to the outputs.

We further assume that the training process is guided by the MSE loss which can be expanded as follows:

$$L(X, \mathbf{W}_d, \mathbf{W}_e) = \frac{1}{n} \sum_{i=1}^{n} \|\mathbf{x}_i - \hat{\mathbf{x}}_i\|^2 = \frac{1}{n} \sum_{i=1}^{n} \|\mathbf{x}_i - \mathbf{W}_d \mathbf{W}_e \mathbf{x}_i\|^2 \quad (2.72)$$

where X is the training dataset that consists of n samples x_i. In other words, we are trying to find a d-dimensional representation of the k-dimensional input that minimizes the input reconstruction error.

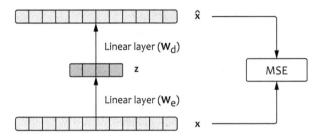

Figure 2.48: A basic linear autoencoder.

The minimization of the reconstruction error generally necessitates the features of z to be characteristic for the manifold of x, but the ability to learn such features is limited to the linearity of the encoding and decoding operations. The encoding operation defined by matrix W_e performs a projection of the k-dimensional space on a d-dimensional hyperplane, so the feature selection essentially boils down to selecting the optimal orientation of this hyperplane in the input space. We can get deeper insights into this process by recognizing the similarities between our model and the principal component analysis (PCA) problem. The PCA problem has several equivalent formulations, and one of them also requires finding a linear transformation of the input space that minimizes the reconstruction error, but additionally constrains the basis of this transformation to be orthogonal:

$$\min_{W} \quad \frac{1}{n} \sum_{i=1}^{n} \left\| x_i - WW^T x_i \right\|^2$$

$$\text{subject to} \quad W^T W = I_d \tag{2.73}$$

where W is a k × d matrix, and I_d is a d × d identity matrix, and the d-dimensional vector $W^T x$ can be interpreted as an embedding. The PCA transformation has multiple useful properties. In particular, the embedding hyperplane obtained using PCA is oriented in a way that maximizes the variance of the projected data, and the embedding features are decorrelated. The linear autoencoder finds the same semantic space as PCA, but converges to a different basis which is not necessarily orthogonal. Consequently, the linear autoencoder achieves the same reconstruction error as the PCA algorithm, but it does not guarantee the nice properties of PCA entailed by the orthogonality constraint. We can, however, modify the basic autoencoder model to enforce the orthogonality and thus make it equivalent to PCA [Teo, 2020]. For example, the orthogonality can be enforced by tying the encoder and decoder weights so that $\mathbf{W}_e^T = \mathbf{W}_d = \mathbf{W}$ and adding a proper regularization on top of the MSE loss:

$$L(X, \mathbf{W}) = \text{MSE}(X, \ \mathbf{W}) + \lambda \left\| \mathbf{W}^T \mathbf{W} - \mathbf{I}_d \right\|^2 \tag{2.74}$$

where the regularization term penalizes non-orthogonal basis vectors, and λ is a regularization weight.

The basic linear model demonstrates the core principle of unsupervised representation learning using autoencoders. The limited-size intermediate representation, that is the information bottleneck, forces the model to learn the most characteristic features of the manifold the input samples live on. The linear model, however, is only able to produce the optimal projections of the input features on a hyperplane which sharply limits the expressiveness of the features it can learn.

2.6.2.2 Stacked Autoencoders

The limitations of the linear autoencoder can be overcome by replacing linear transformations with regular nonlinear dense layers and stacking multiple layers as shown in Figure 2.49. The networks that follow this architecture are referred to as *stacked autoencoders*.

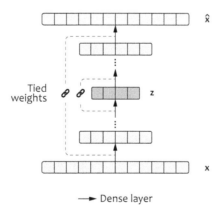

Figure 2.49: A basic stacked autoencoder.

The encoder part of the stacked autoencoder gradually reduces the dimensionality of the input vector $\mathbf{x}$ using a stack of dense layers. In most architectures, the dimensionality of the output monotonically decreases from layer to layer, and the final encoding layer produces embedding $\mathbf{z}$. The decoder part performs the inverse transformation, gradually increasing the dimensionality of the representation and producing the final output $\hat{\mathbf{x}}$ of the same size as the input.

The encoder and decoder parts do not necessarily need to be symmetrical, but symmetrical architectures are often optimal. It is also common to tie the parameters of the same-level encoder and decoder layers, as shown in Figure 2.49, so that

$$\mathbf{W}_m = \mathbf{W}_{n-m+1}^\mathsf{T}, \quad m = 1, 2, \ldots, n/2 \tag{2.75}$$

where m is the index of the layer, $\mathbf{W}_m$ is the weight matrix of layer m, and n is the total number of layers which is assumed to be even. The tied weights help to reduce the number of model parameters and impose the PCA-style regularization as discussed in the previous section.

A stacked autoencoder can be thought of as several nested two-layer autoencoders: the outermost encoder and decoder layers respectively, perform the initial feature extraction and reconstruction; the representation produced by the outermost layers is further approximated by the next pair of layers, and so on. In fact, deep autoencoders are often trained layer by layer, so that the outermost encoder-decoder pair is first trained separately just like a two-layer autoencoder, then the next encoder-decoder pair is trained to approximate the embeddings produced by the first pair, and so on. This helps to reduce the training time and improve the training stability.

The stack of dense layers depicted in Figure 2.49 is one of the most basic autoencoder architectures, and more complex networks can be assembled by stacking convolutional or recurrent layers. Such networks are capable of extracting complex features from a wide range of input structures including vectors, sequences, and tensors. This capability has many important applications in enterprise operations including the following:

FEATURE EXTRACTION Embeddings computed using autoencoders can replace or augment manually designed features for downstream models. This is a generic technique that helps to reduce the feature engineering effort.

SIMILARITY METRICS Distances in the embeddings space can be used to evaluate similarities between entities and search for nearest neighbors. This capability can be used for entity search and retrieval tasks.

NOISE REMOVAL The information bottleneck ensures that the reconstructions produced by the autoencoder retain only the most characteristic features and discard noises (the reconstructions are essentially projections of the input samples on the manifold learned during the training process). This property can be used to de-noise time series, images, and some other types of data.

ANOMALY DETECTION The difference between the input and its reconstruction gauges the deviation from the normal manifold, and this can be used to detect anomalies and outliers. This capability is applicable to a wide range of problems including time series monitoring, visual inspection, and cyber security.

INSTANCE GENERATION We can generate new objects that live on the manifold by sampling random embedding vectors and decoding them. This capability can be used for forecasting and some other tasks.

 We use stacked convolutional autoencoders in recipe R10 (Anomaly Detection) to detect anomalies in internet of things (IoT) data and recipe R11 (Visual Quality Control) to detect manufacturing defects based on images.

In many applications, the above tasks can be solved using a relatively simple stacked architecture as described earlier in this section. These basic models, however, are prone to producing irregular embedding spaces which makes them infeasible for certain applications. We discuss this issue and advanced solutions that address it in the next sections.

2.6.2.3 *Regularization of the Semantic Space*

An autoencoder that is guided solely by the objective to minimize the reconstruction error is prone to overfitting. From the semantic space perspective, this means that two completely different input vectors can be encoded into two close points in the semantic space, and, conversely, two close points in the semantic spaces can be decoded into completely different entities, as illustrated in Figure 2.50 (a). Moreover, points that are randomly sampled from the semantic space can decode into invalid or semantically meaningless entities, which is also depicted in

Figure 2.50 (a). Such an irregular structure of the semantic space can make it infeasible for similarity evaluation, instance generation, and some other tasks which we generally want to solve using autoencoders. Consequently, we want the autoencoder to not just minimize the reconstruction error, but to also construct embedding spaces that exhibit the following properties:

CONTINUITY Two close points in the embedding space should decode into similar entities.

COMPLETENESS Any point sampled from the embedding space should decode into a valid entity.

The concept of a regular embedding space that exhibits these two properties is illustrated in Figure 2.50 (b).

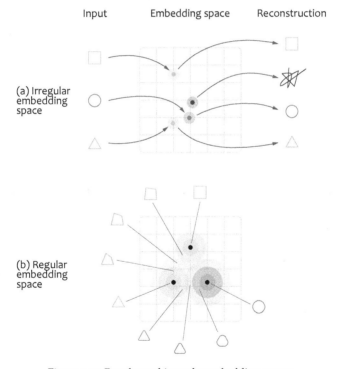

Figure 2.50: Regular and irregular embedding spaces.

The smoothness and regularity of the semantic space can be improved using a wide range of techniques. One of the most basic options is to change the loss function by adding a sparsity penalty for the embedding layer on top of the reconstruction error. Autoencoders that use the loss functions with sparsity penalties are commonly known as *sparse autoencoders*. In particular, we can use L_1 regularization which is the most common choice for sparsity penalization across all machine learning applications:

$$L_{sparse}(\mathbf{x}, \hat{\mathbf{x}}) = MSE(\mathbf{x}, \hat{\mathbf{x}}) + \lambda \sum_{i=1}^{d} | z_i | \qquad (2.76)$$

where λ is a hyperparameter that controls the regularization strength. The L_1 regularization term encourages embedding $\mathbf{z}$ to be sparse, driving some features z_i to zero. Consequently, sparse autoencoders tend to discover a limited number of characteristic features even if the dimensionality of the embedding space is larger than needed to represent the manifold. This basic technique does not fully solve the problem with continuity and completeness of the semantic space, but demonstrates the idea of altering the properties of the embeddings learned by autoencoders using regularization.

2.6.2.4 *Variational Autoencoder*

The autoencoding techniques described in the previous sections provide certain means for controlling and enhancing the structure of the semantic space, but these capabilities might not be sufficient for learning complex manifolds from high-dimensional inputs. We can attempt to overcome the limitations of the basic methods using a probabilistic approach and learn a model of the distribution $p(\mathbf{z} \mid \mathbf{x})$ over the semantic space. Conceptually, this approach can help to learn continuous semantically meaningful spaces provided that we choose a proper distribution model. In this section, we discuss one of the most commonly used realizations of this approach known as the *variational autoencoder* (VAE) [Kingma and Welling, 2014].

The mathematical basis of the variational autoencoder is totally different from the considerations we used to build linear and stacked autoencoders, but the final architecture resembles the regular autoencoder design. Consequently, we begin with a discussion of a more general distribution learning problem, and then relate it back to the autoencoding problem.

Let us start with a basic assumption that we observe samples $\mathbf{x}$ that represent some entities, and these representations are determined by the corresponding unobserved (latent) variables $\mathbf{z}$. Let us also assume that $\mathbf{z}$ are random variables that follow distribution $p(\mathbf{z})$. Our goal is to estimate the distribution of the unobserved variables $p(\mathbf{z} \mid \mathbf{x})$ based on the observed representations. This problem can be approached by defining a parametric model $q(z \mid x)$ that approximates $p(z \mid x)$ and optimizing the model parameters to minimize the approximation error. This error can be quantified using the Kullback-Leibler (KL) divergence which is a measure of distance between two distributions defined as follows:

$$d_{KL}\,(q(x) \parallel p(x)) = \mathbb{E}_{x \sim q}\,[\,\log q(x) - \log p(x)\,] \tag{2.77}$$

Consequently, we want to solve the following optimization problem:

$$\min_{q} d_{KL}\,(q(z \mid x) \parallel p(z \mid x)) \tag{2.78}$$

where q belongs to a certain family of functions that we have to specify. Our first step towards solving this problem is to decompose distribution $p(z \mid x)$ using Bayes' rule:

$$p(z \mid x) = \frac{p(x \mid z)\,p(z)}{p(x)} \tag{2.79}$$

We then can make several simplifying assumptions about the individual terms in this expression. First, let us assume that likelihood that $p(x \mid z)$ is normally distributed around the mean which is computed from z:

$$p(x \mid z) = N(f_\theta(z),\, c \cdot I) \tag{2.80}$$

where f_θ is some deterministic function specified by a vector of parameters θ, and c is a scaling hyperparameter which will be discussed later. We assume that function f_θ is capable of approximating arbitrary complex mappings. Second, we assume that the prior distribution $p(z)$ is simply the standard normal distribution:

$$p(z) = N(0,\, I) \tag{2.81}$$

In other words, we assume a non-informative prior for the unobserved variables. Finally, we assume that the approximation $q(z \mid x)$ is also a normal distribution with the mean and variance computed from x:

$$q(z \mid x) = N(g_\phi(x),\, h_\psi(x)) \tag{2.82}$$

where g_ϕ and h_ψ are deterministic functions parametrized by vector ϕ and ψ, respectively.

Our next step is to obtain a computationally tractable expression for KL divergence using the above assumptions. We start by inserting the Bayesian decomposition of $p(\mathbf{z} \mid \mathbf{x})$ into the definition of the KL divergence 2.77 and obtain the following:

$$
\begin{aligned}
&d_{KL} \left(q(\mathbf{z} \mid \mathbf{x}) \| p(\mathbf{z} \mid \mathbf{x}) \right) \\
&= \mathbb{E}_{\mathbf{z} \sim q} \left[\log q(\mathbf{z} \mid \mathbf{x}) - \log p(\mathbf{x} \mid \mathbf{z}) - \log p(\mathbf{z}) \right] + \log p(\mathbf{x})
\end{aligned}
\tag{2.83}
$$

where the last term was moved out of the expectation operator because it does not depend on $\mathbf{z}$. We can further rearrange the terms as follows:

$$
\begin{aligned}
&\log p(\mathbf{x}) - d_{KL} \left(q(\mathbf{z} \mid \mathbf{x}) \| p(\mathbf{z} \mid \mathbf{x}) \right) \\
&= \mathbb{E}_{\mathbf{z} \sim q} \left[\log p(\mathbf{x} \mid \mathbf{z}) \right] - d_{KL} \left(q(\mathbf{z} \mid \mathbf{x}) \| p(\mathbf{z}) \right)
\end{aligned}
\tag{2.84}
$$

The left-hand side of this expression is the difference between the log-evidence $\log p(\mathbf{x})$ and the KL diversion for the posterior approximation q. Since the KL divergence is non-negative, this difference can be viewed as the *evidence lower bound* which is commonly abbreviated as ELBO. The log-evidence does not depend on q, so the ELBO is maximized when the divergence is minimized with regard to q. Consequently, we can restate the original problem as the ELBO maximization:

$$
\max_{\theta, \phi, \psi} \mathbb{E}_{\mathbf{z} \sim q} \left[\log p(\mathbf{x} \mid \mathbf{z}) \right] - d_{KL} \left(q(\mathbf{z} \mid \mathbf{x}) \| p(\mathbf{z}) \right)
\tag{2.85}
$$

where the subjects of optimization are the parameters of the mapping functions which were introduced earlier, which are θ, ϕ, and ψ.

Let us further assume that we perform the optimization using the stochastic gradient descent (SGD) that approximates the expectation $\mathbb{E}_{\mathbf{z} \sim q} \left[\log p(\mathbf{x} \mid \mathbf{z}) \right]$ with a single-sample mean $\log p(\mathbf{x} \mid \mathbf{z})$. As we established in Section 2.3.1.1, maximization of the negative log-likelihood for normally distributed variables is equivalent to the minimization of the Euclidean distance, so we can express the optimization problem as follows:

$$
\min_{\theta, \phi, \psi} c \|\mathbf{x} - f_\theta(\mathbf{z})\|^2 - d_{KL} \left(N(g_\phi(\mathbf{x}), h_\psi(\mathbf{x})) \| N(\mathbf{o}, \mathbf{I}) \right)
\tag{2.86}
$$

where we also inserted model specifications models 2.81 and 2.82 into the KL divergence term. This form of the optimization problem is computationally tractable, and we can perform the optimization using the following procedure:

1. We start with randomly initialized model parameters θ, ϕ, and ψ.

2. At each SGD iteration, we first compute $g_\phi(\mathbf{x})$ and $h_\psi(\mathbf{x})$, and then sample $\mathbf{z}$ from the corresponding normal distribution 2.82.

3. Next, we compute $f_\theta(\mathbf{z})$ and evaluate the ELBO loss according to expression 2.86.

4. The model parameters are updated based on the loss gradient, and the SGD iterations repeat until the conversion.

It is easy to recognize that this procedure closely resembles autoencoding – functions $g_\phi(\mathbf{x})$ and $h_\psi(\mathbf{x})$ encode the input into embedding $\mathbf{z}$, and $f_\theta(\mathbf{z})$ performs the reconstruction. The key difference is that the encoding process is stochastic because the embedding is sampled, not deterministically computed.

We can implement the encoding and decoding functions of the variational autoencoder using neural networks, but there are two obstacles that need to be addressed in the basic SGD procedure outlined above. The first of these is that the encoding requires two functions, $g_\phi(\mathbf{x})$ and $h_\psi(\mathbf{x})$, to compute the mean and variance of the embedding distribution. This can easily be addressed using a two-head network that produces these two outputs in parallel. Alternatively, we can use only one head that produces one output vector, and divide this vector into two parts which are interpreted as $g_\phi(\mathbf{x})$ and $h_\psi(\mathbf{x})$. The second issue is that the necessity to sample $\mathbf{z}$ from a distribution does not allow connecting the encoding and decoding parts into one network that can be trained using a standard backpropagation algorithm. This issue can be solved by leveraging the fact that a normally distributed random variable with mean $g_\phi(\mathbf{x})$ and variance $h_\psi(\mathbf{x})^2$ can be generated as

$$\mathbf{z} = g_\phi(\mathbf{x}) + h_\psi(\mathbf{x}) \odot \boldsymbol{\eta}, \qquad \boldsymbol{\eta} = N(\mathbf{0}, \mathbf{I}) \qquad (2.87)$$

where $\odot$ is the element-wise product. This reparametrization trick enables the backpropagation of errors from the decoding network to encoding layers because the embedding is *computed* using vector operations, and the random component is added on top.

The above results enable us to implement the variational autoencoder as a single neural network that closely resembles a regular stacked autoencoder, as shown in Figure 2.51. The encoding subnetwork computes $g_\phi(\mathbf{x})$ and $h_\psi(\mathbf{x})$ using two heads, then the embedding $\mathbf{z}$ is produced according to expression 2.87, and the decoding subnetwork computes $f_\theta(\mathbf{z})$.

The entire network is trained using the ELBO loss 2.86. In this context, the ELBO loss can be viewed as a regularization technique – it is a sum of the standard regression loss and KL divergence term that penalizes the deviation from the normal distribution $p(\mathbf{z})$. In expression 2.86,

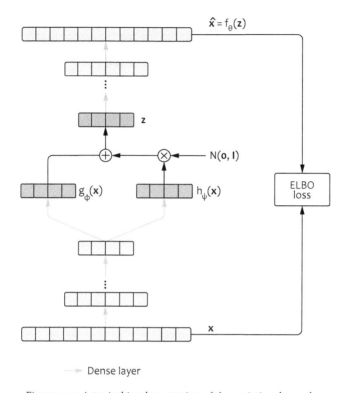

Figure 2.51: A typical implementation of the variational encoder.

constant c, which corresponds to the variance in the likelihood specification 2.80, essentially controls the balance between these two terms.
The penalization of the deviation from some smooth distribution such
as the normal helps to achieve better continuity and completeness of
the semantic space, two desirable properties that were discussed in the
previous section.

 We use the variational autoencoder in recipe
R5 (Visual Search) to learn image embeddings
that can be used for nearest neighbor search.

2.6.3   *Representation of Elements*

Autoencoding is a generic solution for unsupervised representation learning that can be applied to a wide range of entities including vectors, sequences, and tensors. In many applications, however, we are interested not in learning representations of the entire entities, but in learning representations of the individual elements these entities are comprised of. For example, we might be interested to learn embeddings of individual elements in a sequence of discrete elements (tokens). The most common instantiation of this problem is the learning of word embeddings from texts. In this section, we study this problem more thoroughly, and develop a generic algorithm for learning token representations from sequences. This algorithm can be directly applied to a wide range of enterprise problems, and, as we discuss in the next sections, it can also be used as a building block in representation learning solutions for more complex structures such as graphs.

We have discussed in Section 2.4 that a stochastic sequence of tokens $x_1, \ldots, x_T$ can be described using the token distribution conditioned on the context:

$$ p\left(x_t \mid x_{t-h}, \ldots, x_{t-1}, x_{t+1}, \ldots, x_{t+h}\right) \tag{2.88} $$

where the context size h can be assumed to be finite for most practical applications due to the limited memory effects. We further discussed that this distribution can be learned using autoregressive models that essentially reduce the problem to the supervised learning formulation. This creates a foundation for unsupervised learning of representations of individual tokens x_t because the samples and labels needed for training of the autoregressive model are generated from the sequence itself.

We can approach the problem of learning the above distribution in two ways. The first option is to build a model that predicts the middle token x_t based on its context $x_{t-h}, \ldots, x_{t-1}, x_{t+1}, \ldots, x_{t+h}$. The second approach is to build a model that predicts individual tokens of the context based on the middle token. Each of these two approaches has its own advantages and disadvantages depending on a specific application. For the sake of brevity, we focus on the second approach, although the two strategies are, to a large extent, symmetrical, and the same design principles can be applied to both.

Assuming that we want to predict the tokens of the context based on the middle token, we can generate the training samples from the sequence as shown in Figure 2.52.

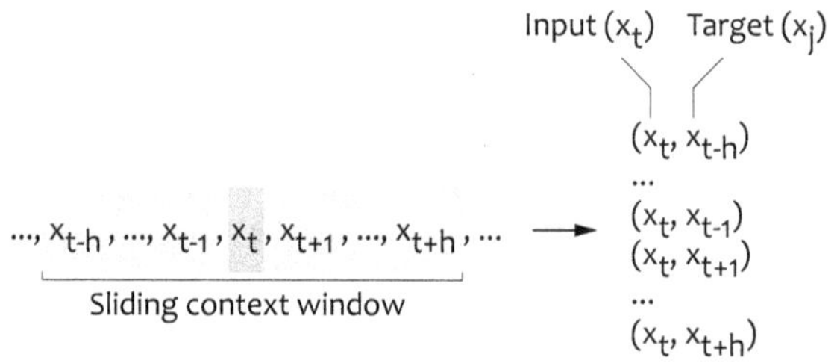

Input (x_t) Target (x_j)

(x_t, x_{t-h})
...
(x_t, x_{t-1})
$\cdots, x_{t-h}, \cdots, x_{t-1}, x_t, x_{t+1}, \cdots, x_{t+h}, \cdots \longrightarrow$ (x_t, x_{t+1})
$\underbrace{\phantom{\cdots, x_{t-h}, \cdots, x_{t-1}, x_t, x_{t+1}, \cdots, x_{t+h}, \cdots}}_{\text{Sliding context window}}$ ...
(x_t, x_{t+h})

Figure 2.52: Generating samples for the context prediction model. The context window moves along the sequence with the stride of one, so we generate $h(2T - h - 1)$ samples for a sequence of length T.

These samples can then be used to train a multinomial classification model, so that the loss for the entire sequence is evaluated as follows:

$$L(x_1, \ldots, x_T) = -\frac{1}{T} \sum_{t=1}^{T} \sum_{\substack{-h \leqslant j \leqslant h \\ j \neq 0}} \log p(x_{t+j} \mid x_t) \tag{2.89}$$

We can further assume that the probability of token x_j being in the context of the middle token x_t can be modeled using the dot product of the corresponding embeddings. This leads us to the following log probability estimate that can be plugged into the above loss function:

$$\log p(x_j \mid x_t) = \log \frac{\exp\left(\mathbf{p}_{x_j}^T \mathbf{q}_{x_t}\right)}{\sum_{v=1}^{V} \exp\left(\mathbf{p}_v^T \mathbf{q}_{x_t}\right)} \tag{2.90}$$

In this expression, vectors $\mathbf{p}$ are the embedding of the corresponding context tokens, $\mathbf{q}$ is the embedding of the middle token, and index v iterates over all distinct tokens (vocabulary). It is important to note that the embeddings for the context and middle tokens are obtained using two different embedding lookup tables, so the same token can be mapped to two different embeddings depending on whether it is in the input (middle token) or candidate output (context token). A neural network that implements this design is shown in Figure 2.53. This solution was originally developed in the context of NLP applications for learning word embeddings from texts, and it is commonly known as Word2Vec [Mikolov et al., 2013a].

The basic model design described above, however, has a limitation that makes it computationally intractable for problems with a large number of distinct tokens. The issue is that the evaluation of the denominator in the softmax function 2.90 needs to be iterated over the all

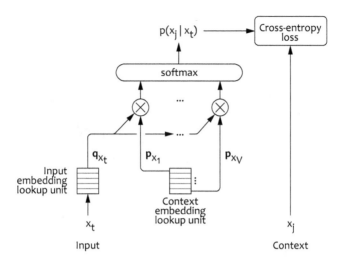

Figure 2.53: Architecture of the basic Word2Vec network.

distinct tokens, and this computation repeats for each training sample. This issue can be resolved by reformulating the problem as a binary classification, so that we take a pair of tokens as the input, and estimate the probability that the second token appears in the context of the first one. This requires changing the sample generation procedure to produce samples, each of which consists of two tokens and a binary target label. The target label equals one when the second token is in the context of the first one, and zero otherwise. The positive samples (labeled as one) can be generated as before using the token pairs from the sliding context window. We also need, however, to generate negative samples (labeled as zero), and this can be accomplished by sampling them from some distribution S over tokens that are *not* in the current context. This distribution can be uniform or skewed in a way that the more frequent tokens are more likely to be selected as negative samples [Mikolov et al., 2013b]. This new sampling process, called *negative sampling*, is shown in Figure 2.54.

The binary mode is trained using the binary cross-entropy loss that requires the evaluation of only two probabilities, regardless of the number of distinct tokens:

$$p(d = 1 \mid x_t, x_j) = \sigma(\mathbf{p}_{x_j}^\mathsf{T} \mathbf{q}_{x_t})$$
$$p(d = 0 \mid x_t, x_j) = 1 - \sigma(\mathbf{p}_{x_j}^\mathsf{T} \mathbf{q}_{x_t}) = \sigma(-\mathbf{p}_{x_j}^\mathsf{T} \mathbf{q}_{x_t})$$

$$(2.91)$$

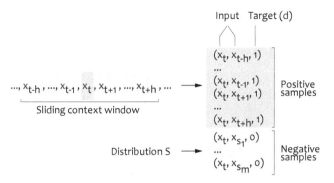

Figure 2.54: Negative sampling.

where d is the target label and σ is the sigmoid function. This allows us to replace the potentially intractable softmax 2.90 with the following:

$$\log p(x_j \mid x_t) = \log \sigma(\mathbf{p}_{x_j}^T \mathbf{q}_{x_t}) + \sum_{x_s \sim S} \log \sigma(-\mathbf{p}_{x_s}^T \mathbf{q}_{x_t}) \qquad (2.92)$$

The number of negative instances x_s sampled for each positive sample is a hyperparameter of the model which is selected based on the size of the training dataset of other considerations.

The Word2Vec model is a relatively simple but generic and powerful solution for learning token embeddings from sequences. It can be applied to a wide range of enterprise use cases including customer analytics where one needs to deal with sequences of events, log analytics where once deals with sequences of tokens, and more traditional NLP applications.

 We use Word2Vec in recipe R2 (Customer Feature Learning) to learn customer embeddings based on event sequences.

2.7   MODELS WITH GRAPH INPUTS

A wide range of enterprise problems involves multiple interconnected or interrelated entities, and the topology of these connections and relations can be extremely important for understanding and predicting the properties of the entities. Examples of such problems include the analysis of interactions between customers and products with the goal of producing personalized recommendations, analysis of financial transactions between economic agents aimed at detecting fraud, and the analysis of connectivity between IoT sensors for detecting failures. The methods developed in the previous sections were designed to predominantly model individual entities, and we cannot apply them directly to problems that involve multiple entities and relations. At the same time, collections of entities and the relations between them can usually be represented as graphs, and we can attempt to develop a generic framework for learning on inputs from graphs. In this section, we review the most common learning tasks associated with graphs and develop a toolkit of supervised and unsupervised methods that will later be used in the use case-specific recipes.

2.7.1 *Machine Learning Tasks on Graphs*

We define graph $G = (V, E)$ as a set of nodes V and a set of edges E that connects these nodes. We denote an edge that goes from node $u \in V$ to node $v \in V$ as $(u, v) \in E$. We further assume that there is at most one edge between any pair of nodes, all edges are undirected so that $(u, v) \in E \Leftrightarrow (v, u) \in E$, and individual nodes can be associated with m-dimensional feature vectors so that we denote the feature vector of node u as x_u.

Graphs can be used to represent a wide range of enterprise environments, and different environments require solving different types of computational problems on the corresponding graph representations. However, the majority of real-world problems can be casted to one of the following generic formulations:

NODE CLASSIFICATION The node classification problem assumes that each node u is associated with a target label y_u. The standard setup is that we are provided with labels for a training subset of nodes $V_{train} \subset V$, and our goal is to build a model that predicts labels for the remaining nodes. The model should leverage both the topology information and known node features x_u to make the prediction.

One common example of enterprise problems that can be expressed as a node classification task is fraud detection. For instance, a social network might need to detect bots in a graph that represents users and social connections. Another illustrative use case is the analysis and prediction of user interests. For example, a photo-sharing service where users can follow each other and subscribe to various interest groups might be looking to predict relevant interest groups for a given user based on their existing relations with other users [Tang and Liu, 2009].

NODE SIMILARITY EVALUATION In some applications, we need to evaluate a similarity score for a pair of nodes based on their position in the graph and the structure of the neighborhood. For example, we can evaluate similarities between products based on a graph that captures how products are grouped by orders.

We use product similarity scores in recipe R7 (Price and Promotion Optimization) to overcome limited data availability.

RELATION PREDICTION In relation prediction problems, the goal is to predict the most likely or missed edges between the nodes in a graph. From the model development standpoint, we usually assume that we are provided with a training subset of edges $E_{train} \subset E$, and the objective is to infer the missing edges.

A classic example of a relation prediction task in enterprise settings is personalized product recommendations: the interactions between users and items can be represented conveniently as a graph, and recommendations can be produced by predicting the most probable edges between the user and item nodes [Ying et al., 2018].

We develop a graph-based recommendation engine in recipe R6 (Product Recommendations).

GRAPH CLASSIFICATION The fourth standard problem formulation is classification or regression over entire graphs. In this setup, the goal is to learn a function that maps a whole graph G to a single label. For example, we can be given a graph of components that represents a complex machine, and our objective may be to predict whether a machine is in a normal or abnormal state. Another typical enterprise use case that can be approached as a graph classification problem is personalized recommendations – user browsing histories or individual web sessions can be represented as graphs of content items or web pages, and the next item a given user is likely to interact with can be predicted using a graph classification model.

We can approach the node classification problem from the representation learning perspective: we first need to develop specialized layers or models that map individual nodes to low-dimensional embeddings, and then use standard output mappers to estimate the target label y_u based on these embeddings. The main challenge is how to capture the topology information, that is the information about a node's role and relations within the graph, in a low-dimensional representation. We spend the next sections developing several solutions, and then discuss how these solutions can be applied to relation prediction and graph classification problems.

2.7.2   Learning Node Representations

We can capture the information about a node's direct and indirect neighbors and its overall role in the graph using a number of methods including manually designed features, algebraic algorithms, unsupervised representation learning, and supervised methods guided by training labels. In this section, we review several basic algebraic methods, and then develop a more general framework for unsupervised node representation learning. The supervised methods will be discussed in the next section.

2.7.2.1   Basic Methods

Assuming the simple graph structure we agreed on in the previous section, graph $G = (V, E)$ can be represented as a $|V| \times |V|$ adjacency matrix $\mathbf{A}$ so that

$$a_{uv} = \begin{cases} 1, & \text{if } (u, v) \in E, \\ 0, & \text{otherwise} \end{cases} \tag{2.93}$$

We can conveniently use the notion of the adjacency matrix to specify various features that characterize the role of the node in the graph.

One of the most basic options is the *node degree* which is defined as the number of edges connected to the node:

$$\deg(u) = \sum_{v \in V} a_{uv} \tag{2.94}$$

The degree of a node can be viewed as a measure of node importance, and it is a highly discriminative feature in most applications. For example, users of a social network who have many connections are very different from most practical standpoints, from users with comparatively fewer connections. The degree metric, however, considers only the nearest neighbors of the node and treats them equally, regardless of their own importance.

We can extend the concept of a degree to account for multi-hop connections. For instance, we can associate each node u with importance value z_u that obeys the following recurrent equation:

$$z_u = \frac{1}{\lambda} \sum_{v \in V} a_{uv} z_v \tag{2.95}$$

where λ is a constant. Since the value for each node is obtained by aggregating the values for its neighbors, this recurrent relationship means that a node is considered important when it is connected to many nodes which are themselves important. It is easy to see that expression 2.95 is effectively the eigenvector equation for the adjacency matrix: we can rewrite it in a matrix form as $\mathbf{Az} = \lambda \mathbf{z}$ to make this link more obvious. This means that values z_u are components of the eigenvector $\mathbf{z}$ of adjacency matrix $\mathbf{A}$, and thus they are referred to as *eigenvector centralities* of the corresponding nodes.

Node degrees and eigenvector centralities are just examples of features that capture the topology of the graph, and we can include these statistics into hand-crafted node feature vectors consumed by the downstream node classification or relation prediction models. Besides that, computing eigenvectors for very large graphs such as social networks is computationally challenging, although efficient iterative algorithms such as PageRank do exist [Page et al., 1999]. However, the idea of summarizing the topology information by means of recurrent (multi-hop) value propagation across the network of nodes is extremely powerful, and we repeatedly use it in the next sections to build more advanced solutions.

2.7.2.2   *Encoder-Decoder Framework*

The Word2Vec algorithm introduced in Section 2.6.3 learns embeddings for tokens in a sequence using the concept of a *context*: tokens are mapped to such embeddings so that the dot product of two embeddings yields the probability of observing the corresponding tokens in the context of each other. In other words, the embeddings are optimized to evaluate the proximity between tokens. Although an ordered sequence of tokens is not a graph (tokens in a sequence can repeat but nodes in a graph cannot), we can then explore the idea of learning embeddings for nodes in a graph based on the ability to evaluate some measure of proximity between the nodes.

Let us first define a general framework that allows for plugging in arbitrary proximity measures. We first assume that each node u is encoded into a d-dimensional embedding z_u using a standard embedding lookup table:

$$z_u = \text{encode}(u) \tag{2.96}$$

We denote a $|V| \times d$ matrix obtained by stacking these embedding vectors as Z. We further assume that each pair of nodes is associated with some proximity value q_{uv}, and this value is estimated based on the corresponding embeddings using a decoding function:

$$\hat{q}_{uv} = \text{decode}(z_u, z_v) \tag{2.97}$$

In other words, this function *decodes* the embeddings into the proximity measure. We assume that the decoding function does not have any learnable parameters, so the training process aims to optimize only the encoding part, that is the embedding lookup table. This requires defining a loss function that guides the optimization process:

$$L(D) = \sum_{(u,v,q_{uv}) \in D} L(\hat{q}_{uv}, q_{uv}) \tag{2.98}$$

In the above, we assume that D is the training dataset that consists of the node pairs with the ground truth proximity labels q_{uv}. Equations 2.96–2.98 provide a general framework, known as the *encoder-decoder* framework, for unsupervised learning of node embeddings [Hamilton et al., 2017].

The encoder-decoder framework requires specifying four components: a pairwise node proximity measure, encoder function, decoder function, and loss function. We have already assumed that the encoder function is a standard embedding lookup unit, but the other three components still need to be specified, and this can be done in many different ways. Let us examine one specific option for the sake of illustration:

- We can assume a proximity measure that is equal to one when a pair of nodes are adjacent, and zero otherwise. Consequently, proximities are given by the entries of the adjacency matrix: $q_{uv} = a_{uv}$.

- We can further assume that the proximity is estimated as a dot product of the corresponding node embeddings:

$$\text{decode}(\mathbf{z}_u, \mathbf{z}_v) = \mathbf{z}_u^\mathsf{T} \mathbf{z}_v \qquad (2.99)$$

- Finally, we choose to use the MSE loss function, so that

$$L(D) = \sum_{(u,v,q_{uv}) \in D} \left\| \mathbf{z}_u^\mathsf{T} \mathbf{z}_v - a_{uv} \right\|^2 = \left\| \mathbf{Z}\mathbf{Z}^\mathsf{T} - \mathbf{A} \right\|^2 \qquad (2.100)$$

The above specification essentially means that we perform the factorization of adjacency matrix $\mathbf{A}$ and learn its lower-rank representation $\mathbf{Z}$ that minimizes the reconstruction error. Consequently, this variant of the encoder-decoder model is known as *graph factorization*. The graph factorization algorithm allows for efficient distributed implementation, and it can be used to learn embeddings in very large graphs – it was originally developed at Yahoo Research to analyze an email communication network with more than 200 million nodes and 10 billion edges [Ahmed et al., 2013].

2.7.2.3   *Proximity Measures Using Random Walks*

The graph factorization algorithm optimizes the embeddings to predict the immediate neighbors of a given node. This leads to embeddings that mostly capture the local structure of the graph rather than the global (multi-hop) context of each node. We can attempt to overcome this limitation by using a different proximity measure. For example, we can normalize the adjacency matrix to make it interpretable as a probability transition matrix, and predict its powers to simulate multi-hop transitions [Cao et al., 2015]. In this section, we explore an even more powerful approach that specifies the proximity measure using random walks.

Let us assume that we have a procedure that traverses the graph starting at a given node u and making N steps by randomly sampling the destination node from the current node's neighbors at each step. The output of such a procedure is a sequence of nodes $(u, v_1, \ldots, v_N)$ which we call a *random walk*. We can then specify the proximity measure as the probability $p_N(v \mid u)$ of visiting node v on a random walk of length N starting at node u:

$$q_{uv} = p_N(v \mid u) \tag{2.101}$$

This is a very different way of defining the proximity measure compared to the deterministic and symmetric measure used in the graph factorization model. The stochastic random walk measure, however, efficiently captures the multi-hop context of a node.

Assuming that we can evaluate the empirical probability of node v to be in the context of node u, we can optimize embedding to approximate this value. This can be done using a dot product of the corresponding node embeddings, but we need to apply the softmax normalization to obtain the valid probabilities:

$$\text{decode}(\mathbf{z}_u, \mathbf{z}_v) = \frac{\exp(\mathbf{z}_u^T \mathbf{z}_v)}{\sum_{k \in V} \exp(\mathbf{z}_u^T \mathbf{z}_k)} = \hat{q}_{uv} \tag{2.102}$$

The embedding can then be learned by minimizing the cross-entropy loss function:

$$L(D) = \sum_{(u,v,q_{uv}) \in D} -\log(\text{decode}(\mathbf{z}_u, \mathbf{z}_v)) \tag{2.103}$$

This specification leads us to the same problem that we had previously with Word2Vec: evaluation of the denominator in the softmax mapper requires computing as many dot products as there are nodes in the graph. We already know that this problem can be tackled using the negative sampling technique introduced in Section 2.6.3 which replaces the multinomial classification problem with a binary classification task. We can simply apply negative sampling to the current case as well, and, moreover, we can use the Word2Vec procedure that implements negative sampling as the off-the-shelf component. Indeed, random walks can be viewed as sequences of nodes, that are sequences of discrete tokens, and we can use arbitrary methods for learning token representations including Word2Vec to learn node embedding from random walks.

The implementation of this idea is known as the Node2Vec algorithm [Grover and Leskovec, 2016]. Its formal specification is provided in box 2.1, and includes two routines. The main one iterates over all nodes in the input graph, generates multiple random walks out of each node, and applies the standard Word2Vec algorithm to the dataset where each sequence is a walk and each token is a node. The random walk is performed by the second subroutine that traverses the graph starting with the given node.

Algorithm 2.1: Node2Vec

Main Node2Vec routine:
  input:
      $G = (V, E)$ – input graph with nodes V and edges E
      N – walks per node

  function node2vec(G):
      walks = []
      for $i = 1$ **to** N **do**
         for u **in** V **do**
            walks.append(random_walk(G, u))
         end
      end

      return word2vec(walks)
  end

Random walk subroutine:
  input:
      $G = (V, E)$ – input graph
      u – start node
      L – maximum walk length

  function random_walk(G, u):
      walk = [u]   *(Initialize the walk (list of nodes))*
      c = u   *(Current node)*
      for $i = 1$ **to** L **do**
         neighbors = G.neighbors(c)
         c = sample(neighbors)   *(Sample the next node)*
         walk.append(c)
      end

      return walks
  end

It is easy to see that this algorithm essentially implements the specification of the encoder-decoder model given by expressions 2.102 and 2.103, but delegates all the complexity associated with negative sampling and other computational aspects to the Word2Vec subroutine. The Node2Vec algorithm highlights the similarity between representation learning on sequences and graphs: we literally use the same model, but specify the *context* in two different ways to appropriately capture the topology of the structure.

The Node2Vec algorithm has one more important aspect that needs to be discussed. We have previously stated that, at each step, the random walk process samples the node to move to from the neighbors of the current node, but we did not specify exactly how this sampling is performed. The most basic option is to sample according to the uniform distribution, so that all neighbors of the current node are equiprobable. This simple strategy, however, does not necessarily capture the topology of the neighborhood around the node in an optimal way. From that perspective, we generally want to find the balance between breadth-first and depth-first searches. The breadth-first search (BFS) tends to generate localized sequences that describe the structural role of the node (hubs, bridges, periphery, etc.), whereas the depth-first search (DFS) produces sequences that describe how nodes are interconnected at a macro level. The ability to employ these two strategies and capture both local and global aspects of the node position is essential for producing useful embeddings.

Node2Vec addresses this problem using an advanced sampling algorithm that can be fine-tuned using hyperparameters. Let us assume a random walk that traversed some node v and then moved to its neighbor node v'. The algorithm now has to choose the next node v'' to move to from all neighbors of v'. In Node2Vec, the transition probabilities are assigned to the candidate nodes according to the following rule:

$$
p(v, v'') \propto \begin{cases} 1/p, & \text{if } d(v, v'') = 0 \\ 1, & \text{if } d(v, v'') = 1 \\ 1/q, & \text{if } d(v, v'') = 2 \end{cases} \tag{2.104}
$$

where $d(v, v'')$ is the length of the shortest path between nodes v and v''. The length of zero means that we return from v' to v, and thus parameter p controls the likelihood of returning to the already-visited nodes and exploring the local structure in a BFS fashion. The length of 1 means that node v'' is connected to both v and v'. Finally, the length of 2 means that we are moving away from v, and thus small values of $q < 1$ make the algorithm more focused on exploring the global structure in a DFS fashion. These three options cover all possible cases because the length of the shortest path between v and v'' cannot exceed 2.

In some applications, the transition rule 2.104 can be customized to incorporate edge weights or domain knowledge. For example, we can increase the transition probability for edges with high weights (strong links) and decrease it for edges with low weights (weak links) if such weights are available. We use this technique in R6 (Product Recommendations) to capture the information about the strength of relationships between products in the catalog.

2.7.2.4   *Usage and Limitations*

The unsupervised methods that follow the encoder-decoder framework, including graph factorization and Node2Vec, can be applied to all problems outlined in Section 2.7.1. First, the node embeddings produced by the encoder can be consumed as input features by the downstream models that perform the actual node classification. Since the topology information is already captured in embeddings, the downstream classification can typically be performed by generic models such as logistic regression [Grover and Leskovec, 2016]. Second, node similarities can simply be computed as distances in the embedding space. Third, relation prediction can be performed by computing edge embeddings based on the corresponding node embeddings, and using them as inputs to the downstream edge prediction model. The edge embeddings can typically be computed using a basic aggregation operation. For example, we can compute embedding z_{uv} for an edge between nodes u and v as an average $(z_u + z_v)/2$ or element-wise product $z_u \odot z_v$ of the corresponding node embeddings. The edge prediction can then be performed using a binary classification model that uses embeddings z_{uv} as inputs and entries of the adjacency matrix as target labels. Finally, graph embeddings for small graphs can also be obtained by aggregating node embeddings [Hamilton et al., 2017].

The encoder-decoder approach, however, has several limitations. First, it is an unsupervised solution, so it cannot be guided by target labels to produce task-specific representations. Second, each node is interpreted as a unique token. This means that we cannot compute embeddings for nodes that are not in the training set, and all embeddings have to be recomputed when the graph changes. The reliance on the node identities also means that we cannot incorporate node feature vectors x_u and transfer learnings across different parts of the graph that have similar or identical structures (topologies) but are comprised of different sets of nodes. We discuss how to overcome these limitations in the next section.

2.7.3   Graph Neural Networks

We previously discussed that embeddings for various structures including vectors, sequences, and tensors, as well as their elements, can be learned using two different approaches – we can build a supervised model and capture the embeddings at certain points of their transformation chain, or we can use unsupervised methods that employ some variant of the information bottleneck to produce dense embeddings. The methods discussed in the previous section implement the latter approach and inherit its limitations. In this section, we focus on the supervised approach and develop a framework for solving the standard learning tasks on graphs in a supervised way.

2.7.3.1   Neural Message Passing Framework

Let us assume graph $G = (V, E)$ where each node $u \in V$ is associated with feature vector x_u. We generally want to build a network that maps each node to dense representation z_u, and then maps these representations to some output for which we have ground truth labels. The complete network can then be trained in a supervised way guided by the discrepancy between the output and ground truth labels, and intermediate representations z_u can be deemed as the node embeddings.

The node embeddings should capture both the structural information about the neighborhood and the node features x_u. We have already seen that methods like eigenvector centrality capture the structural information using iterative value propagation across the graph, so we can attempt to generalize this approach. We can start by initializing node embeddings with the input feature vectors, so that $z_u = x_u$, and then iteratively update each node by aggregating embeddings of the adjacent nodes:

$$m_u^{(k)} = \phi(\{z_v^{(k)}\}), \quad v \in N(u)$$
$$z_u^{(k+1)} = \psi(z_u^{(k)}, m_u^{(k)})$$

(2.105)

where $N(u)$ is the set of adjacent nodes, that is neighborhood, of node u, $m_u^{(k)}$ is the aggregation of the embeddings received from its neighbors at iteration k, ϕ is the aggregation function, and ψ is the update function. The embedding values propagated from the neighborhood to the given node can be thought of as the *messages*, so the iterative process specified by the above equations is commonly referred to as *neural message passing*. Similar to the eigenvector centrality, we expect the process to converge to some final values of z_u that can be interpreted as embeddings. The message passing framework, however, is an abstraction that requires specifying the aggregation and update functions, as well as the overall model design and training procedure.

2.7.3.2 *Network Architecture*

The message passing architecture can be implemented as a neural network provided that we specify the aggregation and update functions appropriately. Let us choose the aggregation function ϕ to be a simple sum of the messages received from the neighbors:

$$\mathbf{m}_u^{(k)} = \sum_{v \in N(u)} \mathbf{z}_v^{(k)} \tag{2.106}$$

Next, we can define the update function ψ as a dense layer that is applied to a node's own embedding and incoming messages. This can be expressed as follows:

$$\mathbf{z}_u^{(k+1)} = g\left(\mathbf{W}_a^{(k+1)}\mathbf{z}_u^{(k)} + \mathbf{W}_b^{(k+1)}\mathbf{m}_u^{(k)}\right) \tag{2.107}$$

In the above, $\mathbf{W}_a^{(k)}$ and $\mathbf{W}_b^{(k)}$ are the learnable linear operators applied at iteration k to the node's own and incoming embeddings, respectively, and g is the element-size activation function such as a sigmoid or ReLu. We can rewrite the update function more concisely in matrix form as follows:

$$\mathbf{Z}^{(k+1)} = g\left(\mathbf{Z}^{(k)}\mathbf{W}_a^{(k+1)\mathsf{T}} + \mathbf{A}\mathbf{Z}^{(k)}\mathbf{W}_b^{(k+1)\mathsf{T}}\right) \tag{2.108}$$

We assume that each iteration is associated with its own linear operator, and thus we can implement a sequence of n updates as a neural network with n layers where parameters $\mathbf{W}_a^{(k)}$ and $\mathbf{W}_b^{(k)}$ are learned independently for each layer (index k iterates from 1 to n). This design is illustrated in Figure 2.55 where a part of the network that corresponds to the computational graph for one of the nodes is presented.

The architecture defined above and its variants are collectively known as *graph neural networks* (GNNs) [Scarselli et al., 2009]. The GNN design is a fundamental building block that can be used to solve various supervised learning and representation learning tasks with graph inputs.

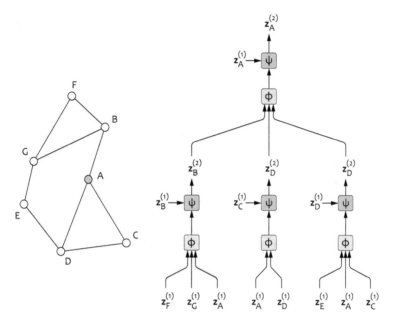

Figure 2.55: Example of a neural message passing network. We assume a two-layer network and show only a fragment of the network that corresponds to the computational graph for node A.

2.7.3.3   Model Training

In the previous section, we outlined the basic GNN architecture, but did not specify how a GNN network can be used to solve standard learning problems such as node classification or relation prediction. In this section, we focus on building such end-to-end solutions.

In node classification problems, we have a training set D of nodes represented by their feature vectors x_u and corresponding class labels y_u. Assuming that there are c classes in total, we can represent a label for node u as c-dimensional one-hot vector y_u. The node embeddings computed by the GNN model can then be mapped to the class probability vectors using the softmax normalization:

$$\hat{y}_u = \text{softmax}\left(W_s z_u^{(n)}\right) \tag{2.109}$$

where we assume a GNN with n layers, $z_u^{(n)}$ are d-dimensional node embeddings, W_s is a $c \times d$ matrix of learnable parameters, and $\hat{y}_u$ are c-dimensional stochastic vectors. We then use the node features as inputs to the first layer of the network, so that $z_u^{(0)} = x_u$, and train it using a regular cross-entropy loss:

$$L(D) = \sum_{u \in D} - \log \sum_{j=1}^{c} y_{uj} \cdot \hat{y}_{uj} \tag{2.110}$$

This design allows us to build node classification models, as well as to learn node embeddings aligned with the target labels which can be used for node similarity scoring and other tasks.

In relation prediction tasks, we can reuse the methods developed earlier for encoder-decoder models. For example, we can use the entries of the adjacency matrix a_{uv} as the ground truth labels, and estimate the probability of relations using dot products of the corresponding node embedding:

$$p(a_{uv} = 1 \mid z_u, z_v) = \sigma(z_u^T z_v)$$
$$p(a_{uv} = 0 \mid z_u, z_v) = \sigma(-z_u^T z_v) \tag{2.111}$$

The GNN can then be trained using the negative sampling loss which we used previously for Word2Vec and Node2Vec models [Yang et al., 2020]:

$$L(D) = \sum_{(u,v) \in D} - \log \sigma(z_u^T z_v) - \sum_{v_n \sim S} \log \sigma(-z_u^T z_{v_n}) \tag{2.112}$$

where dataset D consists of positive samples with $a_{uv} = 1$, and S is the distribution from which the negative instances are sampled. This design is very similar to Word2Vec and Node2Vec (see expressions 2.91 and 2.92), but the key difference is that the lookup embeddings are replaced by an arbitrary neural network, so node embeddings z_u and z_v can potentially capture more complex semantics.

2.8   MODEL CORRECTNESS

All methods developed earlier in this chapter aim to learn functions (networks) that approximate the properties of the data-generating process based on the observed samples. In the previous sections, we implicitly assumed that the input samples cover the manifold that needs to be approximated in a consistent way, so that the gradient descent algorithm is likely to converge to a valid model provided that the model architecture and optimization hyperparameters are chosen correctly. In practice, this assumption can never be taken for granted, and one has to use a broad range of statistical methods and techniques to ensure both the validity of the input data and correctness of the obtained model. A comprehensive treatment of such methods is beyond the scope of this chapter, but we discuss two typical scenarios that illustrate the problem of inconsistent manifold coverage by the available data in the next sections. These two scenarios are very common in enterprise applications, so the checks and corrections described below can be viewed as a part of the standard data validation and preparation checklist.

2.8.1 *Imbalanced Data*

The first typical scenario is a nonuniform coverage of the manifold by the training samples. This problem appears in virtually all enterprise applications, but it is particularly pronounced in applications with rare events. For example, the number of fraudulent transactions in a payment system can be several orders of magnitude less than the number of non-fraudulent transactions, and the number of defective parts in a manufacturing process can be several orders of magnitude less than the number of normal parts. This leads to imbalanced datasets where some areas of the manifold of interest are densely covered by the data samples while other areas have very low coverage density. In the regular gradient descent process, the overall loss used for the model parameters update is computed as a simple average of the per-sample losses, as defined in expression 2.9, and thus the process might fail to capture the curvature of the areas with low coverage density.

The imbalance problem can be approached in several different ways. For the sake of illustration, let us focus on the binary classification problem with real-valued input feature vectors. Assuming that the input dataset is imbalanced, we have the *majority class* that makes up the larger proportion of the data and *minority class* that makes up the smaller proportion. One possible solution for learning a classification model in such a setup is to modify the loss function and assign weights to per-sample losses, so that either the minority samples are *upweighted* or the majority samples are *downweighted* according to the ratio of class cardinalities. This solution is feasible practically and is supported in most machine learning libraries and frameworks, but it is not always optimal because it uses only the original samples without any randomization or interpolation.

The alternative strategy is to explicitly *resample* the dataset by adding or removing samples. We can approach the resampling task in two ma-

jor ways. The first is by *under-sampling* the majority class. Assuming
that there are n_{min} instances of the minority class, we can simply implement this approach by randomly sampling n_{min} instances from the majority class and forming a balanced dataset with $2n_{min}$ samples where
both classes are equally represented. The under-sampling strategy is
generally prone to discarding informative samples and increasing the
variance of the classifier. In certain cases, this issue can be improved
by using more selective under-sampling techniques. For example, we
can under-sample the majority class by removing only the instances
from the so-called *Tomek links* on the borders between the classes and
areas where the classes intermix, as shown in Figure 2.56. We can view
under-sampling as a generalization of the majority class downweight-
ing where zero weights are assigned to individual instances using various algorithms.

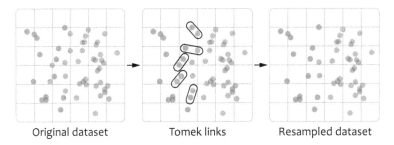

Original dataset   Tomek links   Resampled dataset

Figure 2.56: The majority class under-sampling using Tomek links. Tomek links
occur between two samples that have different classes, but are the
nearest neighbors to each other [Tomek, 1976]. In this example, we
remove only the majority class instance from each link, but other
strategies such as the removal of both instances can be used.

The second option is the *over-sampling* of the minority class. The most
basic implementation of this idea is sampling with replacement – assuming that the majority class contains n_{maj} instances, we sample n_{maj}
points from the minority class, and create a balanced dataset of $2n_{maj}$
samples. This strategy is essentially equivalent to the minority class upweighting discussed earlier because the duplication basically increases
the weights of the corresponding samples in the loss function. However, we can replace this basic duplication by a more advanced randomization or interpolation algorithm. This can help to increase the robustness of the learning process, although we, of course, cannot learn
the minutia of the manifold curvature that are not present in the original data. One of the most commonly used over-sampling algorithms
is Synthetic Minority Oversampling TEchnique, or SMOTE [Chawla
et al., 2002]. The SMOTE algorithm starts by selecting a random mi-

nority class instance **q**, finding its k nearest minority class neighbors, and selecting one of these neighbors **p** at random. The new instance is then created by randomly picking a point at the line segment that connects **q** and **p**, and the process repeats until the desired number of new instances is generated. This algorithm is illustrated in Figure 2.57.

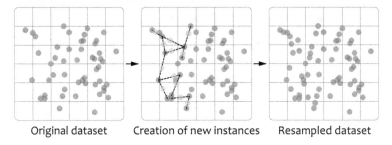

Original dataset   Creation of new instances   Resampled dataset

Figure 2.57: The minority class over-sampling using SMOTE.

The balancing methods described above can be combined in multiple ways. For instance, a hybrid strategy that includes partial under-sampling of the majority class and minority class over-sampling can outperform pure under-sampling [Chawla et al., 2002]. In practice, a specific balancing strategy is designed based on the dataset sizes (it may be unfeasible to under-sample small sets), computational considerations (over-sampling may be computationally infeasible for large sets), model evaluation criteria, feature types, and other factors.

 We discuss the use cases that usually involve imbalanced data in recipes R1 (Propensity Modeling), R10 (Anomaly Detection), and R11 (Visual Quality Control), although all use cases discussed in this book are prone to some degree of data imbalance.

2.8.2 *Observational Data*

The second common scenario that often requires the use of advanced data preparation methods is the analysis and planning of actions that are intended to change the trajectories of entities or produce some other outcomes. In such problems, we usually want to build a model for evaluating the potential causal effect of a specific action on a specific entity, and then use this model to optimally assign actions to entities. In this context, actions are commonly referred to as *treatments* or *interventions*. The development of a model that correctly evaluates the causal effect of the treatment is a challenging problem because the validity of the evaluation can be compromised in many different ways. In this section, we explore some aspects of this problem using a specific use case, and more comprehensive studies that discuss other problematic scenarios are readily available (see, for example, [Guo and Fraser, 2015]).

Consider a telecom company that runs targeted retention campaigns to prevent customer churn. The company wants to develop a model that evaluates the probability of churn for a specific customer provided that this customer is treated with a retention offer, as well as for an alternative scenario where the customer is not treated:

$$p(y \mid \mathbf{x}, a) = f(\mathbf{x}, a) \tag{2.113}$$

where y is the churn event, $\mathbf{x}$ is the customer feature vector, a is a binary variable that indicates whether the customer is treated or not, and f is the model. The development of such a model requires collecting a representative dataset of $(\mathbf{x}, a, y)$ tuples. The ideal approach for collecting such a dataset is as follows: allocate the population of customers into test and control groups, treat the test group, and observe the outcomes during a sufficiently long period of time, as shown in Figure 2.58. It is essential to perform the allocation in such a way that the test and control groups are consistent, so that we can observe both treatment and no-treatment outcomes for similar values of $\mathbf{x}$, isolating the treatment effect from other churn factors that can vary across the customers. This can be accomplished by allocating the test and control groups at random, so that the allocation decisions are independent from the customer features. This approach is known as *randomized experimentation*.

Unfortunately, data collection using randomized experiments is not always feasible in practice. In the example described above, as well as many other scenarios, companies can provide only historical data collected under some biased allocation policy. For example, the telecom company could use manually configured business rules to target specific segments of customers prior to the development of a statistical targeting model. This introduces the *selection bias*, that is the systematic difference between the test and control groups. The problem of evaluating the treatment effects based on the biased data is known as an *observational study*. This term underscores the fact that we do not

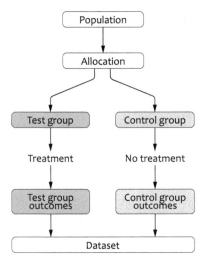

Figure 2.58: Data collection for the treatment effect modeling.

control the allocation policy used for data collection like in random-ized experimentation, but only observe the given allocation process and corresponding outcomes.

The selection bias can make it impossible to learn a model that correctly evaluates the treatment effect for arbitrary instances from the population. An extreme case of this situation is the complete separation of the test and control groups along a certain dimension. In our running example with the telecom company, we might not be able to build a model for evaluating customers from an arbitrary US state if the historical data were collected under a policy that targeted only one specific state.

If the selection bias is limited, so that the test and control groups overlap, we can attempt to correct the bias using resampling. Conceptually, the goal of the resampling process is to ensure that each instance in the test group matches a comparable instance in the control group, so that the groups become consistent. The implementation of this idea requires defining the exact matching criteria which can be done in several different ways.

One of the most common and theoretically well-grounded matching strategies is known as *propensity score matching* [Rosenbaum and Rubin, 1983]. This approach is based on the observation that, for the purposes of the treatment effect analysis, the bias can be fully characterized by the conditional dependency between the treatment assignment a and observed features **x**. Assuming that this dependency can be estimated, the dataset can be rebalanced to reduce the bias. More specifically, we can define the propensity score as the conditional probability of assignment to a particular treatment given the vector of observed features:

$$p(a \mid \mathbf{x}) = g(\mathbf{x}) \tag{2.114}$$

where the score estimating model g is fitted based on the available observational data. In practice, g is typically a low-capacity model such as the basic logistic regression. Once this model is fitted, we can resample the dataset to ensure that the distribution of the propensity scores is approximately the same in both test and control groups. One of the ways to implement such a resampling procedure is to perform one-to-one matching between the test and control groups. We iterate this over all instances in the test group, and, for each instance $\mathbf{x}_i$, we find instance $\mathbf{x}_j$ from the control group that is the nearest neighbor of $\mathbf{x}_i$ in the space of propensity scores:

$$\mathbf{x}_j = \underset{\mathbf{x}_j \in \text{ control group}}{\mathrm{argmin}} \; \left| g(\mathbf{x}_i) - g(\mathbf{x}_j) \right| \tag{2.115}$$

The pair of $\mathbf{x}_i$ and $\mathbf{x}_j$ is then added to the output dataset, instance $\mathbf{x}_j$ is removed from the test group to prevent it from being drawn again, and the process repeats for the next instance from the test group. This procedure creates a dataset where each test instance is matched with a control instance of a similar propensity level. This dataset can be used to evaluate the treatment effect and build downstream models such the one defined previously in expression 2.113.

We continue to discuss the problem of action planning and evaluation in the next chapter and recipes R1 (Propensity Modeling) and R4 (Next Best Action).

2.9 SUMMARY

- In many enterprise applications, it is convenient to view statistical models as components that map observed inputs to hidden properties, expected outcomes, or recommended interventions.

This mapping can be learned based on explicitly provided guiding labels, feedback collected through interactions with the environment, or structural relationship between the parts of the input data.

- Enterprise entities can often be represented as vectors of features that can be mapped to the outputs using a network of transformations that are jointly optimized using the gradient descent algorithm. Common design patterns for such networks include linear layers, nonlinear layers, embedding lookup layers, interaction layers, multi-head and multi-tower architectures.

- Enterprise processes, as well as some entities, can usually be represented as sequences of numerical values or categorical tokens. The typical tasks associated with sequences include sequence classification, element prediction, and sequence-to-sequence mapping. These tasks are performed using specialized blocks such as convolution layers, recurrent layers, and transformers.

- Many enterprise entities are represented as multidimensional structures such as matrices and tensors. The typical tasks associated with these structures include classification, feature extraction, matrix-to-matrix and matrix-to-tuple mappings. These tasks are performed using specialized blocks such as two-dimensional convolution layers.

- Many enterprise problems can be conveniently represented as graphs. Node representations that capture the topology of the graph can be produced using graph neural networks and then used to solve node classification and relation prediction tasks.

- The entity and process representations produced at different stages of the networks can be used for entity similarity evaluation and other tasks. The quality of such representations can be improved using specialized loss functions and model architectures.

- The validity of the model can be compromised by various types of biases in the input data. Some types of biases can be corrected using data resampling techniques.

3

LEARNING CONTROL POLICIES

Many enterprise AI problems can be described as control problems: there is a system, process, or entity that needs to be operated or managed, and we have to develop an algorithm that makes decisions on actions or interventions that need to be taken and learns from the received feedback. The methods discussed in the previous chapter address only the learning part of the problem, and then only in the sense of building a model that approximates the statistical properties of the underlying process or entity based on available data. We did not develop any methodology for optimization of possible actions based on such a model, nor did we specify how the feedback data needs to be collected to ensure correctness of the model.

In this chapter, we focus on the decision-making aspect of AI solutions and study the relationship between models and actions. We first discuss several basic techniques that can be used to make decisions based on model outputs, and then develop a more comprehensive toolkit for learning control policies through interactions with a controlled system or environment.

3.1 BASIC DECISION-MAKING TECHNIQUES

Assuming that we can build a valid statistical model of some process or entity based on the already-available data, we can plug it into an optimization algorithm that evaluates alternative scenarios and determines the optimal action. The optimization algorithm generally needs to incorporate business objectives, constraints, and other considerations, so the exact design of the decision-making procedure depends heavily on a specific use case and application. However, most solutions employ the following generic techniques that are worth discussing at a high level to establish a frame of reference:

RANKING As we discussed in Chapter 2, statistical models are usually built to estimate hidden properties or future states of processes or entities. This estimate is often computed using a chain of contracting transformations that produces intermediate representations of the entity (embeddings) and, finally, outputs scores that describe the required property or state. The embeddings allow us to evaluate distances between the entities, rank entities based on the distance to some reference point, and make the final decision by choosing the most similar items. For example, a visual search service can rank images in the search result list based on their distance to the reference image (query) in the embedding space. We can express this logic more formally for the case of selecting the most optimal entity x_{opt} as

$$x_{opt} = \operatorname*{argmin}_{x} d\left(z(x),\ z(x_0)\right) \tag{3.1}$$

where x are the candidate entities, x_0 is the reference point, z is the embedding function, and d is the distance function. For selecting a set of multiple entities X_{opt}, the decision rule can be expressed as

$$X_{opt} = \{x :\ d\left(z(x),\ z(x_0)\right) < T\} \tag{3.2}$$

where T is the distance threshold parameter which can also be a subject of optimization.

The alternative strategy is to rank items based on the scores or probability estimates that are designed to gauge the goodness (utility) of an entity for a certain objective. These scores and estimates can be produced by regression and classification models, and the final decisions can be made by choosing entities with the highest or lowest scores. For example, an offer-targeting system can send special offers only to customers with a high attrition risk score. We can express this type of decision rule for the case of one entity as follows:

$$x_{opt} = \operatorname*{argmax}_{x} y(x) \tag{3.3}$$

where y is the function implemented by the model, and higher values of the score are assumed to be preferable. In some applications, we might need to balance between multiple objectives, and the goodness of a given entity for each of the objectives is gauged using a separate score. The final decision is then made to achieve a desirable trade-off between the objectives. All three ranking scenarios are illustrated in Figure 3.1.

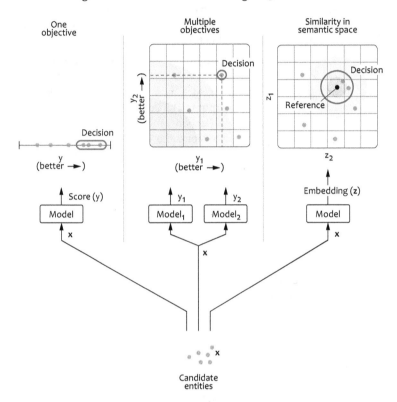

Figure 3.1: Ranking entities using scores and embeddings.

ACTION EVALUATION The ranking methods described above assume that the underlying model estimates the distribution of the goodness score $y(\mathbf{x})$ based on the known state $\mathbf{x}$. This solution can be extended to explicitly account for potential actions and interventions, so that multiple goodness scores conditioned on possible actions a are evaluated, and the final decision is made by selecting the action with the maximum score:

$$a_{opt} = \underset{a}{\mathrm{argmax}}\ y(\mathbf{x},\ a) \tag{3.4}$$

This approach can be used for both discrete and continuous action spaces. For example, an offer-targeting system can evaluate the probability of redemption for several discrete offer types for each consumer and create a personalized offer-to-consumer mapping to maximize the number of redemptions. Alternatively, the system can evaluate the probability of redemption based on the discount percentage, which can be a continuous variable, and determine the optimal value for each customer.

COST-BENEFIT ANALYSIS Although the ranking and evaluation processes can sometimes use models that directly estimate some meaningful business metric such as a profit or loss, we did not assume that the model output $y(x)$ incorporates all business considerations associated with actions and decisions. In our example of the offer-targeting system, the final decisions should be made based not only on the offer redemption probabilities, but also on the offer costs, redemption revenues, and other factors that quantify the bottom line business value. In applications that require performing such cost-benefit analysis, it is common to build an econometric model m that estimates the actual business outcomes such as revenues and profits based on the outputs of the underlying statistical models, and to rank possible actions according to these estimates. This can be expressed as the following extension of the action evaluation task:

$$a_{opt} = \underset{a}{\text{argmax}}\ m(y(x,\ a)) \tag{3.5}$$

MATHEMATICAL PROGRAMMING The above methods assume that we can enumerate and evaluate all possible actions. This can usually be done for small discrete action sets and low-dimensional continuous action spaces that can be traversed and evaluated using, for example, grid search. Many enterprise applications, however, require controlling multiple interdependent parameters, so that each action can be represented by a vector of continuous or discrete variables that can be the subjects for various constraints. For example, a price optimization system might need to set prices for hundreds of related products, multiple time intervals, and under complex inventory and replenishment constraints. The system can use statistical models to evaluate specific pricing plans by estimating the expected profits or revenues, but it cannot evaluate all possible plans. This challenge can often be alleviated by transferring the optimization task to some standard mathematical programming problem such as linear programming or integer programming that can be solved using off-the-shelf optimization algorithms and software.

The four strategies outlined above can be viewed as basic guidelines for designing decision-making and decision-support layers on top of statistical models. In practice, these layers often combine mathematical optimization and various heuristics for handling edge cases, incorporating domain knowledge, and enforcing business policies. We will discuss these aspects in greater detail in the next chapters where we develop use case-specific solutions. However, the framework described above has several fundamental limitations that make it inapplicable or highly inefficient in certain environments. We discuss these issues in the next section, and then develop a completely different framework that can be used as an alternative.

3.2   LEARNING BASED ON INTERACTIONS

The decision-making techniques described in the previous section require valid and accurate models of entities and processes to be available. We described a toolkit for building such models in Chapter 2, but we made several assumptions to simplify the integrations and interactions with the environment:

NO DEPENDENCY ON ACTIONS The input samples are collected by some external process that ensures the completeness and correctness of the data to learn from. This process and the data it collects do not depend on actions taken by the control algorithm.

INSTRUCTIONS For the supervised methods, the target labels are specified by an external process that knows the correct answer, so that the learning process is guided by explicit instructions.

STATIONARITY The environment is relatively static, and the drift of the statistical patterns over time can be addressed using basic methods such as regular model retraining over a sliding time window.

The above assumptions do not always hold true in real enterprise environments, and control algorithms generally need to address the following challenges that can be viewed as an alternative set of assumptions:

DEPENDENCY ON ACTIONS The information to learn from comes as a response to actions and its completeness and distribution depend on the actions taken by the algorithm. It is the responsibility of the algorithm to perform a correct and efficient exploration of the environment.

EVALUATION The environment provides the feedback information about the gains and losses produced by the actions, but it does not tell which action was the optimal or correct one.

NON-STATIONARITY Historical data might not be available, can be incomplete, or become invalid because of changes in the properties of the environment. The control algorithm needs to collect the data dynamically and account for the drift of the environment properties.

In the next sections, we discuss how to build a control algorithm, commonly referred to as an *agent*, that explores the environment having only limited prior knowledge, learns a model that relates actions with outcomes, and produces a control policy that can be used to determine the optimal action in a given state of the environment. The area of machine learning that studies this category of problems is known as *reinforcement learning*.

3.3   REINFORCEMENT LEARNING: BANDIT CASE

Assuming an environment with limited availability or validity of historical data, we might not be able to reliably estimate the value of possible actions at the beginning of the optimization process, and efficient data collection through interactions with the environment becomes a critical task. In this section, we examine the most basic formulation of this problem.

We consider the setup where the control algorithm (agent) needs to choose one action $a_t \in A$ at every time step t from a discrete set A of k possible actions. The chosen action is then applied to the environment, and the algorithm observes the real-valued reward r_t which quantifies the value or loss resulting from the action. The environment is specified by a collection of reward distributions $(p_1(r), \ldots, p_k(r))$, so that each action is associated with a dedicated distribution, and the reward at time step t is sampled from the distribution that corresponds to action a_t:

$$r_t \sim p_{a_t}(r) \tag{3.6}$$

Such an environment is called a *stochastic bandit* by an analogy with a slot machine. It is essential that the rewards at different time steps are assumed to be independent, so that the reward at time step t does not depend on the actions taken before t. However, the reward distributions can be static or can change over time.

We further assume that the reward distributions are initially un-known to the agent, but it can learn some action selection rule for time step t, known as the *control policy*, based on the observed history $a_0, r_0, \ldots, a_{t-1}, r_{t-1}$. The goal of the agent is to learn the policy that maximizes the cumulative reward, also referred to as *return*, collected over T time steps:

$$R = \sum_{t=0}^{T} r_t \tag{3.7}$$

This problem statement is known as a *multi-armed bandit problem*. This formulation underscores the need to explore the environment in order to learn the dependency between the actions and rewards, and to do it efficiently to quickly converge to the return-maximizing policy. At the same time, the multi-armed bandit setup assumes that the agent receives no information about the actions and environment except the action identities and rewards. This is an oversimplification compared to many real-world enterprise problems, but we focus on this formu-lation for now and discuss how to incorporate additional information into the algorithm later in this book.

The agent can make return-maximizing decisions based on the esti-mates of the mean reward for each possible action which is referred to as the *acton value*:

$$Q(a) = \mathbb{E}\left[r_t \mid a_t = a\right] \tag{3.8}$$

where a_t is the action at time t, r_t is the reward at time t, and $Q(a)$ is the value of action a. The value estimates can then guide the optimal action selection. The main challenge is how to balance the exploration of the environment that requires trying different actions to estimate the corresponding reward distributions and exploitation of these learnings through selecting the return-optimal actions. These two objectives are clearly in conflict because the number of time steps is limited, and ev-ery step used for exploration generally reduces the return. Meanwhile, the excessive focus on exploitation reduces the accuracy of the value estimates and suboptimal action selection. We spend the next sections discussing several possible solutions for this problem.

3.3.1 *Greedy Policies*

The agent can estimate the value of action a at time step t by averaging the rewards it has already received through taking this action:

$$Q_t(a) = \frac{\sum_{\tau=0}^{t-1} r_\tau \cdot \mathbb{I}(a_\tau = a)}{\sum_{\tau=0}^{t-1} \mathbb{I}(a_\tau = a)} \tag{3.9}$$

where $\mathbb{I}(\cdot)$ is the indicator function returning the value 1 if its argument is true and 0 otherwise. If action a was not taken before step t and the denominator is thus zero, then some default value can be used for the estimate.

Provided the estimate 3.9, we can consider always taking the action with the maximum expected value:

$$a_t = \underset{a}{\operatorname{argmax}}\ Q_t(a) \tag{3.10}$$

This approach is known as a greedy policy. If the same maximum value estimate is attained by more than one action, the agent can break the tie arbitrarily, for example, selecting one of these actions at random. The greedy policy can achieve good or even optimal results in certain scenarios, but it fails to explore the environment properly in more realistic settings. For example, the greedy policy can be optimal when the rewards are stationary and have zero variance, so the agent sticks to the optimal action right after all alternatives are evaluated once, and this can be ensured by setting sufficiently high default values for $Q_t(a)$. However, if the rewards have relatively high variance or just drift over time, the greedy approach is likely to focus on incorrect actions and deliver suboptimal results. This problem can be addressed by randomizing the policy so that a random action is chosen with a relatively small probability ε:

$$a_t = \begin{cases} \underset{a}{\operatorname{argmax}}\ Q_t(a), & \text{with probability } 1 - \varepsilon \\ \text{random action}, & \text{with probability } \varepsilon \end{cases} \tag{3.11}$$

This solution, known as ε-*greedy policy*, allows control of the bandwidth used for environment exploration through the hyperparameter ε. This simple approach is efficient and is widely used in practice, but it does not necessarily achieve the maximum possible returns and requires the determination of a good value for the exploration rate ε which is a separate problem that needs to be solved. In the next sections, we consider two alternatives that can help to address these concerns.

3.3.2 *Upper Confidence Bound Policy*

The ε-greedy algorithm accounts for potential uncertainty in value estimates $Q_t(a)$ and continuously explores the environment using randomly chosen actions to reduce this uncertainty. The level of uncertainty, however, can be different for different actions and thus choosing the exploring action at random might not be optimal. We can attempt to improve the performance of the algorithm by factoring in the variance of the value estimates.

Let us consider the situation when the agent has the highest value estimate for action a_j at time t. Can the agent be certain that a_j is really optimal? It can be the case when the value estimate for a_j is larger than the estimates for other actions by a margin that is proportional to the variances of these estimates:

$$Q_t(a_j) + B_t(a_j) \geqslant Q_t(a_i) + B_t(a_i) \qquad \text{for all } i \neq j \qquad (3.12)$$

where $B_t(a)$ defines the upper bounds of the intervals where the true action values are located with a sufficiently high probability. If the agent has a reliable estimate for a_j with small $B_t(a_j)$, but other actions are not sufficiently explored so that $B_t(a_i)$ is high and the condition 3.12 does not hold true, then it makes sense to explore the alternative actions further to become more confident that a_j is indeed optimal. This consideration leads to the following action policy that can be contrasted to equation 3.11:

$$a_t = \underset{a}{\text{argmax}} \; [Q_t(a) + B_t(a)] \qquad (3.13)$$

To estimate bounds $B_t(a)$, we can use Hoeffding's inequality. It states that, given n independent random variables $x_1, \ldots, x_n$ bounded by the interval $[0, 1]$, the probability that their sum $x = \sum x_i$ deviates from its true mean by more than ε is limited by the following bound:

$$p(\mathbb{E}\,[x] > x + \varepsilon) \leqslant \exp\left(-2n\varepsilon^2\right) \qquad (3.14)$$

Applying this result to the action value estimates, we get the following:

$$p(Q(a) > Q_t(a) + B_t(a)) \leqslant \exp\left(-2n_a B_t^2(a)\right) \qquad (3.15)$$

where $Q(a)$ is the true action value and n_a is the number of times action a was executed by time t. Denoting the probability on the left-hand side of 3.15 as p and solving for $B_t(a)$, we get the following expression:

$$B_t(a) = \sqrt{\frac{-\ln p}{2n_a}} \qquad (3.16)$$

In order to evaluate 3.16, we can add a requirement that the probability of the action value falling outside of the boundary must decrease sharply as the number of time steps t grows. One convenient choice is to require that $p \leqslant t^{-4}$ so that the probability drops very sharply. This leads to the following expression for the boundary:

$$\exp\left(-2n_a B_t^2(a)\right) \leqslant t^{-4} \qquad (3.17)$$

which we can solve for $B_t(a)$ obtaining a new version of the expression 3.16 that can be fully evaluated for given t and n_a:

$$B_t(a) = \sqrt{\frac{2\ln t}{n_a}} \qquad (3.18)$$

Inserting this into the conceptual equation 3.13, we obtain the final rule for action selection:

$$a_t = \operatorname*{argmax}_{a}\left[Q_t(a) + \sqrt{\frac{2\ln t}{n_a}}\right] \qquad (3.19)$$

This solution is known as the *upper confidence bound* (UCB) algorithm. It generally outperforms the ε-greedy approach because of its more differentiated and efficient exploration, but its customization or extension to environments that are more complex than the basic multi-armed bandits problem is also more challenging. For this reason, the ε-greedy policy is commonly used as an exploration method in many general-purpose reinforcement learning algorithms and practical solutions.

We develop a dynamic content personalization system based on the UCB algorithm in recipe R3 (Dynamic Personalization).

3.3.3 *Thompson Sampling*

The greedy and UCB algorithms do not make any specific assumptions about the distribution of rewards, nor do they estimate these distributions based on the collected feedback. In many practical applications, however, we can build a specific model of the environment and rewards, and then infer the parameters of such a model in a Bayesian way, leveraging the prior knowledge about the problem structure.

Let us start by implementing this idea under the assumption that the rewards are Bernoulli distributed. Suppose we have a discrete set of k possible actions, and the i-th action produces a reward of one with probability θ_i and a reward of zero with probability $1 - \theta_i$:

$$r(a_i) \sim \text{bernoulli}(\theta_i) \tag{3.20}$$

This model can, for example, be used to describe an online ad optimization system with a pool of k ads and a credit paid each time the user clicks on the displayed ad and no credit paid when the user does not click. In this model, action values $Q(a_i)$ are equal to the corresponding θ_i. We can further make a convenient assumption that these action values are beta-distributed, so that the value distribution for the i-th action can be expressed as follows:

$$\theta_i \sim \text{beta}(\alpha_i, \beta_i) \tag{3.21}$$

where α and β are the distribution parameters. The beta-Bernoulli model is a standard choice for this type of problem because the beta distribution is a conjugate prior for the Bernoulli likelihood: when the prior distribution for θ is a beta distribution, and we observe the evidence where each sample is a Bernoulli variable with parameter θ, the posterior distribution for θ given the evidence is also beta. More specifically, if we start with the prior distribution 3.21, take action a_i, and observe reward $r \in \{0, 1\}$, then the posterior distribution for θ_i is also beta and its parameters are updated as follows:

$$(\alpha_i, \beta_i) \leftarrow (\alpha_i + r, \ \beta_i + 1 - r) \tag{3.22}$$

This expression is the update rule for model parameters that can be applied after each action. Assuming that the actions are taken according to the greedy policy based on the action value estimates, we can formulate a complete policy learning algorithm presented in box 3.1. Note that we estimate the action values using the fact that the mean of the beta distribution is given by the following expression over its parameters:

$$\mathbb{E}\left[\theta_i\right] = \frac{\alpha_i}{\alpha_i + \beta_i} \qquad (3.23)$$

Algorithm 3.1: Greedy algorithm for the Bernoulli bandit case

parameters:
$(\alpha_1, \dots, \alpha_k), (\beta_1, \dots, \beta_k)$ – priors

for $t = 0, 1, 2, \dots$ **do**
    Estimate the action values:
    for $i = 1, \dots, K$ **do**
        $\theta_i = \alpha_i / (\alpha_i + \beta_i)$
    end

    Choose the action index that corresponds to the maximum value:
$$i = \operatorname*{argmax}_i \theta_i$$
    Execute the action with index i and observe reward r

    Update the model parameters:
$$\alpha_i = \alpha_i + r$$
$$\beta_i = \beta_i + 1 - r$$

end

Algorithm 3.1 is basically a parametric version of the basic greedy policy. It enables us to specify a reward distribution model and learn its parameters in a Bayesian way, but it inherits all the limitations of the greedy approach including suboptimal exploration.

The alternative approach, known as *Thompson sampling*, alleviates the limitations of the greedy approach by changing how the action values θ_i are estimated at each time step. Instead of computing them deterministically based on the distribution of the parameters, the algorithm samples them from the distribution, as shown in box 3.2. The value estimation procedure is the only difference between algorithms 3.1 and 3.2; all other steps are identical.

Algorithm 3.2: Thompson sampling for the Bernoulli bandit case

parameters:
$(\alpha_1, \ldots, \alpha_k), (\beta_1, \ldots, \beta_k)$ – priors

for t = 0, 1, 2, ... **do**
    Estimate the action values:
    for i = 1, ..., K **do**
        Sample $\theta_i \sim \text{beta}(\alpha_i, \beta_i)$
    end

    Choose the action index that corresponds to the maximum value:
$$i = \underset{i}{\arg\max} \ \theta_i$$
    Execute the action with index i and observe reward r

    Update the model parameters:
$$\alpha_i = \alpha_i + r$$
$$\beta_i = \beta_i + 1 - r$$

end

Similar to the UCB algorithm, Thompson sampling does smart exploration of the environment, accounting for the uncertainty of the reward estimates. The algorithm tends to select either well-explored actions with large mean rewards or actions with high-variance reward distributions that frequently generate large θ samples. The latter can be the case for either underexplored actions or environments with inconsistent or unstable rewards.

Generally, we can use an arbitrary value evaluation model instead of the beta-Bernoulli model. The main steps are the same as in algorithm 3.2. Some distribution is used to sample the parameters needed to evaluate the values for all actions. The action with the maximum value estimate is executed, and the model is updated. It is also not necessary to explicitly estimate values for each of k possible actions as in algorithm 3.2. We can just build a stochastic model of the environment, update its parameters in a Bayesian way based on the observations, and sample the expected future states from this model for different actions to determine the best action. In other words, we can use the model to sample a *scenario* that is likely to occur, and custom logic can be used to estimate the value provided that this scenario realizes.

 We use Thompson sampling to develop an algorithmic price management system in recipe R8 (Dynamic Pricing).

3.3.4 *Non-stationary Environments*

All three algorithms we discussed previously (greedy, UCB, and Thompson sampling) estimate action values based on the observed reward samples and assume the stationarity of the reward distributions. This assumption does not hold true in many practical settings, and we generally need to extend these algorithms with a mechanism that allows the purging of obsolete observations in a controllable way.

The greedy and UCB policies estimate action values $Q_t(a)$ by averaging the observed rewards in accordance with formula 3.9. To simplify the notation, let us focus on one particular action a for which we have n reward samples, and rewrite the expression for its action value in a recursive form:

$$
\begin{aligned}
Q_{n+1} &= \frac{1}{n} \sum_{i=1}^{n} r_i \\
&= \frac{1}{n} \left[r_n + \sum_{i=1}^{n-1} r_i \right] \\
&= \frac{1}{n} \left[r_n + (n-1) \frac{1}{n-1} \sum_{i=1}^{n-1} r_i \right] \\
&= \frac{1}{n} \left[r_n + (n-1) Q_n \right] \\
&= \frac{1}{n} \left[r_n + n Q_n - Q_n \right] \\
&= Q_n + \frac{1}{n} \left[r_n - Q_n \right]
\end{aligned}
\tag{3.24}
$$

The last expression can be viewed as an incremental update rule. At each step, we shift the estimate by one n-th of the difference between the observed and previously estimated values. This suggests that the update step of $\frac{1}{n}$ can be replaced with an arbitrary step α leading to the following:

$$
\begin{aligned}
Q_{n+1} &= Q_n + \alpha\left[r_n - Q_n\right] \\
&= \alpha r_n + (1-\alpha)Q_n \\
&= \alpha r_n + (1-\alpha)\left[\alpha\, r_{n-1} + (1-\alpha)Q_{n-1}\right] \\
&= \alpha r_n + (1-\alpha)\alpha\, r_{n-1} + (1-\alpha)^2 Q_{n-1} \\
&= \alpha \sum_{i=1}^{n}(1-\alpha)^{n-i}\, r_i + (1-\alpha)^n Q_1
\end{aligned}
\tag{3.25}
$$

We can see that the value estimate is the exponentially weighted moving average of the observed rewards r_i. We can control the degree of weighting decay using the coefficient α, and decrease the contribution of the old samples in rapidly changing environments by making $1-\alpha$ small enough. We can use this approach to create a non-stationary version of Thompson sampling, and we use it in the next section as well to develop more advanced reinforcement learning methods.

3.4 REINFORCEMENT LEARNING: GENERAL CASE

The practical usage of the algorithms designed for the basic multi-armed bandit problem is limited in two ways. First, the environment is assumed to be a black box, and the algorithms do not provide any capabilities to incorporate the information either about the current state of the environment, or about properties of the actions. This is a major limitation because many enterprise use cases allow for providing the agent with meaningful information about the context in which the decision needs to be made. The second limitation is that the decisions and rewards at different time steps are assumed to be independent which is also not true in many practical settings because each action changes the state of the environment and, consequently, alters the context for the next decision. In this section, we discuss a more generic problem formulation and corresponding algorithms that help to overcome both limitations.

3.4.1 Markov Decision Process

We consider an agent that interacts with the environment in discrete steps. The internal state of the environment at time t is fully specified by structure $\mathbf{s}_t^f$, and the agent observes it as a complete or partial projection $\mathbf{s}_t$. We call this projection an *observed state* and denote the space of such states as S. The agent then chooses action $a_t \in A$ and applies it to the environment. The environment responds with feedback r_t which is assumed to be a real value. We also assume that this value can be interpreted as the utility of the action for the agent, and thus call it a *reward*. The state of the environment then changes to $\mathbf{s}_{t+1}^f$ and the cycle is repeated. These concepts are summarized in Figure 3.2 where spaces S and A are assumed to be discrete for the sake of illustration.

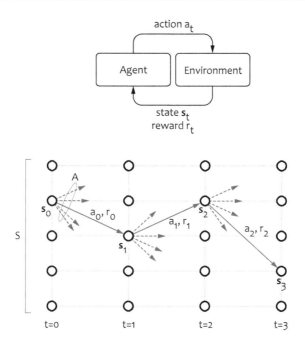

Figure 3.2: The main concepts of the Markov decision process.

The environment is assumed to be stochastic, so that the next state and reward are sampled from the distribution conditioned on the previous states and actions:

$$\mathbf{s}_{t+1}^f, r_{t+1} \quad \sim \quad p\left(\mathbf{s}_{t+1}^f, r_{t+1} \mid (\mathbf{s}_t^f, a_t), \ldots, (\mathbf{s}_0^f, a_0)\right) \quad (3.26)$$

This distribution fully specifies how the transitions between the states happen in the environment, and we refer to it as a *transition function*. We can make the transition function more practical and suitable for the analysis and evaluation by assuming that the next state and reward depend only on the current state and action:

$$s_{t+1}^f, r_{t+1} \quad \sim \quad p\left(s_{t+1}^f, r_{t+1} \mid s_t^f, a_t\right) \tag{3.27}$$

With this assumption, known as a *Markov property*, the setup described above is called a *Markov decision process* (MDP). For virtually all practical purposes, the Markov property assumption does not limit the expressiveness of the model because we can design the state structure to be self-contained.

The Markov decision process is a powerful concept that can be applied to a broad range of problems. As we will discuss later in this book, it can be used to model how marketing actions influence customer behavior, how inventory movement decisions affect product availability in different locations, and how price changes impact profits and revenues.

Thus far, we have set the scene in which the agent makes decisions and takes actions, but we also need to specify the agent's objectives to make the problem statement complete. Let us assume that the agent interacts with the environment for T time steps starting at state s_0^f and observes the following sequence of states, actions, and rewards:

$$\tau = (s_0, a_0, r_0), \ \ldots, (s_T, a_T, r_T) \tag{3.28}$$

This sequence is called a *trajectory*. Each step in the trajectory can be described using a tuple that consists of the initial state, action, reward, and the next state, that is (s_t, a_t, r_t, s_{t+1}), and we refer to such tuples as *transitions*. We define the *return* of the trajectory as a weighted sum of rewards

$$R(\tau) = \sum_{t=0}^{T} \gamma^t r_t \tag{3.29}$$

where $\gamma \in [0, 1]$ is a parameter, called the *discount factor*. The *objective* of the agent can then be defined as the expected return over the distribution of trajectories:

$$J(\tau) = \mathbb{E}_\tau [\, R(\tau) \,] = \mathbb{E}_\tau \left[\sum_{t=0}^{T} \gamma^t r_t \right] \tag{3.30}$$

The discount factor is an important concept that controls the balance between short-term and long-term rewards. If the discount factor is set to 0, the agent that stands at the beginning of the trajectory and contemplates how to maximize the return can focus exclusively on the return r_0 to decide on the first action. If the discount factor is set to 1, the agent needs to focus on the entire sequence of actions because the return is the equally weighted sum of all T rewards, and thus each action needs to be optimized in a multistep context. We refer to the problem statements where the immediate reward dominates as *myopic* optimization, and problems where the multistep goals dominate as *strategic* optimization. The multi-armed bandits discussed in the previous section can be viewed as solutions for the myopic case.

The choice of the discount factor for a particular problem can incorporate both business and technical consideration. On the business side, one should take into account the design of rewards and ultimate business objectives. On the technical side, the optimization for long-term returns is not always tractable in complex environments, and refocusing on shorter-term objectives can help the agent to make progress.

3.4.2   *Policies and Value Functions*

The goal of the agent in the MDP is to learn and exploit the mapping between states and actions that maximize the return. We refer to this mapping as a *policy* and define it as a stochastic function from which actions can be sampled given the current state:

$$a \sim \pi(a \mid s) \tag{3.31}$$

In order to evaluate how good or bad a given policy is, we need to link it to the objective. We do so by defining the *action-value function* for policy π as follows:

$$Q^\pi(s, a) = \mathbb{E}_{s_0=s,\ a_0=a,\ \tau\sim\pi}[\, R(\tau) \,] \tag{3.32}$$

The action-value function evaluates the value of state s and action a assuming that the agent starts to operate at state s, chooses the first action to be a, and then continues to operate under the policy π which is considered to be fixed. We also define the *value function* of a state marginalizing the action-value function by possible actions:

$$V^\pi(s) = \mathbb{E}_{s_0=s,\ \tau\sim\pi}[\, R(\tau) \,] = \mathbb{E}_{a\sim\pi(s)}[\, Q^\pi(s, a) \,] \tag{3.33}$$

We now have to answer two questions. The first is how the agent can evaluate the above functions for a given policy, and the second is how the policy can be optimized provided that the value functions are available. In the next section, we discuss how these two problems can be solved provided that the transition function 3.27 of the environment is known, and then we focus on methods that can learn value functions directly from interactions with the environment.

3.4.3 Policy Optimization Using Dynamic Programming

Let us assume that the transition function 3.27 of the environment is known, and the number of states and actions is small enough to be explicitly enumerated. This enables us to recursively express the value of some state at time t as a weighted sum of values of states to which we can potentially transition by the next time step $t+1$:

$$V^{\pi}(s) = \mathbb{E}_{s_t=s, \pi}\left[R_t \right]$$

$$= \mathbb{E}_{s_t=s, \pi}\left[r_{t+1} + \gamma R_{t+1} \right]$$

$$= \sum_{a} \pi(a \mid s) \sum_{s', r} p(s', r \mid s, a) \left(r + \gamma \mathbb{E}_{s_{t+1}=s', \pi}\left[R_{t+1} \right]\right) \quad (3.34)$$

$$= \sum_{a} \pi(a \mid s) \sum_{s', r} p(s', r \mid s, a) \left(r + \gamma V^{\pi}(s')\right)$$

where R_t is a shortcut for the return after time step t:

$$R_t = \sum_{i=t+1}^{T} \gamma^{i-t-1} r_i \quad (3.35)$$

Equation 3.34, known as the *Bellman equation*, efficiently reduces the evaluation problem of a given time length to subproblems of shorter time length. It is the foundation of a whole family of algorithms, referred to as *dynamic programming* algorithms, for solving MDP problems with known transition functions. We discuss below one particular strategy for evaluating and improving action policies using the dynamic programming approach.

Assuming a discrete set S of states, the Bellman equation can be viewed as a system of $|S|$ equations in $|S|$ unknowns $V^{\pi}(s)$. This system can be solved analytically, but an iterative solution is usually more practical. We can start with arbitrary initial values $V_0^{\pi}(s)$ for all states, and then iteratively update them as follows:

$$V_{k+1}^{\pi}(s) \leftarrow \sum_{a} \pi(a \mid s) \sum_{s', r} p(s', r \mid s, a) \left(r + \gamma V_k^{\pi}(s')\right) \quad (3.36)$$

At each iteration, we update all states and then repeat the process until the convergence. The convergence condition can be, for example, to stop when all the changes in the value estimates are sufficiently small:

$$\max_{s} | V_{k+1}^{\pi}(s) - V_k^{\pi}(s) | < \text{threshold} \tag{3.37}$$

Algorithm 3.36 is known as *iterative policy evaluation*. It provides a practical way for assessing the state values under a given policy, and we can use this capability as a basis for comparing policies to each other and making policy improvements.

The second question that we need to answer is how a given policy $\pi(a \mid s)$ can be improved or proved to be optimal provided that the corresponding value functions $V^{\pi}(s)$ can be estimated as described above. We can evaluate the value of any action at any state, using the Bellman equation as follows:

$$
\begin{aligned}
Q^{\pi}(s, a) &= \mathbb{E}_{s_t = s, \, a_t = a, \, \pi} \left[r_{t+1} + \gamma V^{\pi}(s_{t+1}) \right] \\
&= \sum_{s', r} p(s', r \mid s, a) \left(r + \gamma V^{\pi}(s') \right)
\end{aligned}
\tag{3.38}
$$

This enables us to compare the initial policy with alternatives that take a different action in a particular state, and make improvements if a better option is available. One simple alternative is to follow a greedy approach and modify the old policy so that it takes the action that seems best according to the value estimate:

$$
\pi(a \mid s) \leftarrow
\begin{cases}
1, & \text{if } a = \underset{a}{\text{argmax}}\ Q^{\pi}(s, a) \\
0, & \text{otherwise}
\end{cases}
\tag{3.39}
$$

If several actions have equal value estimates, the tie can be broken by giving some non-zero probability to each of them. Performing the update 3.39 for all states, we either obtain a better policy, or confirm that the current policy is optimal by finding that no modifications were done or that the modifications resulted in an equivalent policy that is as good as the current one. This process is known as *policy improvement*.

The policy evaluation and policy improvement processes have symmetrical inputs and outputs: the evaluation requires some policy as an input and produces the value function as an output. The improvement requires the value function as an input and produces a new policy as an output. The improvement process cannot generally produce an optimal policy in one pass because it is tied to the value function evaluated under some suboptimal policy, but the evaluation and improvement steps can be chained together and applied iteratively. The combined process created this way is known as *policy iteration,* and its overall lay-out is shown in Figure 3.3. We start with arbitrary policy π_0, estimate the corresponding value function using dynamic programming which iteratively cycles over all states refining the estimates using rule 3.36, execute policy improvement for all states using rule 3.39, and then re-peat this two-step process until convergence to the optimal policy π_*.

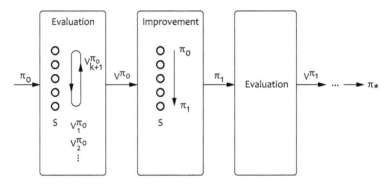

Figure 3.3: The policy iteration process.

The dynamic programming approach is essentially an optimization algorithm that can find an optimal sequence of actions provided the specification of the environment (transition function) and observabil-ity of the full environment state needed to evaluate this specification. Its computational complexity also grows with the number of states, imposing certain limitations on the dimensionality of the problems it can be applied to. In the enterprise AI context, this makes dynamic pro-gramming applicable to the environments for which we can build good mathematical models such as supply chains, but more dynamic prob-lems and problems with limited observability such as personalization require different tools. Reinforcement learning, which can be defined as a collection of methods for approximate solving of MDP problems in settings where dynamic programming is not applicable or compu-tationally intractable, offers many useful techniques and components that can be applied to a wide range of enterprise problems. We spend the next few sections discussing the main categories of reinforcement learning algorithms and shaping out the toolkit for solving specific use cases later in the book.

3.4.4   *Value-based Methods*

The policy improvement process discussed in the previous section demonstrated one particular way of doing policy optimization using value functions. More generally, the agent can construct a policy using either $V^{\pi}(\mathbf{s})$ or $Q^{\pi}(\mathbf{s}, a)$:

- If both the value function $V^{\pi}(\mathbf{s})$ and the transition function are available, the agent can enumerate all possible actions in the current state $\mathbf{s}$, compute the next state $\mathbf{s}'$ or distribution of states assuming a certain action is taken, evaluate the corresponding $V^{\pi}(\mathbf{s}')$, and then choose the action with the maximum expected return $\mathbb{E}\left[r + V^{\pi}(\mathbf{s}')\right]$. This approach works well for deterministic environments where we can compute the next state for each possible action. The game of chess is the classic example of such an environment. In enterprise applications, some manufacturing and supply chain problems can be handled using this approach.

- If action-value function $Q^{\pi}(\mathbf{s}, a)$ is available, the agent can directly evaluate all possible actions in the current state and choose the optimal one. This does not require knowing the transition function of the environment, and generally makes $Q^{\pi}(\mathbf{s}, a)$ preferable over $V^{\pi}(\mathbf{s})$.

Since value functions make policy construction and optimization relatively straightforward, there is a wide class of reinforcement learning algorithms that compute or estimate these functions explicitly. These algorithms are collectively known as *value-based methods*. If the transition function of the environment is known, the value functions can be computed, for example, using dynamic programming. If the transition function is not known to the agent, it can attempt to sample transitions from the environment and learn an approximation of the value function using statistical methods.

When the agent needs to learn the value functions from samples, $V^{\pi}(\mathbf{s})$ has the advantage of requiring less data than $Q^{\pi}(\mathbf{s}, a)$. The agent generally needs to collect enough samples to cover the space of state-action combinations $S \times A$ to learn $Q^{\pi}(\mathbf{s}, a)$, but it is enough to cover just the space of states S to learn $V^{\pi}(\mathbf{s})$. However, the considerations discussed at the beginning of this section typically dominate over this argument, and most value-based algorithms use $Q^{\pi}(\mathbf{s}, a)$ or some of its variations.

In principle, we can use any supervised learning model, either linear or nonlinear, to approximate $V^{\pi}(\mathbf{s})$ and $Q^{\pi}(\mathbf{s}, a)$. Since deep neural networks provide flexible and generic approximators, it is natural to consider them for this purpose, and the reinforcement learning algorithms that use deep learning approximators have indeed proved themselves to be very efficient in practice. This category of algorithms is generally known as *deep reinforcement learning*. We discuss several fundamental methods from this group in the next sections, and use them as a foundation for developing more specialized solutions in other parts of the book. However, the agent is more than just a value function approximator, and we need to develop a framework that combines environment sampling, function learning, and policy optimization into one seamless algorithm. In the next section, we build such a framework using the ideas from dynamic programming.

3.4.4.1 *Monte Carlo Sampling*

Let us assume that we have a generic approximator $Q_\phi^\pi(s, a)$ specified by a vector of parameters ϕ that can be used to learn a value function based on training samples, each of which includes a state-action pair and target value label collected under some policy π:

$$\{ ((s, a),\ Q^\pi(s, a)) \} \xrightarrow{\text{train}} Q_\phi^\pi(s, a) \tag{3.40}$$

To build a complete agent, we also need to specify how to sample the data needed to train the approximator and how to construct the action policy provided that the approximator has been trained. One possible approach is as follows:

1. Start with some, perhaps random, initial policy π. Sample a number of trajectories $\tau_1, \ldots, \tau_n$ from the real environment or a simulator of the environment.

2. Group all trajectories according to their initial state s and the first action taken by the agent a. For each group, estimate the target Q-value label as the average return in the group:

$$Q_{tar}^\pi(s, a) = \frac{1}{m_{s,a}} \sum_{\tau_i} R(\tau_i) \tag{3.41}$$

where $m_{s,a}$ is the number of trajectories in a group, and τ_i iterates over these trajectories.

3. Optimize the approximator parameters ϕ that minimize the prediction error for the Q-values, that is the following loss function:

$$L(\phi) = \sum_{s,a} \left(Q_{tar}^\pi(s, a) - Q_\phi^\pi(s, a) \right)^2 \tag{3.42}$$

4. Construct a new policy using the greedy or ε-greedy approach based on the value function approximation $Q_\phi^\pi(s, a)$.

This approach is called *Monte Carlo sampling* because it estimates the value function simply as the empirical mean of returns. The disadvantage of the Monte Carlo approach is its low sample efficiency: we need to collect multiple complete trajectories for each possible combination of a state and action to estimate the target value 3.41.

3.4.4.2 *Temporal Difference Learning*

We can overcome some of the limitations of Monte Carlo sampling by learning based on individual transitions rather than on complete trajectories. This approach is enabled by the recursive nature of the value function that allows it to be expressed in terms of a single transition (s, a, r, s'). To see it more clearly, let us rewrite the Bellman equation 3.34 as follows:

$$Q^\pi(s, a) = \mathbb{E}_{s', r \sim p(s', r \mid s, a)} \left[r + \gamma \mathbb{E}_{a' \sim \pi(s')} \left[Q^\pi(s', a') \right] \right] \quad (3.43)$$

The Bellman equation can be viewed as an update rule that produces a new estimate $Q^\pi(s, a)$ based on the previous estimates $Q^\pi(s', a')$ using the expectations that can be evaluated using individual transitions. To turn this concept into a concrete algorithm, we need to specify how exactly the outer and inner expectations in expression 3.43 are evaluated.

The outer expectation generally requires to be integrated over the distribution of the state-action pairs. If the transition function is unknown, this can be done by calculating the average over multiple transition samples. In particular, we can choose to update the value estimate on every new transition. If the environment is deterministic, this approach is perfectly accurate. If the environment is stochastic, the estimation using just one sample is noisy, but it allows for instant updates and reduces expression 3.43 to the following:

$$Q_{tar}^\pi(s, a) = r + \gamma \mathbb{E}_{a' \sim \pi(s')} \left[Q^\pi(s', a') \right] \quad (3.44)$$

The inner expectation, that corresponds to Q-value target labels, generally requires to be integrated over the policy. However, this can be done explicitly because the policy is known, and there are several alternatives that work well in practice. The main options include the following:

Q-LEARNING The inner expectation over the policy can be approximated by the maximum value over all actions that lead to state $\mathbf{s}'$:

$$Q^\pi_{\text{tar:QL}}(\mathbf{s}, a) = r + \gamma \max_a Q^\pi(\mathbf{s}', a) \tag{3.45}$$

This approach is known as *Q-learning*. It picks the value-maximizing action instead of the action that was actually taken by the policy π, and thus it produces Q-values that correspond to the optimal (greedy) policy instead of Q-values for policy π. This creates an additional force that steers the learning process in the direction of the optimal policy. Q-learning has good theoretical properties and is widely used in practice as a foundation for many deep reinforcement learning algorithms.

SARSA The second alternative is to approximate the expectation by the value that corresponds to the actually taken action a':

$$Q^\pi_{\text{tar:SARSA}}(\mathbf{s}, a) = r + \gamma Q^\pi(\mathbf{s}', a') \tag{3.46}$$

This approach is known as *SARSA*, the acronym derived from the tuple of variables $(\mathbf{s}, a, r, \mathbf{s}', a')$ required for its evaluation. SARSA can be viewed as a single-sample approximation of the inner expectation, consistent with the single-sample approximation of the outer expectation we used to obtain the generic template 3.44 for the value function.

EXPECTED SARSA The third alternative is to explicitly evaluate the expectation over the policy:

$$Q^\pi_{\text{tar:ESARSA}}(\mathbf{s}, a) = r + \gamma \sum_{a'} \pi(a' \mid \mathbf{s}') Q^\pi(\mathbf{s}', a') \tag{3.47}$$

This solution is known as *expected SARSA* because it can be viewed as an extension of the SARSA estimate. The expected SARSA algorithm is the most accurate approximation of the concept 3.44 from the three options we just discussed.

Since the target value labels in expressions 3.45–3.47 are computed based on the next-step state $\mathbf{s}'$ and action a', the approximation error given by expression 3.42 is called the *temporal difference error*, and the whole family of algorithms that use the Bellman decomposition for value function estimation, including Q-learning and SARSA, are also referred to as *temporal difference learning*.

The target value label estimated using one of the above methods can be used to compute the approximation error for $Q^\pi_\phi(\mathbf{s}, a)$ and then update the approximator in a similar manner to what was done in the Monte Carlo sampling. This process is summarized in algorithm 3.3 which can be viewed as a generic template for implementing temporal difference learning algorithms, including Q-learning and SARSA. For the sake of clarity, we assume an approximator that can be updated using gradient descent, but any other supervised learning algorithm can be used.

Algorithm 3.3: Temporal Difference Learning

parameters and initialization:
α – learning rate

ε – policy construction parameter

ϕ – approximator parameters

$Q_{tar}^{\pi}(s, a)$ – Q-learning, SARSA, or expected SARSA

for step $= 1, 2, \ldots$ **do**
Construct an ε-greedy policy based on $Q_{\phi}^{\pi}(s, a)$:

$$\pi_{\phi}(a \mid s) = \begin{cases} 1 - \varepsilon, & \text{if } a = \underset{a}{\text{argmax }} Q_{\phi}^{\pi}(s, a) \\ \varepsilon/(k-1), & \text{otherwise} \end{cases}$$

where k is the total number of actions allowed in the state

Collect n transitions $(s_i, a_i, r_i, s_i', a_i')$ under π_{ϕ}

for $i = 1, \ldots, n$ **do**
Calculate labels y_i using $Q_{tar}^{\pi}(s_i, a_i)$
end

Calculate the loss based on the temporal difference error:

$$L(\phi) = \frac{1}{n} \sum_i \left(y_i - Q_{\phi}^{\pi}(s_i, a_i) \right)^2$$

Update the approximator parameters:

$$\phi = \phi - \alpha \nabla_{\phi} L(\phi)$$

end

The concepts described above provide a solid foundation for creating value-based reinforcement learning algorithms, but most concrete algorithms make additional improvements to increase computational stability and performance. In the next sections, we review two Q-learning algorithms that are commonly used in enterprise applications, but we first have to discuss one more important aspect of temporal difference learning.

3.4.4.3 *On-policy vs Off-policy Learning*

A careful examination of the Q-value expressions 3.45–3.47 reveals one important fact about the usage of the transition samples. In the case of SARSA, the target labels in expression 3.46 are computed using the actual action a' taken by the current policy π. This means that the transition samples are tied to the policy they were collected under, and they are valid only until we modify the policy. In other words, we cannot reuse the collected samples across multiple steps in algorithm 3.3, and n transitions collected at each step have to be discarded at the end of the step. In the case of Q-learning, the target labels in expression 3.45 do not account for the actual action, and thus the samples can be reused across updates. In other words, the target labels in Q-learning depend on the destination state s' of the transition, but do not make assumptions on how we got to it. It could happen under a policy that took action a'_i or another policy that took a'_j, or even against the intent of the policy but because of a random fluctuation in the environment.

The algorithms that can utilize only the data generated under the current policy, like SARSA, are called *on-policy* algorithms, and the algorithms that separate policy learning from the action policy, like Q-learning, are known as *off-policy* algorithms. The ability to reuse samples across multiple updates makes off-policy learning significantly more sample-efficient than on-policy learning. We will see later that this property has far-reaching consequences that influence the design of the algorithms.

3.4.4.4 *Fitted Q Iteration (FQI)*

We previously stated that reinforcement learning aims at solving the problem of strategic (multiple steps ahead) action optimization through online learning in interactive environments. Many reinforcement learning algorithms are designed to solve these two parts, strategic optimization and online learning, simultaneously, but we can consider solving each of these problems individually. Multi-armed bandits, for example, solve online learning but not strategic optimization. In this section, we consider a version of Q-learning that does the opposite – it solves the strategic optimization problem under the assumption that the data is already collected and there are no interactions with the environment. This algorithm, known as *fitted Q iteration* (FQI), can be viewed as a generalization of supervised learning, and it could be very handy when we need to learn how to optimize sequences of action strategically based on historical data [Ernst et al., 2005]. FQI can also be viewed as Q-learning stripped to its bare essentials, so it is useful for illustration purposes as well.

Let us start with the input depicted in Figure 3.4. We assume that we have a number of trajectories that are prerecorded under some action policy, and the goal is to learn the value function from this data.

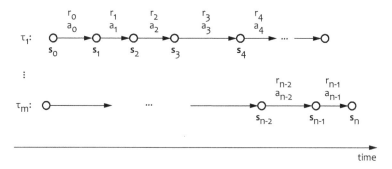

Figure 3.4: An example of the input data for the FQI algorithm.

We can apply the Q-learning concepts to this setup by following the main steps of the template algorithm 3.3:

1. Start by cutting the trajectories into individual transitions and labeling them with the immediate rewards that are interpreted as the initial approximations of the target Q-values:

$$(s_0, a_0) : y_0 = r_0$$
$$(s_1, a_1) : y_1 = r_1$$
$$\ldots \tag{3.48}$$
$$(s_{n-1}, a_{n-1}) : y_{n-1} = r_{n-1}$$

2. Fit a supervised model Q_ϕ to predict the immediate reward. This means to find the model parameters vector ϕ_1 that minimize the loss

$$L(\phi_1) = \frac{1}{n} \sum_{i=0}^{n-1} (y_i - Q_{\phi_1}(s_i, a_i))^2 \tag{3.49}$$

3. Update the training labels using the Q-learning rule 3.45:

$$y_0 \leftarrow r_0 + \gamma \max_a Q_{\phi_1}(s_1, a)$$
$$y_1 \leftarrow r_1 + \gamma \max_a Q_{\phi_1}(s_2, a)$$
$$\dots$$
$$y_{n-1} \leftarrow r_{n-1} + \gamma \max_a Q_{\phi_1}(s_n, a)$$

(3.50)

4. Fit the next model Q_{ϕ_2} to predict the new labels using the same error function 3.49. The model is now capable of predicting the sum of rewards for two steps ahead. Repeat the process updating the training labels at each iteration as follows:

$$\text{iteration } k: \quad y_i \leftarrow r_i + \gamma \max_a Q_{\phi_{k-1}}(s_{i+1}, a)$$

(3.51)

This produces a sequence of models Q_{ϕ_k} where each subsequent model predicts the rewards for a longer time horizon. The stopping condition can be set based on the discount factor (stop when γ^k is small) or convergence to some fixed value.

The above algorithm produces value model $Q_\phi(s, a)$ that can further be used to construct the action policy. For example, we can do it using the greedy or ε-greedy approach. We can think of FQI as a generalization of regular supervised learning that is typically used to train models for predicting one-step-ahead outcomes based on the current state. This extension basically propagates the cumulative reward backwards from the later transitions to the earlier ones to capture the strategic context.

The FQI algorithm, in principle, can use any supervised model as a value function approximator. In practice, neural networks are often a good choice for FQI, as well as for many other reinforcement learning algorithms. The FQI algorithm with a neural approximator is called *neural fitted Q* and commonly abbreviated as NFQ [Riedmiller, 2005].

 We use FQI to develop a next best action model for marketing applications in recipe R4 (Next Best Action).

3.4.4.5   *Deep Q-Networks (DQN)*

The second Q-learning algorithm we consider is *Deep Q-Networks* (DQN) [Mnih et al., 2015]. It is one of the most versatile and commonly used deep reinforcement learning methods. DQN can be viewed as a version of the temporal difference learning algorithm 3.3 with three important customizations:

DEEP NEURAL APPROXIMATOR The DQN algorithm uses a deep neural network for Q-value approximation. The specific network architecture, however, is not prescribed by the DQN algorithm itself, and it is highly dependent on a specific problem and designs of the state and action spaces. For example, DQN can use basic fully connected networks for problems with low-dimensional states and advanced computer vision network architectures to learn policies for video game playing based directly on the game's screenshots.

REPLAY BUFFER Algorithm 3.3 uses each transition only once to update the approximator parameters which is not optimal from several standpoints. First, this basic approach is sample-inefficient when the parameters are updated using stochastic gradient descent because the update is done iteratively, and we capture only a fraction of the information carried by the loss function at each step. (This fraction is determined by the learning rate α.) Ideally, the transitions need to be reused in multiple updates. Second, each update in algorithm 3.3 is done using a batch of transitions that are collected sequentially, so these transitions are highly correlated in most practical settings. This impacts the stability of the updates because the variance between the batches can be high. These considerations are generally valid for any approximator, but become particularly prominent for complex high-capacity models such as deep neural networks.

The above problems can be mitigated by storing transitions in a relatively large buffer and randomly sampling batches needed for stochastic gradient descent from there. The size of the buffer needs to be limited and fine-tuned to ensure an adequate rotation of transitions, so that new samples are continuously added and obsolete samples are similarly removed. This solution, called a *replay buffer*, helps with both the reuse and decorrelation of samples.

Note that the replay buffer is a suitable solution for off-policy methods, but not for on-policy methods, so it cannot be viewed as a generic extension of the template algorithm 3.3.

TARGET NETWORKS The second limitation that compromises the computational stability of algorithm 3.3 is the tight coupling between target labels Q_{tar}^{π} and the value approximator Q_{ϕ}^{π}. At every step, the target labels are computed using the current value approximator, and then the approximator is immediately updated to track the difference between the estimates and target, that is $Q_{tar}^{\pi} - Q_{\phi}^{\pi}$. This causes the training targets to move at every step, so that $Q_{tar}^{\pi}(s, a)$ can be different for the same pair of (s, a) at adjacent time steps, destabilizing the learning process.

This problem can be mitigated by maintaining two copies of the approximator. One copy – let us keep the notation Q_{ϕ}^{π} for it, emphasizing that it is specified by the set of parameters ϕ – is continuously updated and used to construct the policy, just like it is used in algorithm 3.3. The second copy, called the *target network*, is used to calculate the target labels. The target network is specified by another set of parameters ϕ_{tar}, and thus we denote it as $Q_{\phi_{tar}}^{\pi}$. The target network is not updated at every time step, but it is periodically refreshed by replacing ϕ_{tar} by ϕ. In other words, the target network $Q_{\phi_{tar}}^{\pi}$ is replaced by a copy of the policy network Q_{ϕ}^{π} every q time steps. The update frequency q needs to be fine-tuned for each application: larger networks and more complex environments generally require more steps to align with new targets, smaller networks and simpler environments can do it faster.

The above modifications are collected together in algorithm 3.4. The layout is similar to the generic temporal difference learning algorithm, but the use of deep neural networks enables the learning of complex value functions on high-dimensional inputs, and the replay buffer and target networks support this by improving the computational stability. The DQN algorithm can be further improved using more advanced buffer management and Q-values estimation techniques that can be used separately or jointly [Hessel et al., 2017].

We use DQN to develop a personalization agent in recipe R4 (Next Best Action) and price management agent in recipe R7 (Price and Promotion Optimization).

Algorithm 3.4: DQN

parameters and initialization:
  ϕ – parameters of the policy network Q_ϕ^π
  ϕ_{tar} – parameters of the policy network $Q_{\phi_{tar}}^\pi$
  α – learning rate
  q – frequency of target updates
  Initialize $\phi_{tar} = \phi$

for step $= 1, 2, \ldots$ **do**
  Construct an ε-greedy policy π_ϕ based on $Q_\phi^\pi(s, a)$

  Collect n transitions under π_ϕ and add to the buffer

  Update the policy network:
    Sample a batch of n_b transitions from the buffer

    Calculate target Q-values for each sample in the batch:

$$y_i = r_i + \gamma \max_{a'} Q_{\phi_{tar}}^\pi(s', a')$$

    where the initial condition is defined by setting
    $Q_{\phi_{tar}}^\pi(s, a) = 0$ for last states of the trajectories

    Calculate the loss:

$$L(\phi) = \frac{1}{n_b} \sum_i \left(y_i - Q_\phi^\pi(s_i, a_i) \right)^2$$

    Update the policy network parameters:

$$\phi = \phi - \alpha \nabla_\phi L(\phi)$$

  If the step number is divisible by q:
    Update the target network: $\phi_{tar} \leftarrow \phi$
end

3.4.5 *Policy-based Methods*

The core idea of the value-based methods discussed in the previous
section is to estimate the expected values of potential actions and then

construct the policy based on these estimates. The disadvantage of this approach is that the policies are constructed from Q-values in a heuristic way, such as the ε-greedy rule, and it creates certain inefficiencies. The alternative approach is to learn the policy function directly, so that the gap between the value estimates and policy construction is eliminated. To learn the policy directly, we can parametrize the policy by a vector of learnable parameters θ as follows:

$$\pi_\theta(a \mid \mathbf{s}) = p(a_t = a \mid \mathbf{s}_t = \mathbf{s}, \, \theta_t = \theta) \tag{3.52}$$

Similar to the value function, we can use an arbitrary supervised model, such as a deep neural network, to approximate the policy function and optimize its parameters using a standard training algorithm such as stochastic gradient descent. The policy-based approach overcomes some limitations of value-based learning, providing the following advantages:

MORE ACTION TYPES Most value-based methods assume discrete low-cardinality action spaces. In Q-learning, for example, we search for the value-maximizing action by iterating over all possible actions and evaluating them individually. This approach becomes intractable for high-cardinality action spaces and continuous action spaces. Some value-based methods work around this issue by using special value functions that can be maximized analytically (for example, a quadratic function [Gu et al., 2016]), but the policy-based solutions are generally more flexible.

MORE EXPRESSIVE POLICIES In the value-based methods, the expressiveness of the policy is limited by the algorithm one uses to construct it from Q-values. For example, an ε-greedy policy focuses only on the action with the maximum Q-value, so it cannot express a complex probability distribution over actions. The ε-greedy policy cannot converge to a deterministic policy either, because the exploration factor ε is fixed. Alternative solutions exist, such as mapping of Q-values to action probabilities using softmax, but such simple mappings do not allow the expression of arbitrary stochastic policies. The direct optimization of the policy function addresses this problem in a more flexible way.

At the same time, the direct optimization of the policy function imposes certain limitations that make the basic policy-based methods sample inefficient. In the next section, we develop a concrete policy-based algorithm and investigate its limitations in more detail.

3.4.5.1   *REINFORCE*

The classic implementation of the policy-based learning approach is the *REINFORCE* algorithm [Williams, 1992]. The core idea of REINFORCE is to explicitly evaluate the gradient of the policy function π_θ with respect to its parameters θ and then perform the gradient ascent on these parameters to maximize the expected return.

Recall that the objective of the agent is to maximize the expected return over the distribution of trajectories:

$$J(\pi_\theta) = \mathbb{E}_{\tau \sim \pi_\theta} [\, R(\tau) \,] = \mathbb{E}_{\tau \sim \pi_\theta} \left[\sum_{t=0}^{T} \gamma^t r_t \right] \tag{3.53}$$

The agent can maximize the objective by performing the gradient ascent in the space of the policy parameters using the following parameter update rule:

$$\theta \leftarrow \theta + \alpha \cdot \nabla_\theta J(\pi_\theta) \tag{3.54}$$

where α is the learning rate and $\nabla_\theta J(\pi_\theta)$ is the *policy gradient*. The evaluation of the policy gradient is a nontrivial problem, but we can obtain the closed-form expression for it. Let us start with the observation that one needs to integrate over the distribution of actions and states that depend on the policy parameters θ in order to evaluate the policy gradient:

$$\nabla_\theta J(\pi_\theta) = \nabla_\theta \mathbb{E}_{\tau \sim \pi_\theta} [\, R(\tau) \,] \tag{3.55}$$

This task can be viewed as an instance of a more general problem where we have distribution $p(x \mid \theta)$ and are looking to estimate the gradient with respect to θ of the expectation of some function $f(x)$:

$$\nabla_\theta \mathbb{E}_{x \sim p(x \mid \theta)} [\, f(x) \,] \tag{3.56}$$

We can reduce the above expression as follows:

$$\nabla_\theta \mathbb{E}_{x \sim p(x \mid \theta)} [\, f(x) \,]$$

$$= \nabla_\theta \int f(x) p(x \mid \theta) \, dx$$

$$= \int \nabla_\theta (f(x) p(x \mid \theta)) \, dx$$

$$= \int f(x) \nabla_\theta p(x \mid \theta) + p(x \mid \theta) \nabla_\theta f(x) \, dx \quad \text{(chain rule)}$$

$$= \int f(x) \nabla_\theta p(x \mid \theta) \, dx \qquad (\nabla_\theta f(x) = 0)$$

$$= \int f(x) p(x \mid \theta) \frac{\nabla_\theta p(x \mid \theta)}{p(x \mid \theta)} \, dx \qquad \left(\times \frac{p(x\mid\theta)}{p(x\mid\theta)} \right)$$

$$= \int f(x) p(x \mid \theta) \nabla_\theta \log p(x \mid \theta) \, dx \qquad \left(\partial \log x = \frac{\partial x}{x} \right)$$

$$= \mathbb{E}_x [\, f(x) \nabla_\theta \log p(x \mid \theta) \,]$$

This result allows us to reduce the original expression 3.55 as follows:

$$\nabla_\theta J(\pi_\theta) = \mathbb{E}_{\tau \sim \pi_\theta} [\, R(\tau) \nabla_\theta \log p(\tau \mid \theta) \,] \tag{3.57}$$

Finally, we leverage the Markov property of MDP to expand the probability of the trajectory into a product of transition probabilities (or, alternatively, the sum of log-probabilities) obtaining the final expression for the gradient:

$$\nabla_\theta J(\pi_\theta) = \mathbb{E}_{\tau \sim \pi_\theta} \left[\sum_{t=0}^{T} R_t(\tau) \cdot \nabla_\theta \log \pi_\theta(a_t \mid s_t) \right] \tag{3.58}$$

where R_t stands for the return after the time step t:

$$R_t(\tau) = \sum_{i=t}^{T} \gamma^{i-t} r_i \tag{3.59}$$

Expressions 3.54 and 3.58 are sufficient to build an agent that optimizes the policy based on the observed trajectories, but we need to specify how the expectation over the trajectories is evaluated. One possible way is to estimate the expectation using just one trajectory sample, similar to how we solved a similar problem in SARSA. This leads to the algorithm presented in listing 3.5. For the sake of concreteness, we assume that the policy function π_θ is implemented using a deep neural network, although other types of approximators can be used.

Algorithm 3.5: REINFORCE

parameters and initialization:
  α – learning rate
  θ – parameters of the policy network π_θ

for step $= 1, 2, \ldots$ **do**
  Sample trajectory $\tau = s_0, a_0, r_0, \ldots, s_T, a_T, r_T$ under π_θ

  Compute the policy gradient:

  $$\nabla_\theta J(\pi_\theta) = \sum_{t=0}^{T} R_t(\tau) \cdot \nabla_\theta \log \pi_\theta(a_t \mid s_t)$$

  Update the network parameters:

  $$\theta = \theta + \alpha \nabla_\theta J(\pi_\theta)$$

end

Historically, the REINFORCE algorithm was the first implementation of the policy gradient approach, and it has several major shortcomings that motivated the development of more advanced methods. The first major limitation is that the policy gradient depends on the actual actions in the trajectory. This means that REINFORCE is an on-policy algorithm, and the transitions collected to evaluate the policy gradient need to be discarded after each parameter update, making the algorithm sample-inefficient. We will discuss one possible way of addressing this issue in Section 3.5.1. The second problem is that each gradient evaluation needs to directly compute the returns from step t till the end of the trajectory, which implies that a complete trajectory needs to be collected for each evaluation. In this sense, REINFORCE is a Monte Carlo method just like the Monte Carlo value function learning introduced in Section 3.4.4.1. Consequently, the policy gradient estimate has a high variance. This issue can be mitigated using parametric value approximators, similar to what we did in temporal difference learning. We expand this idea in the next section.

3.4.6 Combined Methods

We have seen that the policy gradient approach has certain advantages over the value-based methods because it potentially supports a wider range of action spaces and policy functions. At the same time, the basic implementations of the policy gradient such as REINFORCE estimate the return directly from trajectory samples (expressions 3.58) similar to Monte Carlo sampling in the value-based approach. This leads to the same shortcomings, namely, the low sample efficiency and high variance of the estimate.

In light of the above, we can pose the following question: is it possible to improve the sample-efficiency and computational stability of the basic policy gradient algorithm using the techniques that we previously developed for DQN and other value-based methods? The answer to this question is affirmative, and, moreover, it turns out that the policy-based and value-based methods can be combined in a natural and beneficial way, producing a whole family of high-performance algorithms. In this section, we first discuss a generic framework that demonstrates the approach, and then develop a concrete algorithm that combines policy gradient with DQN.

3.4.6.1   Actor-Critic Approach

Let us start by reviewing the policy gradient solution developed in the previous section. We have shown that the policy function can be optimized by performing a gradient ascent in the space of parameters in the direction of the maximum return which was defined as follows:

$$\nabla_\theta J(\pi_\theta) = \nabla_\theta \mathbb{E}_{\tau \sim \pi_\theta} [\, R(\tau) \,] \tag{3.60}$$

The REINFORCE algorithm evaluates this gradient using complete trajectories τ as

$$\nabla_\theta J(\pi_\theta) = \mathbb{E}_{\tau \sim \pi_\theta} [\, R(\tau) \cdot \nabla_\theta \log p(\tau \mid \theta) \,] \tag{3.61}$$

The disadvantage of this approach is the high variance of the return estimate $R(\tau)$. We can attempt to decrease the variance using a value approximator instead of a single-sample estimate, similar to what we did in the value-based methods. This leads to the following expression that can be evaluated using individual transitions instead of complete trajectories:

$$\nabla_\theta J(\pi_\theta) = \mathbb{E}_{s \sim \rho^\pi, a \sim \pi_\theta} \left[Q_\phi^{\pi_\theta}(s, a) \cdot \nabla_\theta \log \pi_\theta(a \mid s) \right] \tag{3.62}$$

where $\rho^\pi(s)$ is the state distribution under policy π. This design involves two learnable functions. The first one is the policy function π_θ specified by its vector of parameters θ, and it is referred to as the *actor*.

The second function is the value function Q_ϕ specified by another vector of parameters ϕ, and it is referred to as the *critic*. Consequently, the methods that follow this design approach are collectively known as *actor-critic* algorithms. The basic implementation of the actor-critic algorithm is presented in listing 3.6 where the expectation over states and actions in expression 3.62 is estimated based on a single sample. The actor-related part is similar to REINFORCE, and the critic-related part corresponds to the temporal difference algorithm.

Algorithm 3.6: Basic Actor-Critic

parameters and initialization:
  θ – parameters of the actor network π_θ
  ϕ – parameters of the critic network Q_ϕ
  α_θ, α_ϕ – learning rates

for step $= 1, 2, \ldots$ **do**
  Sample transition s, a, r, s', a' under policy π_θ

  Update the actor:
    Compute the policy gradient:

$$\nabla_\theta J(\pi_\theta) = Q_\phi^{\pi_\theta}(s, a) \cdot \nabla_\theta \log \pi_\theta(a \mid s)$$

    Update the actor network parameters:

$$\theta = \theta + \alpha_\theta \nabla_\theta J(\pi_\theta)$$

  Update the critic:
    Calculate the target value:

$$y = r + \gamma Q_\phi^{\pi_\theta}(s', a')$$

    Compute the loss for the critic based on the temporal difference error:

$$L(\phi) = \left(y - Q_\phi^{\pi_\theta}(s, a) \right)^2$$

    Update the critic network parameters:

$$\phi = \phi - \alpha_\phi \nabla_\phi L(\phi)$$

end

Since the gradient 3.62 is used to update the parameters of the actor function, the critic can be viewed as a component that generates the reinforcement signal for the actor by moderating (amplifying or de-amplifying) the gradient, depending on the assessment of the expected value. This is advantageous because the signal produced by the critic is generally less noisy and less sparse than the raw rewards used in the policy gradient algorithms. The density and smoothness of this estimate can be controlled by the design and hyperparameters of the value function.

The actor-critic architecture imposes several challenges as well. First, it requires at least two approximators that need to operate in concert, which creates additional challenges and requires the use of specialized stabilization techniques. Second, the basic implementation of actor-critic has two parts that require on-policy learning mode. The first part is the policy gradient that still relies on the assumption that the transitions are sampled under the action policy π_θ. This prevents experience bufferization and repay limiting the sample efficiency. The second part is the critic that is updated using single-sample target value estimates that depend on the actual actions a', similar to SARSA. The alternative is to use Q-learning estimates that do not depend on the actual actions, but this would constrain us to discrete action spaces, eliminating an important advantage of the policy gradient. These limitations can be addressed in several different ways, and we discuss one particular solution in the next section.

3.4.6.2 *Deep Deterministic Policy Gradient (DDPG)*

We can attempt to improve the sample efficiency of the basic actor-critic algorithm by developing a version that works in the off-policy mode and, ideally, use advanced Q-learning algorithms such as DQN to implement the critic. This requires solving the two problems outlined in the previous section:

ACTOR SIDE First, we need to evaluate the gradient of policy $\pi_\theta(a \mid s)$ based on transitions collected under another policy $\beta(a \mid s) \neq \pi_\theta(a \mid s)$. We call β a *behavior policy*.

CRITIC SIDE Second, we need to figure out how to compute target Q-values for both continuous and discrete action spaces.

One possible way to address these problems is to replace a stochastic policy $\pi_\theta(a \mid s)$ by a deterministic policy $\pi_\theta(s)$. This assumption leads to the following simplifications:

ACTOR SIDE When we assume a stochastic policy, the objective function in the on-policy mode is as follows:

$$J(\pi_\theta) = \mathbb{E}_{s \sim \rho^\pi, a \sim \pi_\theta} [\, \pi_\theta(a \mid s) \, Q^\pi(s, a) \,] \tag{3.63}$$

and its gradient is given by expression 3.62. In the off-policy mode, the objective transforms into

$$J_\beta(\pi_\theta) = \mathbb{E}_{s \sim \rho^\beta, a \sim \beta} [\, \pi_\theta(a \mid s) \, Q^\pi(s, a) \,] \tag{3.64}$$

where ρ^β is the state distribution under behavior policy β. The evaluation of the gradient becomes more complex in this case, but the deterministic policy assumption eliminates the integration over the action space resulting in the following computationally tractable expression:

$$\nabla_\theta J_\beta(\pi_\theta) = \mathbb{E}_{s \sim \rho^\beta} [\, \nabla_\theta Q^\pi(s, \pi_\theta(s)) \,] \tag{3.65}$$

CRITIC SIDE On the critic side, the deterministic policy assumption results in the following expression for the target values:

$$y = r + \gamma Q_\phi^{\pi_\theta}(s', \pi_\theta(s')) \tag{3.66}$$

This eliminates the dependency on the actual action a' enabling us to use the off-policy value learning methods for the critic.

The above results allow us to build actor-critic solutions on top of robust off-policy algorithms. For example, we can use DQN as a foundation and build a complete actor-critic algorithm around it. One specific implementation of this approach, known as *deep deterministic policy gradient* (DDPG) is presented in box 3.7 [Silver et al., 2014; Lillicrap et al., 2015].

The overall layout of DDPG is similar to DQN, and it relies heavily on the two main stabilization techniques introduced in DQN, target networks and experience replay. Both actor and critic are represented by two network instances, so that one network is continuously updated and the other is used to calculate target Q-values. For both actor and critic, the target values and losses needed for parameter updates are computed based on the transitions sampled from the buffer.

At the same time, there are several differences between DQN and DDPG. First, DDPG constructs the policy by adding noise to the output of the actor network instead of using the ε-greedy logic. This modification is needed to support continuous action spaces. Second, DDPG gradually updates the target networks at every step instead of doing infrequent but complete replacements. Finally, the target values for the

---

Algorithm 3.7: DDPG

parameters and initialization:
  ϕ, ϕ_{tar} – parameters of the critic networks Q_ϕ^π
  θ, θ_{tar} – parameters of the actor networks π_θ
  α – target update rate

for step $= 1, 2, \ldots$ **do**
  Construct a policy that select actions as $\pi_\theta(s) + \varepsilon$ where ε is a noise component that ensures exploration

  Collect transitions under the constructed policy and add them to the buffer

  Update the network parameters:
  Sample a batch of transitions $B = \{(s_i, a_i, r_i, s_i')\}$ from the buffer

  Calculate target Q-values for each sample in the batch:

  $$y_i = r_i + \gamma Q_{\phi_{tar}}^\pi(s_i', \pi_{\theta_{tar}}(s_i'))$$

  Update critic network parameters ϕ using

  $$\nabla_\phi L(\phi) = \nabla_\theta \frac{1}{|B|} \sum_i \left(y_i - Q_\phi^\pi(s_i, a_i)\right)^2$$

  Update actor network parameters θ using

  $$\nabla_\theta J(\pi_\theta) = \nabla_\theta \frac{1}{|B|} \sum_i Q_\phi^\pi(s_i, \pi_\theta(s_i))$$

  Update the target networks:
  $\phi_{tar} \leftarrow \alpha\phi_{tar} + (1 - \alpha)\phi$
  $\theta_{tar} \leftarrow \alpha\theta_{tar} + (1 - \alpha)\theta$

end

---

critic are calculated using the determinist policy estimate 3.66 instead of regular Q-values.

We use DDPG to develop a supply chain management agent in recipe R9 (Inventory Optimization).

3.5 COUNTERFACTUAL POLICY EVALUATION

In the previous sections, we assumed that the control policies are
learned through continuous interaction with the environment. We
also discussed that some algorithms, such as SARSA, require all
interactions to be performed strictly under the latest version of the
continuously updated policy, and some algorithms, such as DQN,
can reuse transitions collected under old versions of the policy. We
referred to these two groups as on-policy and off-policy learning,
respectively.

In enterprise applications, however, we can rarely assume that the
agent can freely interact with the real environment. For example, inconsistent or random exploratory actions can lead to customer dissatisfaction in marketing applications, revenue losses in price management
applications, and safety risks in production operations. This creates a
need for a framework that allows us to evaluate new policies to ensure
their quality before they are deployed to production and learn new
control policies based on the interactions collected under some limited-
risk policy. In other words, we are seeking to answer the following two
questions:

- Assuming that we have data collected under a fixed behavior
  policy β, how do we evaluate the performance of some other
  policy π?

- How to learn a new policy π based on the interactions collected
  under a given behavior policy β?

The first question is known as the *counterfactual policy evaluation*
(CPE) problem because we aim to evaluate a hypothetical result that
could have happened had the actual behavior policy been replaced
with the alternative policy. This problem can be viewed as a generalization of the treatment analysis problem discussed in Section 2.8.2.
The second question can be viewed as a generic formulation of the basic off-policy learning capability introduced in Section 3.4.4.3, and we
refer to it as the *off-policy policy learning* problem. We develop a generic

method that can be applied to these two problems in the next section, and then discuss more specialized techniques that can be used in certain applications.

3.5.1 Importance Sampling

Let us assume that we have collected a number of trajectories under a known behavior policy β, and we want to evaluate the state value function $V^\pi(s)$ for some policy π based on these trajectories. We also assume that every action taken under π is also taken with non-zero probability under β:

$$\text{for any } a, s: \quad \pi(a \mid s) > 0 \Rightarrow \beta(a \mid s) > 0 \tag{3.67}$$

The value function for the action policy is defined as the expected return over the trajectories produced under this policy. This function can easily be estimated for β by averaging the returns of the collected trajectories. Since the distribution of trajectories generated under π is different from β, we can attempt to estimate the value function for π as a weighted average of the collected returns, where the weights are computed based on the ratio of trajectory probabilities under the behavior and evaluated policies. This approach is known as *importance sampling*.

Importance sampling requires the evaluation of the ratios of trajectory probabilities, so we can start by expressing the probability of generating a specific trajectory $\tau = (s_t, a_t, s_{t+1}, \dots, s_T)$ starting at state s_t and taking actions according to policy π is as follows:

$$p(\tau \mid s_t; a \sim \pi) = \prod_{j=t}^{T-1} \pi(a_j \mid s_j) \, p(s_{j+1} \mid s_j, a_j) \tag{3.68}$$

where $p(s_{j+1} \mid s_j, a_j)$ is the transition function of the environment. The ratio of trajectory probabilities under π and β, called the *importance sampling ratio*, can then be estimated as follows for an arbitrary segment of the trajectory:

$$
\begin{aligned}
\rho_{t:T-1}(\tau) &= \frac{\prod_{j=t}^{T-1} \pi(a_j \mid s_j) \, p(s_{j+1} \mid s_j, a_j)}{\prod_{j=t}^{T-1} \beta(a_j \mid s_j) \, p(s_{j+1} \mid s_j, a_j)} \\
&= \prod_{j=t}^{T-1} \frac{\pi(a_j \mid s_j)}{\beta(a_j \mid s_j)}
\end{aligned}
\tag{3.69}
$$

This means that the importance sampling ratio does not depend on the transition function of the environment, but only on the ratio of the action probabilities under two policies. In the next two sections, we show how the regular policy evaluation and learning algorithms can be modified to operate in the off-policy mode provided that the importance sampling weights can be estimated.

3.5.1.1 *Evaluation*

Assuming that we have collected trajectories $\tau_1, \ldots, \tau_n$ under the behavior policy β, we can estimate the importance sampling ratio for each of them using expression 3.69, and we can then estimate the expected return for policy π as follows:

$$V^\pi = \mathbb{E}_{\tau \sim \pi}[\, R(\tau)\,] = \frac{1}{n} \sum_{i=1}^{n} \rho_{0:T_i-1}(\tau_i) \cdot R(\tau_i) \qquad (3.70)$$

where $R(\tau_i)$, T_i, and $\rho(\tau_i)$ are the observed return, duration, and importance sampling ratio for trajectory τ_i, respectively. This estimator is unbiased, but its variance can be very high when π and β are substantially different from each other. The high variance of the estimate is one of the biggest challenges in importance sampling, and many advanced variants of the basic procedure described in this section were developed to mitigate this issue.

We can use the same approach to obtain other standard value functions for π. For example, we can break down the value estimate by state obtaining the state value function:

$$V^\pi(\mathbf{s}) = \frac{1}{n} \sum_{i=1}^{n} \rho_{t_i(\mathbf{s}):T_i-1}(\tau_i) \cdot R_{t_i(\mathbf{s})}(\tau_i) \qquad (3.71)$$

where $t_i(\mathbf{s})$ is the first time that the state $\mathbf{s}$ was observed in trajectory τ_i, and $R_{t_i(\mathbf{s})}(\tau_i)$ is the return of the trajectory τ_i after the time step $t_i(\mathbf{s})$. These estimates can be used to evaluate multiple policies π and compare them to each other, as well as validate that new (candidate) policies are better than the baseline policy β used in production. However, it is worth emphasizing that the behavior policy β must be known in order to evaluate the importance-sampling weights, and this often represents a challenge in real-world enterprise applications.

3.5.1.2 *Learning*

The importance-sampling weights can be used not only to rebalance the returns in the value function estimates as we did in the previous section, but also to adapt on-policy learning algorithms to off-policy policy learning. Let us consider REINFORCE, a typical on-policy learning algorithm, as an example. The regular version of the algorithm optimizes the parameters of the policy function π_θ to maximize the following objective, as discussed in Section 3.4.5.1:

$$J(\pi_\theta) = \mathbb{E}_{\tau \sim \pi_\theta} [\, R(\tau) \,] \tag{3.72}$$

Assuming that the trajectories are sampled under behavior policy β, we can define the off-policy learning objective as

$$J(\pi_\theta) = \mathbb{E}_{\tau \sim \beta} [\, \rho(\tau) \cdot R(\tau) \,] \tag{3.73}$$

where $\rho(\tau)$ is the importance sampling ratio for policies β and π_θ evaluated over the entire trajectory τ. Computing the policy gradient for this objective as described in Section 3.4.5.1, we obtain the following:

$$\nabla_\theta J(\pi_\theta) = \mathbb{E}_{\tau \sim \beta} \left[\sum_{t=0}^{T} \rho_{0:t-1}(\tau) \cdot R_t(\tau) \cdot \nabla_\theta \log \pi_\theta(a_t \mid s_t) \right] \tag{3.74}$$

This is a modified version of expression 3.58 which can be plugged into the REINFORCE algorithm 3.5 transforming it into an off-policy policy learning method. The same approach can be used to modify other on-policy algorithms such as SARSA.

The importance sampling technique and its advanced versions enable one to log trajectories collected under a certain baseline policy, as well as the probability distributions over the possible actions at every step, and then replay these logs against an arbitrary off-policy learning algorithm to learn a new policy. We apply this approach to some enterprise use cases later in this book.

 We use importance sampling for policy learning and evaluation in recipe R4 (Next Best Action).

3.5.2 *Action Rejection Sampling*

Importance sampling provides a generic framework for off-policy policy learning and evaluation that can be applied to a wide range of problems. In many environments, however, we can use simpler and more robust evaluation procedures provided that certain simplifying assumptions hold. In this section, we describe an alternative evaluation method that can be used in many bandit-case environments [Li et al., 2010].

In the bandit case, we assume that the state of the environment at each time step is independent from the previous state and, consequently, each trajectory represents a sequence of independently drawn transition tuples $(\mathbf{s}_t, a_t, r_t)$. Let is us further assume that we initially gather the trajectories in such an environment under a policy that chooses an action at each time step uniformly at random:

$$\beta(a \mid \mathbf{s}) = \text{uniform}(a_1, \ldots, a_k) \tag{3.75}$$

where k is the total number of possible actions. Assuming that we have a trajectory τ collected under β and deterministic candidate policy $\pi(\mathbf{s})$ that needs to be evaluated, we can iterate over τ rejecting all transitions where policies β and π do not match and accumulate rewards for all transitions where the policies do match, as summarized in algorithm 3.8.

Algorithm 3.8: Action Rejection Sampling

inputs:
    $(\mathbf{s}_0, a_0, r_0, \ldots, \mathbf{s}_T, a_T, r_T)$ – trajectory collected under β
    π – policy to be evaluated

$R = 0,\ n = 0$
for $t = 0, 1, \ldots, T$ **do**
    if $\pi(\mathbf{s}_t) = a_t$ **do**
        $R = R + r_t$
        $n = n + 1$
    end
end

return R/n *(Estimated return under policy π)*

This approach produces an unbiased estimate of the return under policy π because the probability of obtaining a certain trajectory by fast-forwarding through unmatched transitions is the same as the probability of obtaining this trajectory by playing policy π against the actual environment. Both assumptions introduced earlier (bandit environment and equiprobability of actions under the behavior policy) are essential for ensuring such an equivalence between the simple log replay performed by algorithm 3.8 and real policy execution.

 We use the action rejection method to evaluate contextual bandits in R3 (Dynamic Personalization).

3.6 SUMMARY

- Basic decision automation techniques include entity ranking, action evaluation, and cost-benefit analysis. Problems that require optimizing multiple interdependent variables can be approached using mathematical programming methods.

- The basic representation and mapping learning methods might not be applicable in highly dynamic environments and environments that require active exploration. These scenarios are addressed in reinforcement learning.

- Environments where the response distributions at different time steps can be assumed to be independent are known as stochastic bandits. The optimal control policies for such environments can be learned using bandit algorithms.

- Stateful environments that can be modeled using a Markov decision process require strategic action optimization. The main categories of policy control learning algorithms for such environments include value-based, policy-based, and combined methods.

- In enterprise environments, off-policy learning and evaluation based on the observational data play an important role. One of the most generic frameworks for this category of problems is importance sampling.

Part II

CUSTOMER INTELLIGENCE

Customer analytics and personalization are among the most important areas of enterprise AI because digital touchpoints and modern communication channels provide numerous opportunities for improving customer experience, as well as business outcomes, using data-driven methods. Moreover, it is well known that the demographics, interests, intents, and expectations of customers can be extremely diverse, and thus customer experiences that are supposed to fit everyone's needs may not do so, which makes personalization a mission-critical capability for many businesses. Customer experience engineering is also associated with a wide range of expenses including advertising, offers and promotions, and customer support and retention. These costs can also be subjects of the data-driven optimization.

In this part, we look at the methods that leverage customer data, both behavioral such as clickstream, and static such as demographics, to optimize customer experiences and learn compact representations of a customer that can be used by marketing analysts and downstream transactional systems. Later in this book, we will discuss methods that combine customer data with other pieces of information including content and product data, to improve the quality and efficiency of personalization.

Recipe

1

PROPENSITY MODELING

Customer Intent Prediction for Experience Personalization

One of the most common problems in marketing data science is the estimation of the probability of an individual customer performing a certain action such as a website visit, in-store purchase, or account cancellation. In many applications, the action of interest is directly observable, and we are interested in predicting that such an action will recur in the future based on what we currently know about the customer. For example, an online retailer typically maintains a database with customer profiles as well as orders, and they can attempt to build a model that predicts the probability of a purchase based on a profile. In other applications, however, the action of interest may not be observed directly, and we would be interested to estimate the likelihood that a given customer is currently performing a certain activity or has performed it in the past. A typical example is fraud detection where the fraudulent act might not be observed explicitly but can be revealed using a risk scoring model trained on manually flagged past cases of fraud. Once the probabilities of actions (commonly referred to as *propensities*) are estimated, a personalization system or marketing operations team can decide on the optimal action for each customer. For example, it could be a personalized offer chosen based on the propensity to purchase a certain brand, a retention package offered based on the probability to cancel the service subscription, or an account blocking based on the fraud risk score.

The problem of propensity scoring outlined above is fairly broad, and there are many specific problem statements in existence that differ in assumptions about the environment, possible actions that can be taken based on the predicted scores, and downstream operationalization processes. For example, we can assume that the environment is relatively static and patterns learned based on historical data are generally valid for predictions, or we can assume that historical data is becoming obsolete very quickly and so the system needs to learn online. For another example, one can make a decision on whether or not to provide a customer with a retention offer based on the basic unconditional probability of account cancellation. Alternatively, one might be looking to make this decision based on how this probability changes depending on different offer types and how these change over time, so that both the offer type and timing can be personalized. In this recipe, we focus on a relatively basic setup where the environment is assumed to be static and we are looking to estimate unconditional probabilities of actions or events. We will come back to the alternative problem statements in other recipes later in this book.

R1.1   BUSINESS PROBLEM

We start with the analysis of the typical model inputs, desired outputs, and marketing use cases that can be improved using such a model. This analysis will help to properly define the technical design goals and constraints in the next section.

In most B2C industries, including retail, digital media, and telecom, the company can record customer actions and the history of interactions with a customer at the level of individual events such as clicks, purchases, or phone calls. We can also assume that each event can be encoded as a vector of categorical or real-valued features such as an event timestamp, event type, user's geo location, transaction total, and so on. Consequently, an event history of length m can be represented as a $k \times m$ matrix where k is the size of the event vector. In many cases, the company also maintains customer account (profile) records that include demographics, preferences, and other non-event data that can be used as additional inputs which can also be encoded as a vector. This layout is depicted in the upper part of Figure R1.1. We can attempt to get several insights based on this input as discussed in the next sections.

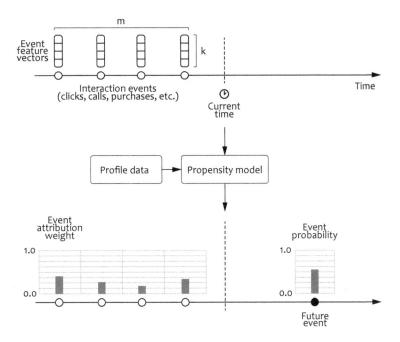

Figure R1.1: The main inputs and outputs of the event-level propensity model.

R1.1.1 *Scoring*

One of the central goals of propensity modeling is to estimate the probability of a certain outcome such a purchase or click based on the above inputs. This generally requires collecting a number of customer profiles with event histories, attributing each profile with a target label which can be a binary or real-valued variable, training a classification or regression model that approximates the dependency between the input history and the target label, and then scoring profiles for which the outcomes are not yet known. Once the scores are computed, one can operationalize them in many different ways depending on a specific use case. For example, consider the problem of optimal distribution of special offers to customers. We can build a propensity model that estimates the probability of the offer redemption using historical campaign data, and then, assuming that each offer is associated with some cost C and potentially drives incremental revenue R when redeemed, the expected incremental profit for customer u will be

$$\text{profit}(u) = p(\text{redemption} \mid u) \times (R - C)$$
$$- (1 - p(\text{redemption} \mid u)) \times C$$

(R1.1)

where the first term represents the expected gain from the redemption event and the second term represents the loss associated with an ignored offer. This estimate enables us to make a targeting decision with regard to individual customers and determine the optimal number of customers to be targeted to maximize the sum of incremental per-customer profits, that is the return on investment (ROI).

In practice, it is common to build multiple propensity models that are focused on different aspects of customer experience. For example, Booking.com, an online travel agency, reported that its customer-facing applications are backed by more than a hundred models that estimate various user propensities such as the likelihood to change the traveling dates, travel with family or alone, and travel for leisure or for business. These scores are then used to optimize various suggestions, tooltips, and messages in the user interface [Bernardi et al., 2019].

We should also take note that, among all propensity modeling use cases, there is an important category of applications where the length of the event history is a major constraint. Examples include customer churn prediction and fraud detection where it is preferable to identify risks at early stages, in-session personalization and recommendations that rely only on a handful of clicks collected in the current web session, and market segments like luxury goods where customers make relatively few transactions. The ability to make an accurate prediction based on short event sequences is a major design goal in such cases.

R1.1.2 *Event Attribution*

The second important problem that we choose to address in this recipe is the quantitative analysis of the event history itself and the understanding of what drives customers to certain outcomes. For instance, a telecom company might be interested to not only identify customers who are likely to cancel their subscriptions, but also to understand event patterns that are typical for such customers, in order to design retention packages. This generally requires assigning attribution weights to all events in the history, as illustrated in Figure R1.2. The attribution weight vectors can then be clustered to determine typical patterns, or aggregated by marketing channels or other criteria to analyze what drives customers to certain outcomes.

The two outputs described above, that is the probability of a certain outcome and the contribution of various events and other factors into this outcome, correspond to the lower part of Figure R1.1. Note that, in terms of the scenario planning framework, the goals we set

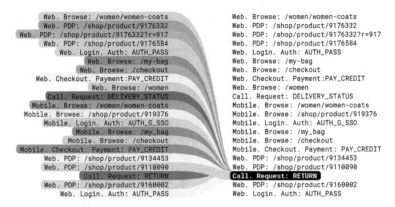

Figure R1.2: An example of visualization for web events attribution weights. The darker color corresponds to the bigger contribution, so that `Call. Request: DELIVERY_STATUS` event appears to be a precursor for `Call. Request: RETURN` event.

basically correspond to the analysis and forecasting of customer trajectories which we chose to be represented as event histories. We discuss how one can achieve these goals using machine learning methods in the next section.

R1.2   SOLUTION OPTIONS

Customer data usually represent a mix of attributes such as the age, gender, payment plan, and event sequences. This suggests two modeling approaches. The first one is to aggregate the event sequences into a fixed set of features, concatenate it with the customer attributes, and then build a vector-input model using the designs discussed in section 2.3. The second option is to focus on the analysis of event sequences and use sequential model architectures described in section 2.4. We discuss these two approaches separately in the next two sections.

R1.2.1   Models with Aggregated Features

One of the most basic techniques for propensity scoring is so-called *look-alike modeling* with aggregated features. This approach is based on the assumption that the future behavior of a customer who needs to be scored is likely to follow the behavioral patterns of customers who were in a similar state at some time in the past. The typical design of such a look-alike model is illustrated in Figure R1.3, and the implementation process usually includes the following steps:

- First, we have to specify the target label based on the outcome that we are wanting to predict. It can be a click on a banner, a purchase, account cancellation, or an aggregated metric such as the total customer spend over the next three months.

- Second, we need to engineer customer features. The feature vector can include account data (age, location, or payment method), and aggregated features derived from the event history. Examples of aggregated features include total spend over a certain period of time, frequency of purchases or clicks, time since the last purchase, as well as the breakdown of these aggregates by product categories, marketing channels, and time intervals. Each customer is thus mapped to a fixed-length vector because the number of features does not depend on the length of the event history.

- Third, we have to collect a number of representative customer records, compute the target label and features for each record, and fit a model that estimates the training label based on features. This is illustrated in the upper part of Figure R1.3: assuming that each customer is represented by a vector $\mathbf{x}$ of k features, and we have n training samples, the input of the model training process will be an $n \times k$ design matrix and n-dimensional vector of target labels $\mathbf{y}$. Depending on the target label, we can either fit a regression model f_r that estimates a real-valued target such as the purchase total as

$$y = f_r(\mathbf{x}) \tag{R1.2}$$

or a classification model f_c that estimates the probability of a binary outcome such as a conversion event as

$$p(y = 1) = 1 - p(y = 0) = f_c(\mathbf{x}) \tag{R1.3}$$

or otherwise a multinomial classification model f_{mc} that produces a tuple that specifies the distribution of probabilities over several classes of possible outcomes $c_1, \ldots, c_l$:

$$(p(y = c_1), \ldots, p(y = c_l)) = f_{mc}(\mathbf{x}) \tag{R1.4}$$

The fitting process, of course, includes multiple sub-steps including feature selection, algorithm selection, hyperparameter tuning, validation, and diagnostics.

- Finally, the model can be evaluated for new customers, as shown in the lower part of Figure R1.3. The input vector will typically be computed on the time interval with the same length as for the training, but with an offset so that its end matches the scoring time. Note that the time intervals used for computing features and training labels are not necessarily adjacent as we might need to include a time buffer that is required to take a marketing action. For example, we might be interested to identify customers who are likely to churn in two months to treat them with a retention package, but not customers who are likely to churn in less than a month which leaves no time for treatment.

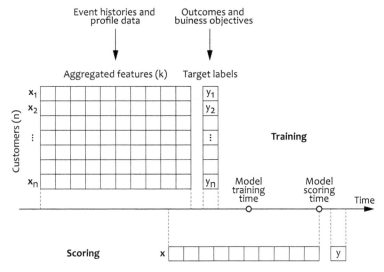

Figure R1.3: A typical layout of the input data for look-alike model training and scoring.

The common implementation choices for look-alike modeling include traditional machine learning methods such as linear regression, logistic regression, gradient boosted decision trees, and neural networks with vector inputs. However, regardless of the model type, the basic approach described above has several important limitations:

EVENT AGGREGATION. One of the main disadvantages of the traditional look-alike model design is that the information about individual events and their temporal structure can be lost in aggregation. Theoretically speaking, it is always possible to design an aggregation schema that preserves all the information that is essential for accurate prediction and attribution, but it is not always achievable in practice.

ENGINEERING EFFORT. The feature engineering effort for look-alike modeling can be considerable for several reasons. First, event histories are often available in the form of application logs or other sources with volatile, fragmented, and poorly documented data schemas, and one needs to understand the semantics of these data to engineer meaningful features. Second, even if the event-level data is readily accessible, designing a good information-preserving aggregation strategy is usually a nontrivial problem.

EXPLAINABILITY. A look-alike model is typically a standard classification or regression model, so one can typically use standard techniques such as Shapley values to explain how exactly the prediction depends on the input features. This, however, does not necessarily help to understand the event patterns and evolution of the customer behavior over time because the input features are aggregated.

These limitations can only be addressed to a certain extent within a framework with aggregated features, which can be more or less critical depending on a specific application. However, we can attempt to develop an alternative framework that allows us to efficiently model and analyze event sequences whenever it is necessary. We explore this approach in the next section.

R1.2.2   *Event Sequence Modeling*

One of the standard solutions for sequence modeling is recurrent neural networks (RNNs) introduced in Section 2.4.4. The RNN approach offers several benefits including a large collection of models developed in the context of natural language processing and other applications, ability to handle variable-size input structures, higher accuracy compared to the models with aggregated inputs, and advanced interpretability features.

R1.2.2.1   *Scoring*

One of the most basic RNN-based designs for propensity scoring is shown in Figure R1.4. It is a pure long short-term memory (LSTM) network that consumes a k-dimensional event vector at each step. So the training set is a $k \times m \times n$ tensor where m is the maximum length of the event history and n is the number of samples. The output is produced based on the final state of the LSTM cell using a dense layer. The hidden state vector **h** can be viewed as a low-dimensional embedding of the customer which evolves over time as the customer history grows.

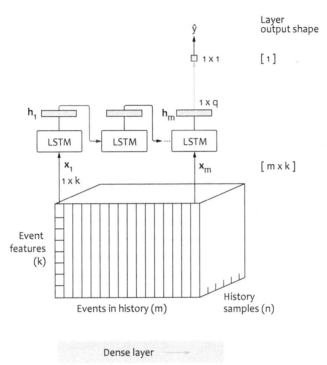

Figure R1.4: The design of a basic event-level propensity model using LSTM. The size q of the hidden state vector is a hyperparameter of the model.

The LSTM-based propensity model helps to reduce the engineering effort because feature engineering for individual events is generally easier than for the entire customer history. It can also achieve higher accuracy than aggregated-input models because of proper handling of temporal event patterns. In particular, it can outperform aggregated-input models on short event histories. This can be useful in applications where it is important to detect certain behavioral traits at early stages. For example, in customer churn prevention, a service provider is generally interested to identify high-risk customers at as early a stage as possible to start handling them accordingly. Another important example is session-based recommendations where the majority of event sequences can be as short as 2-3 events. In such settings, advanced collaborative filtering methods such as factor models might not be applicable, and more basic methods, such as nearest neighbors, are not especially accurate, but RNN-based models can perform reasonably well [Hidasi et al., 2015]. Because of these benefits, RNN-based architectures were tested by many technology companies including Netflix, Google, and Snap with generally positive results [Hidasi et al., 2015; Wu et al., 2017; Yang et al., 2018].

R1.2.2.2   *Event Attribution*

Although the basic LSTM architecture is able to learn the event patterns efficiently, it does not provide convenient tools for event attribution analysis. One possible approach is to analyze the dynamics of the hidden state vector. Since the hidden state is basically a customer embedding that can capture the semantics of customer behavior, it can potentially provide nontrivial insights into the evolution of the customer state and correlate these with the events [Lang and Rettenmeier, 2017]. The shortcoming of this approach is that LSTM does not provide any guarantees with regard to the orientation or semantic meaning of the dimensions of the hidden state, so this type of analysis can be involved and complicated.

A more robust solution can be created by using the attention mechanism introduced in Section 2.4.6. The attention mechanism can help to improve the accuracy of the model, and it also enables event attribution by producing the attention weights. The detailed design of a propensity model with an attention layer is shown in Figure R1.5. This design closely follows the description provided in Section 2.4.6. The intermediate outputs of the LSTM cells $\mathbf{h}$ are mapped to the scalar attention weights a, and the history vector $\mathbf{s}$ is computed as a weighted sum of all intermediate outputs. Note that the history vector $\mathbf{s}$ produced by the top layer of the model can be augmented with profile features, thanks to the flexibility of neural networks that allow the concatenation of multiple inputs.

The attention layer can be used to produce a vector of m attention weights for any event history. These vectors then can be used in several different ways. First, individual vectors can be analyzed in isolation to understand what drove a particular customer to a particular state or outcome. Second, weight vectors can be averaged by customer cohorts to analyze typical event patterns and differences between the cohorts. Finally, one can attempt to cluster customers in the space of weight vectors to determine cohorts based on the event patterns. We demonstrate

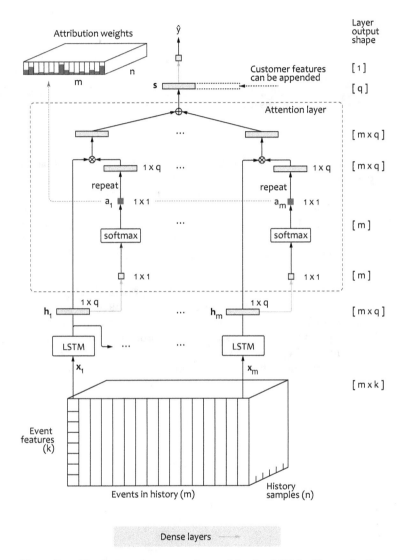

Figure R1.5: The design of a propensity model using LSTM with an attention layer.

the first two techniques in action in the next section, and come back to the third idea in recipe R2 (Customer Feature Learning).

R1.3   PROTOTYPE

 The complete reference implementation for this section is available at https://bit.ly/37013Pr

In this section, we implement a basic prototype of the LSTM-based propensity model according to the blueprint we developed in the previous section. We aim to demonstrate the mechanics of the model in a clear and illustrative way, so we use a toy setup that allows us to examine every detail but avoids the complexities and controversies of real-world datasets. Model testing in a more realistic setup with real-world data is, of course, also important, and we get to this in the next section.

We are going to prototype a basic workflow presented in Figure R1.6 that consists of a simple data generator, model training and validation steps, and analysis of the attention weights computed using the model. The main outputs of this workflow are the propensity model that can be used for scoring of new event histories and attention weights that can be used for the history analysis, so it addresses the main business goals we posed at the beginning of this recipe.

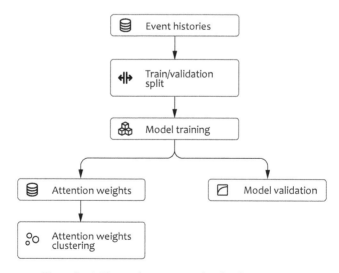

Figure R1.6: The implementation plan for the prototype.

We start by generating a dataset of event histories with a simple pattern. The structure of this data is shown in Figure R1.7. Each event history is a sequence of 20 events, and each event is represented by just one real value. The histories are labeled as either *positive* or *negative*. In both positive and negative samples, the event values follow a smooth sine pattern, but two randomly chosen samples around 12th and 16th positions are amplified in positive samples, as clearly visible in Figure R1.7. We then add white Gaussian noise, so the pattern becomes less apparent but is still recognizable, as shown in Figure R1.8. We generate a balanced dataset of 10,000 event histories (samples) with half of them being positives and the other half negatives.

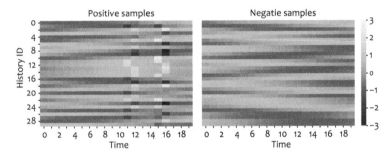

Figure R1.7: A sample of the input data for the prototype model before adding noise.

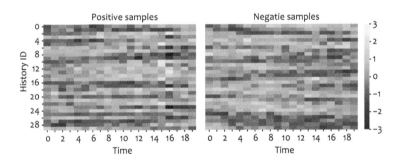

Figure R1.8: A sample of the input data for the prototype model after adding noise.

The event values, including the ones amplified in the positive samples, are zero-centered, so the average history in both positive and negative cohorts is a zero line as shown in Figure R1.9. Consequently, we cannot differentiate between the cohorts based on the mean event values.

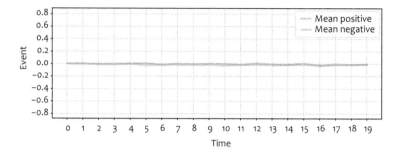

Figure R1.9: Event values averaged by positive and negative cohorts.

The next step is to specify and train the model. We implement LSTM with an attention mechanism according to the architecture shown in Figure R1.5, and then use 75% of the samples for training, and 25% for validation. The ROC curve and confusion matrix for the fitted model are shown in Figure R1.10, and it is a reasonable result providing a relatively high level of noise and illustrative purpose of this prototype.

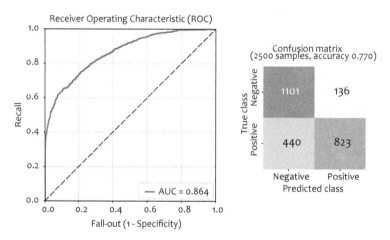

Figure R1.10: The ROC curve and confusion matrix for the prototype model.

At every model evaluation for a given input sequence of events, the attention weights are computed internally, and their values can be captured and analyzed. For example, Figure R1.11 shows a plot of attention weights for one of the event histories. We can see that the attention weights peak between the 12th and 16th positions because this is where the differentiators between the positive and negative samples are located. Averaging the attention weights by cohorts, we see that this pattern is persistent, and the positive cohort has a distinctive signature in the space of the attention weights, as shown in Figure R1.12. Note that the model puts the emphasis on the end of the event history in both positive and negative cohorts because the presence and the absence of the amplified event samples are both informative.

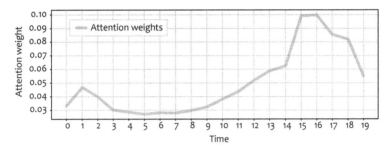

Figure R1.11: An example of attention weights for a specific event history.

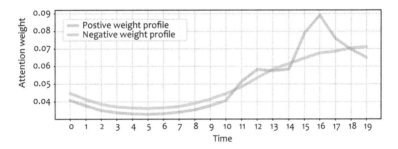

Figure R1.12: Attention weights averaged by positive and negative cohorts.

A more practical and generic way of analyzing the space of attention weights is clustering. For instance, computing attention vectors for all event histories and projecting these vectors onto a two-dimensional plane using t-SNE, we observe the separation of positive and negative cohorts, as illustrated in Figure R1.13. This result is not particularly useful because the target labels have to be known in advance to train the model, but it can be useful in real-world settings where positive and negative cohorts have sophisticated internal structures. For example, a telecom company that uses this approach to build a churn model can attempt to cluster the churned customers in the space of attention weights and analyze typical patterns such as frequent calls to customer support, multiple billing plan changes, and usage of certain services.

The prototype developed above demonstrates how to prepare the inputs and process the outputs of the event-level propensity model.

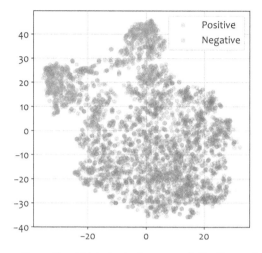

Figure R1.13: Event histories in the space of attention vectors.

In practice, a propensity scoring solution usually includes many more steps such as the comparison with baseline models and hyperparameter tuning. We discuss some aspects of this broader scope in the next section.

R1.4   CASE STUDY

 The complete reference implementation for this section is available at https://bit.ly/3r0H1IP

Let us now evaluate the event-level propensity model in a more realistic setup. We choose to use a larger dataset with a realistic feature layout created based on statistics collected from a digital media company that sells its services on a subscription basis. The dataset includes about 9,000 user profiles with basic demographic and subscription features. For each user, daily usage statistics that include the number of viewed and previewed media items, as well as in-application time, are available, and the total number of daily usage records is about 2.3M. The short samples of the profile and log tables are provided below.

```
User profiles: 8979 rows x 7 columns
+-------+----------+------+--------+-------------+------------+---------+
|  uid  | location |  age | gender | reg_channel |  reg_date  | outcome |
|-------+----------+------+--------+-------------+------------+---------|
|   0   |       15 |  17  | female |           3 | 2014-10-21 |    1    |
|   1   |       13 |  40  | female |           9 | 2006-05-26 |    0    |
|   2   |       14 |  23  | male   |           9 | 2007-03-25 |    1    |
|   3   |        1 |  19  | female |           3 | 2014-11-02 |    1    |
|   4   |        1 |   0  | nan    |           9 | 2014-11-08 |    1    |
|   5   |       21 |  21  | male   |           9 | 2007-10-12 |    1    |
|   6   |        1 |   0  | nan    |           7 | 2014-04-16 |    1    |
|   7   |        5 |   0  | nan    |           9 | 2013-02-06 |    1    |
|   8   |       13 |  18  | female |           9 | 2013-02-06 |    0    |
|   9   |        5 |  29  | male   |           9 | 2013-02-12 |    1    |
+-------+----------+------+--------+-------------+------------+---------+

Usage logs: 2324214 rows x 5 columns
+-------+------------+---------+----------+------------+
|  uid  | date       |  views  | previews |  duration  |
|-------+------------+---------+----------+------------|
|   1   | 2015-02-18 |      5  |       2  |       209  |
|   1   | 2015-04-12 |     12  |       3  |       376  |
|   1   | 2015-06-01 |      4  |       2  |       136  |
|   1   | 2015-07-22 |     12  |      17  |       562  |
|   1   | 2015-09-12 |     40  |       8  |      1021  |
|   1   | 2015-11-02 |     46  |      17  |      1261  |
|   1   | 2015-12-22 |     18  |       6  |       539  |
|   1   | 2016-02-11 |      5  |       9  |       238  |
|   1   | 2016-04-01 |     20  |       6  |       559  |
|   1   | 2016-05-23 |      6  |       0  |       197  |
+-------+------------+---------+----------+------------+
```

The semantic meaning of the profile fields is as follows:

- uid – user ID
- location – user location (city or region)
- age – user age
- gender – user gender
- reg_channel – user's registration channel
- reg_date – user's registration date
- outcome – a binary flag that indicates whether the user took a specific action of interest or not

The fields in the usage logs table have the following meaning:

- date – activity record date
- views – how many media items the user has consumed
- previews – how many media items the user has previewed
- duration – how much time the user spent in the application

The dataset is balanced, and it contains approximately the same number of customers who did and did not take the action of interest. We use this dataset to develop and compare two models that predict the outcome label. The first model is based on aggregated features, and we use it as a baseline. The second model is based on the architecture we used in the prototype. Consequently, we have two modeling pipelines as shown in the implementation plan in Figure R1.14.

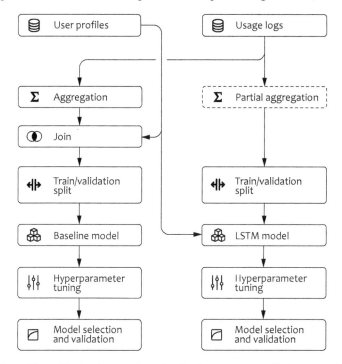

Figure R1.14: The implementation plan for the outcome prediction example.

In the baseline pipeline, we aggregate logs computing the total number of views, previews, and total duration for each user. These aggregated metrics are then combined with the profile features. The baseline model represents a stack of three dense layers, and the sizes of these layers are optimized using the hyperparameter search. Finally, the result is validated using the hold-out samples.

In the LSTM pipeline, the aggregation step is optional – the usage logs can be consumed by the model directly. However, in this particular dataset, the average length of the event history is about 260 events with the longest one coming close to 800 events, so we chose to partly aggregate daily records into weekly buckets. The second difference is that the LSTM model has two separate inputs; events and profiles, that have different shapes and are processed by separate network towers. The events are processed by LSTM, while the profiles are processed by a single dense layer. The outputs are then concatenated and passed through several dense layers on the top of the model.

The validation results for the baseline and LSTM models are shown in Figure R1.15. The LSTM model outperforms the baseline in this setup, although the baseline can also be improved with a more elaborate feature design. For example, one can replace the total number of views and previews with several more granular aggregates such as the totals for the last month, quarter, and year. In practice, however, both aggregated and sequential approaches are valid and important, and one should evaluate both of them when solving a specific problem.

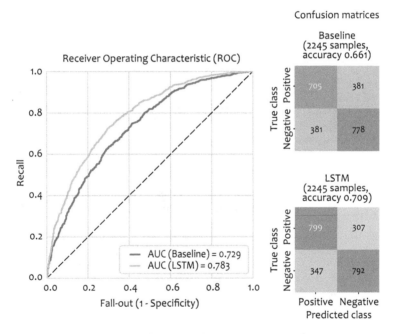

Figure R1.15: The ROC curves and confusion matrices for the baseline and LSTM models on the media subscriptions dataset.

Both models provide basic introspection capabilities such as feature importance analysis, but LSTM can be enhanced with the attention layer to analyze event patterns using the techniques we discussed in the previous section. The feature engineering process is generally simpler and more straightforward for sequential models, although both approaches require thoughtful consideration in that regard. For example, one can consider rescaling daily metrics into weekly metrics to avoid very long sequences that might not be handled well by LSTMs because of the signal decay.

R1.5   VARIATIONS AND EXTENSIONS

We conclude this recipe with a brief discussion of additional topics related to the efficiency and practical usage of the sequential propensity scoring methods that were developed in the previous sections.

R1.5.1   *Advanced Sequential Models*

In this recipe, we demonstrated that sequential models can provide certain advantages over the models with aggregated features both in terms of accuracy and interpretability. We used the LSTM-based design as an example, but a broader range of sequential architectures, including transformers introduced in Section 2.4.7, can be applied to the propensity scoring and other customer analytics problems. We will continue to develop solutions using other types of sequential models in the next recipes.

 We discuss transformer-based customer behavior models in recipe R6 (Product Recommendations).

R1.5.2   *Convolutional Models*

Customer behavior models inspired by traditional NLP architectures such as RNNs and transformers are a good choice for many applications, but they are not the only option. A powerful alternative solution is convolutional neural networks (CNNs). It is indeed convenient to visualize event sequences as rows of pixels, as we did in Figure R1.6, or two-dimensional bitmaps in case the events are vectors, and then to use a one-dimensional or two-dimensional convolutional network to process such bitmaps. This approach makes sense because event sequences would normally have spatial patterns both along the time axis and along the event dimensions.

R1.5.3 *Target Label Design*

Every propensity model requires the design of a training label, and the design of this label is the key to getting meaningful business results. In this recipe, we assumed relatively basic labels constructed using individual events such as conversions or clicks. In practice, the design of the target labels can be far more complex to incorporate immediate, strategic, engagement, and monetary considerations to ensure that the model addresses the right business goals. Consequently, the problem of the label design should be studied in a broader context that includes the formalization of business objectives, model operationalization, and marketing actions optimization. We discuss these topics more thoroughly in the next recipes.

 We discuss the relationship between business objectives, labels, and action in recipe R4 (Next Best Action) where we develop a framework that not only estimates the propensities, but prescribes marketing actions.

R1.5.4 *Operationalization*

The design of the target label is not the only customization one needs to make in order to build an end-to-end solution for a specific business problem using propensity modeling. The solution development process for most problems includes exploratory data analysis, creation of auxiliary models for data preparation, creation of one or several propensity models, reconciliation and operationalization of the scoring results, and efficiency measurements. The design of such a process depends heavily on the business problem, data availability, and other factors, so it is challenging to specify a framework or template that fits all problems and situations. In the next recipes, we will discuss more operationalization techniques and examples in the context of specific use cases.

R1.6 SUMMARY

- Propensity scoring is the approach to customer analytics and personalization problems that are based on estimating the probability of a given customer behaving in a certain way. Typical use cases include the propensity to click, conversion, fraud, and churn.

- Operationalization of propensity models requires the design of training labels that reflect the business objective, creating a model that allows estimation of the propensities, and analyzing the event attribution weights.

- The traditional approach to propensity modeling is to aggregate individual events from the customer history and to fit a generic linear or nonlinear approximator.

- More specialized models that process event sequences can outperform models with aggregated inputs. In particular, RNNs offer a comprehensive toolkit for this type of modeling and they are commonly used in practice.

- Event-level models can help to reduce the feature engineering effort, improve the overall accuracy, and detect high-propensity customers in the early stages of their journeys.

- RNN models offer advanced capabilities for event-level analysis of customer behavior. An example of such capabilities is the attention mechanism that can be used to analyze individual event histories and identify typical patterns by clustering the space of attention weights.

Recipe

2

CUSTOMER FEATURE LEARNING

Learning Representations for Customer Analytics and Personalization

---

Many marketing analytics and personalization problems, including propensity modeling, product recommendations, and customer segmentation require engineering a representation of a customer that properly captures demographic and behavioral traits. These representations need to be useful for computing similarities between customers, informationally complete to be consumed as inputs by downstream models, and, ideally, semantically interpretable.

In recipe R1 (Propensity Modeling) we discussed several approaches for creating customer representations. One of the options was the manual engineering of aggregated features. The second alternative was to use the hidden state vector of the LSTM-based model as a customer embedding that compactly represents the event history, preserving the information about the chronological order of the events. In this recipe, we study how to create useful customer representations and representations of other related entities, in greater detail.

We use the term Customer2Vec to refer to the class of methods and algorithms that help to create compact customer representations, but the synonymous terms User2Vec and Client2Vec are also common in the industry. The same nomenclature is often used for other entities, and we will discuss Item2Vec and Session2Vec problems in this recipe as well.

R2.1   BUSINESS PROBLEM

The customer representation problem can be viewed from several different perspectives. The first of these is the complexity of feature engineering and the level of effort associated with it. Feature engineering for customer entities can be relatively straightforward in most basic environments where each customer is represented by just a few attributes such as age, location, or registration date. Many companies, however, have access to a much broader range of customer data including transaction histories, clickstream logs, and social connection graphs. Unlike the basic demographic attributes which typically have a clear structure and semantic meaning, these alternative datasets can be unstructured and noisy which makes representation engineering more challenging.

For instance, consider the clickstream data that is available as a web server log where each event is represented by a timestamp, event type, and multiple pairs of event attribute names and values as shown below:

```
1607008 | web_thumb_click | prod_id:8330 | page:3 ...
```

The semantics of the attribute fields might not be properly documented, can be changed at the developer's discretion, and complex semantic dependencies can exist between the events. These factors make it challenging to manually engineer behavioral features based on such logs without information losses. The problem becomes even more complicated if we attempt to incorporate product metadata replacing product identifiers in the above log with a collection of product attributes and their values. The information about product categories and styles the customer interacted with and the sequence of interactions can improve the customer feature vector, but combining all these pieces with minimal information losses is a challenge.

The second aspect of the representation engineering problem is that we might need to create embeddings not only for customers, but for other entities such as web sessions, products, and even individual product attributes. For example, a personalization or recommendation system might need to make a decision based on the current web session if the user is anonymous or the quality of personalization depends largely on the current usage context and micromoment [Arora and Warrier, 2016]. This requires compiling a semantic representation of a session that summarizes the real-time context that informs personalization decisions. Another typical use case is the inclusion of new products for which behavioral data are not yet available, into personalized recommendations. This problem, commonly referred to as the *cold start problem*, can be approached in several different ways, one of which is to compute embeddings for individual product attributes and features based on behavioral data, and then to synthesize embeddings for new products according to their attributes and features. These examples suggest that one can benefit from developing a flexible and generic embedding learning toolkit that can be applied to the entities and data sources that are typical in marketing operations.

The third and final perspective on the customer representation problem is how embeddings are used and what functional flows can be improved using representation learning algorithms. One canonical use case is customer segmentation which generally requires the specification of a customer representation space and then performing clustering in this space. More broadly, embeddings can be consumed by a wide range of personalization and recommendation models as inputs. This versatility makes representation learning an important problem that can substantially simplify and improve many marketing intelligence workflows.

We summarize the above considerations in Figure R2.1 that depicts how data sources, different types of embeddings, and downstream models are related.

R2.2   SOLUTION OPTIONS

The event-level propensity models that we developed in recipe R1 (Propensity Modeling) are based on the architectures that are widely used in NLP. Customer analytics and NLP indeed have a lot in common because both disciplines deal with sequences of tokens (events and words, respectively) with complex semantic relationships. More specifically, it is easy to recognize that entities like customers, sessions, and orders can be thought of as texts comprised of event-words or product-words. Provided that the deep learning methods in the field of NLP have advanced tremendously from the relatively basic designs such as LSTM to much more powerful solutions, we can also attempt to go beyond the basic sequential models and experiment with a wider range of NLP techniques in the context of customer analytics. In the next sections, we entertain this idea starting with relatively basic methods and gradually moving on to more advanced architectures.

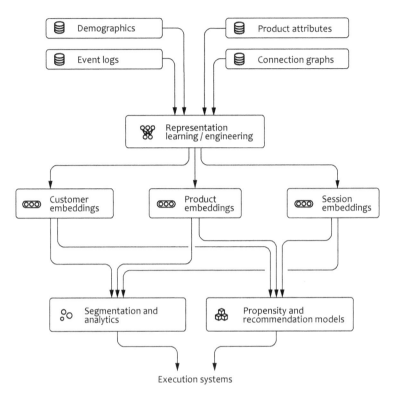

Figure R2.1: The role of representation learning in the context of customer analytics and personalization.

R2.2.1 *Learning Product Embeddings Using Word2Vec*

As an introductory example, consider a database of customer orders in which each order normally includes multiple products (e.g. a grocery business). We can interpret each order as a sentence and each product as a word and apply the standard Word2Vec model introduced in Section 2.6.3 to learn product embeddings, as shown in Figure R2.2.

This class of models, known as Item2Vec [Barkan and Koenigstein, 2016], can produce useful product embeddings that capture purchasing or browsing patterns and reveal the affinity between products that are perceived or used in similar ways by customers. We discuss the usage of embeddings produced in this way comprehensively in the next sections, and demonstrate that these embeddings are often aligned with canonical product categorizations, such as music genres (in the case of media products) or departments (in the case of a department store).

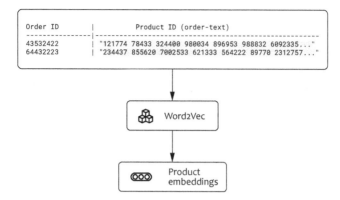

```
Order ID          |          Product ID (order-text)
----------------  |----------------------------------------------------------
43532422          | "121774 78433 324400 980034 896953 988832 6092335..."
64432223          | "234437 855620 7002533 621333 564222 89770 2312757..."
```

Word2Vec

Product
embeddings

Figure R2.2: The basic Item2Vec model.

R2.2.2   *Mixing Behavioral and Content Features*

The beauty of the Word2Vec approach is that the basic solution described in the previous section can be extended in many ways to incorporate multiple heterogeneous data sources. For example, one can incorporate content data by replacing product IDs with product attributes [Arora and Warrier, 2016]. In this way, orders or web sessions can be represented as flat sequences of product attributes and attribute embeddings can then be learned, as illustrated in Figure R2.3.

This approach blends behavioral data efficiently with product data, capturing both purchasing patterns and attribute-based product similarities. The obtained attribute embeddings can be rolled up into product embeddings, then session embeddings, and finally customer embeddings. This rolling-up process can usually be done through simple averaging. For example, a product embedding can be computed as the average of the embeddings of all its attributes.

The above approach can be extended to incorporate even less-structured content data. For example, one can replace product attributes with human-readable textual product descriptions (lists of words instead of lists of attributes) if structured attributes are not available or not informative enough, and embeddings can be learned using the same off-the-shelf Word2Vec algorithm [Stiebellehner et al., 2017]. Surprisingly, one can obtain good results this way without dealing with complex feature engineering or fragile relevancy tuning, which are required by traditional hybrid recommendation algorithms.

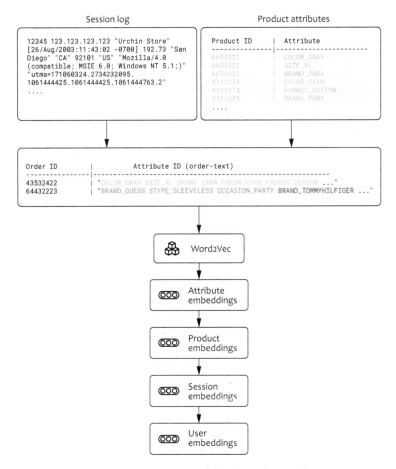

Figure R2.3: An Item2Vec model with product attributes.

The embeddings learned using the Item2Vec methods discussed in this and previous sections can be useful in several applications, including the following:

ITEM-TO-ITEM RECOMMENDATIONS Product embeddings computed using Item2Vec allow for measuring distances between products in the semantic space, and this can be used to build an item-to-item recommender system [Phi et al., 2016].

USER-TO-ITEM RECOMMENDATIONS Embedding roll-up enables the computing of customer embeddings, which in turn enables user-to-item recommendations or similar personalization use cases [Phi et al., 2016; Arora and Warrier, 2016].

CONTEXTUAL RECOMMENDATIONS Consider the following scenario: a customer who visits an online fashion store might be shopping in several different modes or contexts. They might be looking for a specific product, a specific style, or a certain combination of products, such as socks and shoes. Understanding this context is essential for a personalization system. This can be done by computing session embeddings and then measuring the distance between the session and personalizable items, such as products, in the semantic space.

AUTOMATED FEATURE ENGINEERING Item2Vec models learn embeddings in an unsupervised way from data that is easy to engineer (e.g. sequences of product IDs), which makes them a good feature extraction component that can be integrated with downstream customer models. We develop this idea further in the following sections.

ANALYTICS AND SEGMENTATION Similar to the recommendation and propensity modeling use cases, products and customers can be analyzed and segmented more efficiently in embedding spaces than in spaces of manually engineered features. We explore this idea more thoroughly in Section R2.3 where we build prototypes.

R2.2.3 *Learning Customer Embeddings*

The Item2Vec models described in the previous sections can produce customer embeddings using roll-ups, but this is not the only approach. Another natural solution is to use Doc2Vec instead of Word2Vec.

Word2Vec learns from plain sequences of tokens and uses the notion of a sentence only to reset the learning context. It does not support any hierarchical relationships, such as product $\rightarrow$ order $\rightarrow$ customer. This is clearly a limitation because the distribution of events in a customer journey depends not only on the global event patterns but also on the context of a specific customer. In the NLP world, an equivalent problem is the learning of sentence embeddings, as opposed to word embeddings. One of the standard solutions for this problem is Doc2Vec, which directly generates sentence embeddings. We can adapt Doc2Vec to learn customer embeddings from customer-sentences. The difference between these two approaches can be clarified as follows:

- Word2Vec is based on the idea that word representation should be good enough to predict surrounding words (e.g. "the cat sat on the" predicts "mat"). This makes sense for product representations as well (e.g. "wine cheese" predicts "grapes").

- Doc2Vec is based on the idea that a sentence (document) representation should be good enough to predict words in the sentence. For example, "the most important → thing" may be the best prediction on average, but "the most important → feature" may be the best prediction for a text on machine learning. Similarly, a good customer embedding should predict future events for that specific customer. Customer embeddings obtained by averaging the product embeddings associated with customer interaction history do not necessarily achieve this goal.

The Doc2Vec approach to learning customer embeddings is illustrated in Figure R2.4 [Phi et al., 2016; Zolna and Romanski, 2016]. The main difference between this schema and the designs we presented in the previous steps is that the algorithm outputs embeddings for customers (sentences), not products (words). This category of models is commonly referred to as User2Vec, Client2Vec, or Customer2Vec.

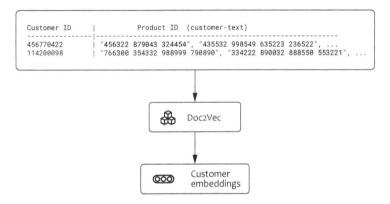

Figure R2.4: The basic Customer2Vec model.

R2.2.4   *Unsupervised Embedding Learning from Logs*

We have seen that the sequential modeling approach allows one to blend behavioral and content data in various ways as well as to produce embeddings for different levels of aggregation, such as attributes, products, and customers. These embeddings can then be absorbed as features by downstream models such conversion propensity or price sensitivity scoring models. In some cases, the quality of embeddings can be high enough to completely eliminate manually engineered features and replace them with embeddings that are automatically generated by Item2Vec or Customer2Vec algorithms [Seleznev et al., 2018].

We can, however, develop even more advanced and autonomous Customer2Vec solutions by recognizing that the customer-as-a-text paradigm not only helps to leverage NLP methods for customer analytics purposes, but can also be taken literally because customer data often originates in application logs which are basically semi-structured texts. For example, consider a website or mobile application that continuously logs events with a timestamp, event type (e.g. click or view), event attribute (e.g. page ID and click coordinates), and other fields. Consider also a data scientist who is tasked with engineering features for some models out of these log files. In practice, this task can be quite challenging because one needs to study log samples thoroughly, understand the semantics of fields, learn how multiple related events can be stitched together, examine corner cases, and so on. However, one can approach the problem from a different angle: event names and attributes can be automatically concatenated into discrete tokens, which can be grouped into customer-sentences, and then Customer2Vec can be applied [Seleznev et al., 2018]. This approach is illustrated in Figure R2.5 where the tokens are obtained by concatenating the event names, attributes, and values. This example demonstrates how the Customer2Vec approach can reduce the engineering effort and simplify the operationalization of customer analytics solutions.

R2.2.5   *Semi-supervised Embedding Learning*

Our next step is to further develop the idea of automated embedding generation for downstream models. The methods described in the previous sections partly solve this task, but the limitation is that Word2Vec and Doc2Vec are unsupervised methods that provide no guarantees regarding the predictive power of the produced embeddings. We can attempt to ensure certain guarantees by combining unsupervised representation learning with supervised learning that provides additional guidance and orients the embedding space.

One possible way to implement this idea is shown in Figure R2.6 [Seleznev et al., 2018]. On the left-hand side, there is a standard Word2Vec model (continuous bag of words version) that consumes the context, which consists of one-hot encoded tokens (products, events, etc.). Then, it maps them to embeddings using the embedding matrix $\mathbf{W}$, passes through the nonlinear hidden layer, and unfolds the hidden vector into

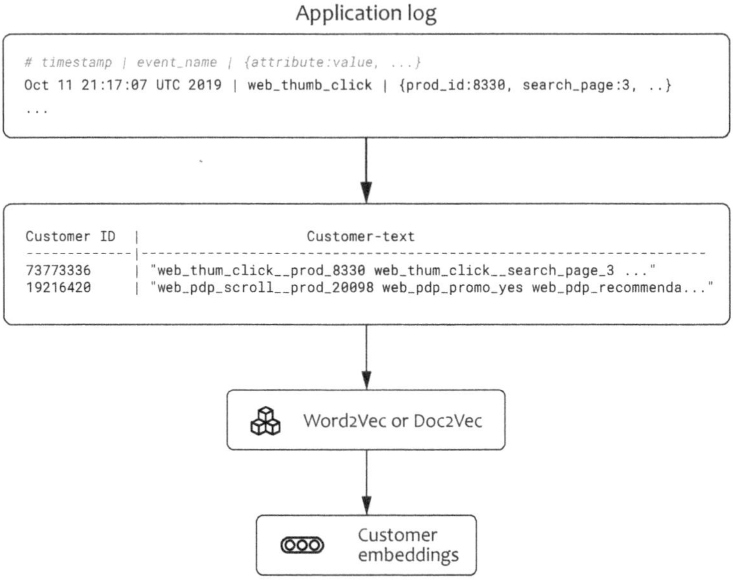

Application log

```
# timestamp | event_name | {attribute:value, ...}
Oct 11 21:17:07 UTC 2019 | web_thumb_click | {prod_id:8330, search_page:3, ..}
...
```

```
Customer ID |                    Customer-text
------------|--------------------------------------------------------------
73773336    | "web_thum_click__prod_8330 web_thum_click__search_page_3 ..."
19216420    | "web_pdp_scroll__prod_20098 web_pdp_promo_yes web_pdp_recommenda..."
```

Word2Vec or Doc2Vec

Customer embeddings

Figure R2.5: Unsupervised customer embedding learning from application logs using Customer2Vec model.

token probabilities using the output matrix and, finally, softmax operation. The output is the predicted token based on the input context. On the right-hand side is a regular supervised model that predicts one or several business metrics of interest, such as conversions, based on the same customer texts. This model can be viewed as a simulator of the downstream models that are supposed to consume the customer embeddings. The left and right networks are structurally independent but trained simultaneously – the embedding weights are shared or copied between the networks after each training epoch.

This guided learning helps to align the semantic space with the business metrics and improve the predictive power of embeddings. We can also draw some parallels between this approach and LSTM-based propensity model discussed in recipe R1 (Propensity Modeling). In the case of guided Word2Vec, we start with an unsupervised method but enhance it with supervised guidance. In the case of LSTM, we start with a supervised model but extract embeddings from the hidden layer or attention layer. Thus, both models can be viewed as hybrids. Moreover, one can use a multi-output LSTM model that predicts several metrics based on the same hidden layer [Zolna and Romanski, 2016], which

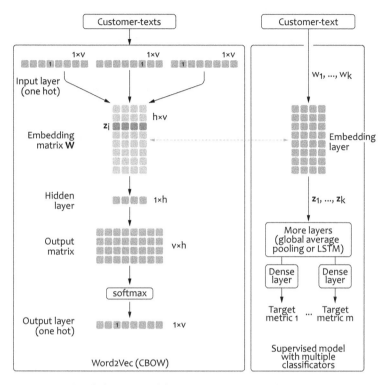

Figure R2.6: Guided training of the Customer2Vec model. In the graphics, v is the size of the input vocabulary (number of distinct tokens), h is the dimensionality of customer embeddings, m is the number of guiding metrics, and k is the number of tokens in one customer history. Consequently, matrix $\mathbf{W}$ consists of v embedding vectors $\mathbf{z}$, and both Word2Vec and the supervised model use it to map each input token w to the corresponding embedding.

makes the LSTM schema even more similar to the guided Word2Vec model described above.

R2.2.6 *Autoencoder-based Models*

In the NLP world, pioneering solutions with relatively basic architectures such as Word2Vec were gradually succeeded by more complex, deep, and specialized architectures. Personalization and recommendation models followed a similar trajectory, and it is not uncommon to use more complex architectures than the vanilla LSTM and Word2Vec models we discussed previously. This can be illustrated with the autoencoder-based Customer2Vec model which can be used as an alternative to the Word2Vec approach [Baldassini and Serrano, 2018; Seleznev et al., 2018].

The conceptual architecture of the autoencoder-based Customer2Vec is relatively straightforward. The input of the model is an aggregated fixed-length customer representation, which can be a vector of manually engineered features or a bag-of-words vector produced from the customer-text. This input is encoded into a low-dimensional representation using one or several neural layers, and the original input is then reconstructed from this condensed representation. The network is trained to minimize the reconstruction error, and the low-dimensional representation is interpreted as a customer embedding. Optionally, the model can be extended with guiding metrics so that the overall loss function is a weighted sum of the reconstruction loss and guides losses, as shown in Figure R2.7.

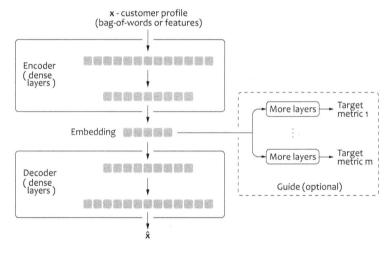

Figure R2.7: An autoencoder-based Customer2Vec model.

In practice, this approach may or may not provide advantages compared to Word2Vec, depending on the input data and use case, but in general, it is a competitive alternative.

R2.2.7   *Incorporation of Graphs, Texts, and Images*

We have seen in the previous sections that the Customer2Vec concept is flexible enough to extract informative signals from behavioral, content, structured, and unstructured data. In this section, we briefly discuss how the Customer2Vec toolkit can be extended to incorporate graphs, texts, and images into the analysis.

The need to incorporate graphical data often appears in financial institutions such as banks that work with a large number of very different customers, including individuals, companies from various industries, and public services. The financial institution observes transactions between these entities and can build a graph in which nodes represent entities and edges correspond to transactions and interactions. We can obtain valuable insights about the needs of individual entities, their operational efficiency, and roles in the global value chain by examining the topology of this graph. For example, a manufacturer that transacts with a large number of international suppliers and carriers has different needs compared to a manufacturer that interact with just a few suppliers and carriers. Embeddings that capture such signals can be used to segment entities, recommend relevant financial services, and perform other customer analytics and relationship management activities.

We can learn customer embeddings based on interaction graphs using Node2Vec, a generic algorithm for learning node embeddings introduced in Section 2.7.2.3. Node2Vec maps each node in the graph to a sequence of related nodes by randomly traversing the graph outward from the given node, and then learns dense sequence embeddings using the regular Word2Vec algorithm. Applied to transaction graphs and financial entities, this procedure naturally captures common interaction patterns and produces meaningful entity embeddings [Barbour, 2020]. The embeddings produced by Node2Vec can be concatenated with embeddings produced by other Customer2Vec models and consumed by downstream processes. The graph-based approach can, of course, be used in many applications besides the financial sector. For example, product recommendations can be made based on the graph of interactions between customers and products [Eksombatchai et al., 2018; Ying et al., 2018]. We elaborate on this topic in recipe R6 (Product Recommendations).

The need to incorporate texts, images, and videos into customer and item embeddings often arises in content-rich applications such as retail and media services. In many cases, content data can be easily mapped to dense embeddings using pretrained NLP and computer vision models available from public repositories. In particular, we will discuss the mapping of product images in recipe R5 (Visual Search) and the mapping of textual product descriptions in recipe R6 (Product Recommendations). This approach works well when we need to extract generic topics from texts and images, and make them available for the down-stream analysis or models. For example, we can expect that images of shoes will be well separated from the images of dresses in the em-bedding space produced using off-the-shelf computer vision models. This approach, however, does not necessarily work in applications that require embeddings to be aligned with domain-specific objectives. In such cases, we can train networks in a supervised way to map cus-tomers or items to vectors where the domain-specific classes or metric levels become well separable, and use these vectors as embeddings. We will discuss such methods in detail in recipes R5 and R6 as well.

R2.3   PROTOTYPE

    The complete reference implementation for this
section is available at https://bit.ly/3LGHbNr

In this section, we develop a prototype that demonstrates how event histories can be processed using Word2Vec and Doc2Vec models to cap-ture sequential patterns. We consider a toy model of an online apparel store that sells two categories of products: hats and dresses. Each cate-gory is represented by two products, so we have 4 products in total (2 hats and 2 dresses). Next, we assume two classes of customers:

CLASS A The 'category' shoppers who come to buy either a hat or a dress. They tend to browse only one category during one session, but can switch to another category in a different session.

CLASS B The 'look' shoppers who come to buy both a hat and a dress. They tend to browse products from both categories in every ses-sion.

These two classes of shoppers are specified using two simple Markov chains shown in Figure R2.8.

It is easy to check that both models generate product sequences where all four products are equiprobable. We can do it analytically by checking that the flat distribution over products is in fact the sta-tionary distribution for both chains. The stationary distribution π for a

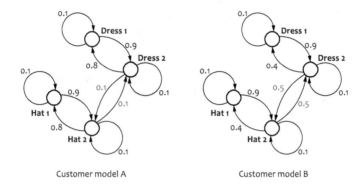

Figure R2.8: Two customer models used for data generation. The models are structurally identical, but have different cross-category transition probabilities.

Markov chain with transition matrix $\mathbf{P}$ satisfies the condition $\pi = \pi\mathbf{P}$, and this indeed holds for the first model and flat π:

			Hat 1	Hat 2	Dress 1	Dress 2
Hat 1	0.25	0.25	0.1	0.9	0.0	0.0
Hat 2	0.25	0.25	0.4	0.1	0.5	0.0
Dress 1	0.25	0.25	0.0	0.0	0.1	0.9
Dress 2	0.25	0.25	0.5	0.0	0.4	0.1

(The first two columns are transposed vectors $[0.25\ 0.25\ 0.25\ 0.25]^{\mathsf{T}} = [0.25\ 0.25\ 0.25\ 0.25]^{\mathsf{T}}$.)

The same is true for the second model. For the purpose of prototyping, we generate 10,000 browsing histories for each of two models, and each history is a sequence of 50 products. We also assume that each event history corresponds to exactly one customer, so that the history representation and customer representation are synonymous. First, we merge the generated histories together to produce a corpus of 20,000 history-sentences, and feed them into the Word2Vec model to compute embeddings for the products. Examples of embedding vectors are as follows:

$$\text{Hat } 1 \rightarrow [\ 1.80 \quad 2.10 \quad 0.44 \quad -1.99\ ]$$
$$\text{Hat } 2 \rightarrow [\ 1.11 \quad 2.14 \quad 1.94 \quad -1.47\ ]$$
$$\text{Dress } 1 \rightarrow [\ -0.97 \quad -1.52 \quad -1.56 \quad 2.65\ ]$$
$$\text{Dress } 2 \rightarrow [\ -0.50 \quad -3.05 \quad -0.51 \quad 1.65\ ]$$

We can see that the model properly captures category semantics, so that the embeddings for dresses are alike and the embeddings for hats are alike, while dresses and hats are dissimilar.

The second step is to develop a Doc2Vec model that produces customer embeddings. As we discussed above, product frequencies are the same for both models, so one cannot tell which customer model produced a given sequence based solely on the product frequency metrics. Consequently, we want customer embeddings produced by Doc2Vec to be more useful than the basic product frequency histograms, so that we can determine the customer class based on the embedding. To demonstrate how two customer classes separate in the semantic space, we feed the corpus of history-sentences into the Doc2Vec model that produces an embedding for each history, randomly subsample 4,000 embeddings, and project them onto a two-dimensional plane using singular value decomposition (SVD). An example result is shown Figure R2.9 where the embedding projections are color coded according to the true customer classes. These true classes are not visible to the Doc2Vec model, but the model manages to separate two cohorts of customers reasonably well, based on the sequential event patterns.

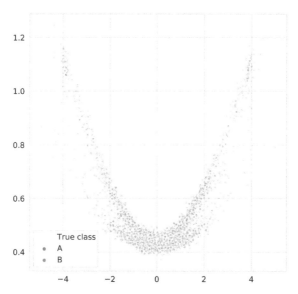

Figure R2.9: Customer embeddings projected onto a two-dimensional plane using truncated SVD.

R2.4   CASE STUDY

 The complete reference implementation for this section is available at https://bit.ly/3KeVAA6

Our next step is to test the ideas we discussed earlier on a bigger and more realistic dataset. We use a dataset created based on online grocery transaction data. This dataset consists of about 3 million transactions (orders) that collectively include about 50 thousand products (items). Each order is a collection of items that were sequentially added to an online shopping cart and thus each order line is attributed with the sequence number, as shown in the example below.

```
Customer orders: 31433254 rows x 3 columns
+-------------+-----------+-------------------+
|  order_id  |  item_id  |  add_to_cart_seq  |
+-------------+-----------+-------------------+
|     431534 |       198 |                1 |
|     431534 |     12427 |                2 |
|     431534 |     10258 |                3 |
|     431534 |     25133 |                4 |
|     431534 |     10326 |                5 |
|     473747 |       198 |                1 |
|     473747 |     12427 |                2 |
+-------------+-----------+-------------------+
```

The second part of the dataset is the item metadata which includes human-readable item descriptions and mappings to the grocery store departments, as illustrated in the following sample.

```
Items: 49220 rows x 3 columns
+-------------+----------------------------------+---------------+
|  product_id | product_name                     | department    |
+-------------+----------------------------------+---------------+
|       26225 | Artificially Flavored Candi...   | snacks        |
|       11391 | Lavander & Aloe Lotion           | missing       |
|       24737 | Organic Micro Broccoli Spro...   | produce       |
|       19383 | Soup, 99% Fat Free New Engl...   | canned goods  |
|        6440 | 100% Organic Tarragon            | pantry        |
|       17358 | Crossovers Maple Syrup Blen...   | dairy eggs    |
|       30246 | Micellar Makeup Remover Wip...   | personal care |
|       38666 | Wheat Hot Dog Rolls              | bakery        |
|        7812 | Salisbury Steak Home Style ...   | frozen        |
|        3822 | Green Magic Chia Squeeze         | snacks        |
+-------------+----------------------------------+---------------+
```

We create order-sentences concatenating the corresponding item IDs, and then feed the corpus of such sentences into the Word2Vec model to learn item embeddings. The quality of the obtained embeddings can be assessed in several ways. One basic validation is to review the nearest neighbors in the semantic space for individual products. Consider the following two examples where the first product in each table is the starting point, and its nearest neighbors are listed under it sorted by the distance:

```
+-----------------------------------------+-------------+
| product                                 | similarity  |
+-----------------------------------------+-------------|
| > Bag of Organic Bananas                |      1.000  |
| Organic Banana                          |      0.744  |
| Banana                                  |      0.720  |
| Organic D'Anjou Pears                   |      0.524  |
| Organic Bosc Pear                       |      0.487  |
| Organic Raspberries                     |      0.485  |
| Organic Green Seedless Grapes           |      0.466  |
| Organic Large Extra Fancy Fuji Apple    |      0.464  |
+-----------------------------------------+-------------+


+-----------------------------------------+-------------+
| product                                 | similarity  |
+-----------------------------------------+-------------|
| > Organic Lowfat 1% Milk                |      1.000  |
| Organic Reduced Fat Milk                |      0.863  |
| Organic Homestyle Waffles               |      0.653  |
| Organic Yokids Lemonade                 |      0.624  |
| Organic Mini Homestyle Waffles          |      0.620  |
| Organic Whole Milk                      |      0.613  |
| Medium Cheddar Cheese Block             |      0.606  |
| Organic Whole String Cheese             |      0.597  |
+-----------------------------------------+-------------+
```

These examples confirm that the embeddings capture the semantics of product categories. We can take one more step in this direction, and make a projection of all embeddings onto a two-dimensional plane using t-SNE to visualize the structure of the semantic space. In Figure R2.10, this projection is color coded using the ground truth department labels. These labels are not exposed to the Word2Vec model in any way, but we can see that the semantic space is aligned with them in the sense that the items that belong to the same department tend to cluster in the semantic space as well.

The clusters in Figure R2.10 do not perfectly match the department labels, but this is not the goal – the embeddings produced by Item2Vec and Customer2Vec modes are expected to capture behavioral patterns, not just reproduce the canonical categorization. However, it is expected that the behavioral patterns are partly aligned with the basic attributes.

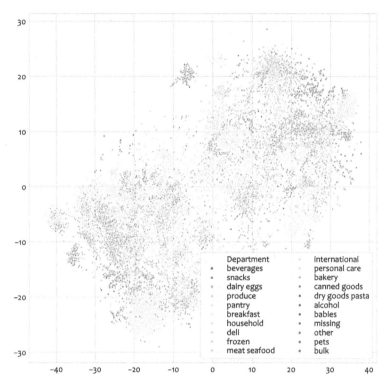

Department		International
•	beverages	•	personal care
•	snacks	•	bakery
•	dairy eggs	•	canned goods
•	produce	•	dry goods pasta
•	pantry	•	alcohol
•	breakfast	•	babies
•	household	•	missing
•	deli	•	other
•	frozen	•	pets
•	meat seafood	•	bulk

Figure R2.10: An example of the semantic space for online grocery items. The 200-dimensional embeddings computed by a Word2Vec model are projected onto a plane using t-SNE.

R2.5 SUMMARY

- Most personalization models and customer analytics processes require customer and product representations as inputs. These representations can be engineered manually or learned using statistical models.

- Customer and item representations often need to be engineered based on event sequences or semi-structured data such as web server logs. This problem can be efficiently tackled using sequential and NLP models that can be adapted to wide range of text-like inputs.

- Word2Vec and Doc2Vec models are powerful tools for learning customer, item, and session representations based on event sequences such as store transactions, online orders, and raw application logs. These models can be extended to incorporate product attributes and customer demographic fields.

- Training of unsupervised Word2Vec and Doc2Vec models can be guided using target labels created based on the business metrics of interest. This helps to produce embeddings that properly capture the information needed for predicting the business metrics.

- Supervised neural networks provide an alternative to guided Word2Vec. One network can be used to produce embeddings for multiple entities (e.g. customers and products), and it is often possible to extract embedding vectors at different points (layers) of the network depending on features and entities of interest.

- The quality of embeddings can be assessed using their predictive power when they are used as inputs to the downstream classification or regression models, analysis of the nearest neighbors in the semantic space, and clustering.

- Embeddings produced by Customer2Vec, Item2Vec, and Session2Vec models can be used in customer analytics, in-session personalization, product recommendations, and promotion targeting applications.

Recipe

3

DYNAMIC PERSONALIZATION

Recommending Products, Offers, and Content Using Contextual Bandits

---

The customer analytics and personalization methods discussed in the previous recipes, as well as many other traditional methods, assume the availability of historical data for model training and relative stationarity of the environment. This is so that the trained models will remain valid for the time period needed for their operationalization. These assumptions are acceptable for many use cases provided that we implement appropriate experiment planning, model quality checking, and retraining processes. This will ensure model correctness and proper control and mitigation of the issues related to nonstationarity. In certain scenarios, however, it is challenging or impractical to adapt traditional methods because the environment is highly dynamic, and various overheads and efforts associated with model retraining and other adjustments become prohibitively high. In this section, we explore alternative solution approaches that are designed from the ground up to operate in dynamic settings and to do it as efficiently as possible.

R3.1 BUSINESS PROBLEM

We consider an online recommendation system that has a collection of k items such as products, ads, or banners. We assume that the system operates in discrete time, so it receives a request for a recommendation from user u_t at time step t, determines the recommended item a_t, and presents it to the user. We also assume that the recommendation system has access to the database of user and item profiles that are represented by feature vectors **u** and **a**, respectively, and can be used to optimize the recommendation decision. This environment is depicted in Figure R3.1.

Once the recommended item is presented to the user, the system observes reward r_t. The reward is usually designed based on the business metrics of interest. For example, we can attempt to maximize the click-through rate. In this case, we can use the reward value of one each time the user clicks on the recommended item, and zero otherwise. In more complex scenarios, such as product recommendations on a retail website, the reward can incorporate monetary metrics such as the order total or customer lifetime value estimates. The overall performance of the system is measured as the sum of rewards, also known as *return*, over a certain number of time steps across all users. We also use the term *impression* to refer to one item exposure to a user, so the number of time steps is equal to the number of impressions in this setup.

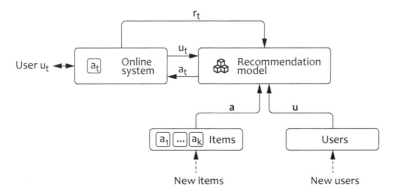

Figure R3.1: The main components of the dynamic recommendation environment.

This environment generally allows the use of personalization methods that rely on historical data, such as propensity scoring from recipe R1 (Propensity Modeling) or recommendation models from recipe R6 (Product Recommendations), to score the items and select the optimal one. However, the problem changes significantly if we add the requirement that the system needs to operate in a constantly changing environment. More specifically, let us assume that new items and users are added at a relatively high rate, and the old items and users fade away. A typical example of such settings is a newsfeed recommendation system where news stories are constantly added and then gradually become obsolete. Another example of this problem is an online retailer that runs many short-term promotional campaigns in parallel, so the collection of promotional banners that are shown to users on the website is frequently updated.

The assumption about the continuously changing collection of items and inflow of new users means that the system should use the profile data whenever possible, but it should also handle the situation efficiently when item profile, user profile, or both, are missing or potentially obsolete. The latter case, that is, making recommendations based on incomplete profile data, is known as the *cold start problem*. In the next section, we discuss several solution options that address these challenges.

R3.2   SOLUTION OPTIONS

Dynamic content personalization requires solving several problems including cold-start optimization, personalization using known user and item features, feature design, and offline performance evaluations. We discuss these tasks separately and build a complete solution step by step.

R3.2.1   *Context-Free Recommendations*

Let us first consider an extreme scenario where neither item nor user profiles are available. The system starts to process recommendation requests having a collection of k items, but there is no historical data, no item or user features, and all users are new. We cannot personalize recommendations in this case, at least until the same users start to return, but we can attempt to optimize the overall click-through rate in a nonpersonalized way. This setup is also known as *context-free optimization* because all recommendation requests are identical and do not include any contextual information such as user features.

One of the most basic solutions for the context-free optimization problem is to randomly split the traffic into k streams, returning item a_i to all requests in stream i until enough rewards are collected to determine the best-performing item in a statistically correct way. After this, switch all requests to that item to maximize the mean reward over the entire user population. This approach is illustrated in Figure R3.2 (a) where we refer to the split testing phase as *exploration*, and the reward optimization phase as *exploitation*.

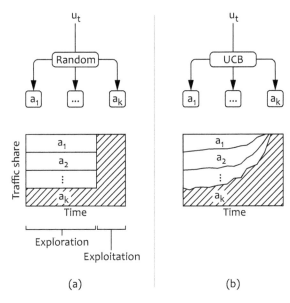

Figure R3.2: Design options for context-free recommendations in a dynamic environment using split testing (a) and multi-armed bandit algorithm (b). In the traffic share graphs, item a_k is assumed to be optimal in terms of a click-through rate, and the hatched area corresponds to the total number of recommendation responses with this item.

An alternative solution can be implemented using multi-armed bandits introduced in Section 3.3. In the multi-armed bandits formulation, we consider each item a as an action, dynamically estimating item values $Q_t(a)$ at each time step, making recommendations balancing between exploration and exploitation based on these estimates, and gradually converging to the return-maximizing routing policy. This formulation allows us to use a wide range of bandit algorithms, including the ε-greedy and UCB algorithms. The bandit approach is illustrated in Figure R3.2 (b). From the theoretical standpoint, multi-armed bandits achieve better returns compared to two-step split testing described above, but both methods are widely used in practice, and the choice between the two depends on several considerations:

- Split testing explicitly aims to produce statistically significant value estimates for each item. Multi-armed bandits do similar estimates internally, but the goal is to rank items by their performance rather than by measuring the absolute values. Consequently, split testing is often preferred in experiments where the results need to be analyzed or multiple metrics need to be tracked. This can be the case, for example, in testing of new product designs where the goal is to measure the performance of each design and explain the results, not only to determine the best-performing option.

- The multi-armed bandits approach is preferred when efficiency and automation are the primary goals. For example, limited-time offers and other short-term campaigns can be difficult to optimize using split testing, but multi-armed bandits can produce good results. Multi-armed bandits may also be preferable in low-traffic scenarios where split testing requires too much time to produce statistically significant estimates, and in scenarios where split testing is prohibitively inefficient because of the high costs of lost opportunities (e.g. luxury products).

- Split testing and multi-armed bandits can also be viewed as two different points on the trade-off line between value estimation and optimization: split testing tends to produce statistically significant estimates faster but achieves relatively low returns; multi-armed bandits tend to produce relatively high returns but take more time steps to determine the best item with statistical significance.

R3.2.2   Basic Contextual Recommendations

We next consider the scenario where the recommendation context with user and item features is available. In a static environment, the standard solution is to build a model that estimates the expected reward $\hat{r}(\mathbf{u}, \mathbf{a})$ as a function of the context, that is the concatenation of the user and item feature vectors, to score all items using this model, and to recommend the item with the maximum score. This approach, entertained further in recipe R6 (Product Recommendations), assumes that the model is trained on the historical data, deployed to production where a new batch of interactions is collected, and then the model is retrained, as sketched in Figure R3.3 (a). In a dynamic environment, this approach faces several headwinds:

- If the historical data is not available, we need to either make random recommendations until a sufficient batch of samples is collected or to develop an auxiliary recommendation algorithm, for example rule-based, as an alternative to completely random recommendations. If the training data were collected under a nonrandom recommendation algorithm, we might need to account for selection biases as discussed in Section 2.8.2.

- The two main categories of recommendation algorithms, collaborative filtering and content-based filtering, require behavioral data. In classic content filtering, user profiles need to include past interactions with the items, so that a new item is recommended based on its similarity to past items. However, the similarity metric can be computed purely on the item's content attributes. In collaborative filtering, both user and item profiles need to include interaction data. Consequently, many standard algorithms cannot handle new users or items efficiently even if we manage to train the models on historical data.

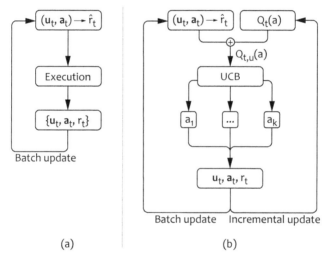

(a)   (b)

Figure R3.3: Contextual recommendations in a dynamic environment (a) using collaborative filtering or content filtering and (b) UCB with warm start.

We can improve the handling of new items and users by combining a recommendation model with a multi-armed bandit algorithm. One possible implementation of this idea is to estimate the user-specific item value as a sum of two components. The first of these is the context-free (non-personalized) action value $Q_t(a)$ which we used in the previous section. The second component is the personalized estimate of the reward $\hat{r}_t(\mathbf{u}, \mathbf{a})$ at time t produced using a static recommendation model. Consequently, the user-adjusted item value function is as follows:

$$Q_{t,u}(a) = Q_t(a) + \hat{r}_t(\mathbf{u}, \mathbf{a}) \tag{R3.1}$$

The final recommendation is then made using ε-greedy and UCB logic [Li et al., 2010]. In other words, we modify the standard context-free algorithm by shifting the context-free value estimate $Q_t(a)$ towards the user-specific bias $\hat{r}_t$. This design, known as multi-armed bandit with warm start, is depicted in Figure R3.3 (b). The user profile generally includes both demographic and behavioral features, and the item profile includes content attributes and behavioral features, so the estimate $\hat{r}_t$ can be more or less accurate depending on what data is available. The advantage of this approach is that potentially inaccurate reward estimates for new users and items produced by the model, as well as obsolete estimates in non-stationary environments, are corrected using a context-free algorithm.

The warm start design is an intermediate solution that heuristically combines the advantages of personalized and context-free methods. Our next step is to develop a contextual multi-armed bandit that seamlessly integrates the personalization model with the control logic of a bandit algorithm.

R3.2.3   *LinUCB*

In this section, we develop a contextual version of the UCB algorithm. The basic idea is to use a supervised model that can be incrementally updated at every time step to estimate item value $Q_t(a)$ and its upper confidence bound $B_t(a)$ based on the context that includes both item and user profiles. We then plug these estimates into the UCB algorithm, as illustrated in Figure R3.4. Compared to the basic designs presented in Figure R3.3, this approach eliminates the separation of the contextual and context-free parts and enables end-to-end incremental updates.

One of the main challenges of implementing the above concept is the estimation of the confidence bound. To make this problem tractable, we assume that the item value is a linear function of the context. Denoting the context for item a at time t as $x_{t,a} = (u_t, a_t)$, we can express this assumption as

$$Q(a) = \mathbb{E}\left[r_{t,a} \mid x_{t,a}\right] = x_{t,a}^T \theta_a^* \tag{R3.2}$$

where θ_a^* is the unknown coefficient vector associated with item a. Let us also assume that context vector $x_{t,a}$ has d dimensions, and we have accumulated m samples for item a at time step t. We can then define a $m \times d$ design matrix D_a whose rows correspond to m observed context vectors, and m-dimensional vector r_a whose elements corre-

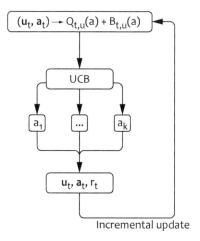

Incremental update

Figure R3.4: Contextual recommendations in a dynamic environment using LinUCB.

spond to m observed rewards $r_{t,a}$ for item a. The model coefficients can then be estimated using ridge regression as

$$\hat{\theta}_a = A_a^{-1} D_a^T r_a \tag{R3.3}$$

where $A_a = D_a^T D_a + I_d$, and I_d is the $d \times d$ identity matrix. As shown in the box below, the upper confidence bound for the item value can be estimated as

$$B_t(a) = (1 + \alpha)\sqrt{x_{t,a}^T A_a^{-1} x_{t,a}} \tag{R3.4}$$

where α is a constant, calculated based on the desired confidence level. The item selection rule in the UCB algorithm then becomes:

$$a_t = \underset{a}{\mathrm{argmax}} \left(x_{t,a}^T \hat{\theta}_a + (1 + \alpha)\sqrt{x_{t,a}^T A_a^{-1} x_{t,a}} \right) \tag{R3.5}$$

This solution is known as LinUCB [Li et al., 2010]. The complete algorithm that includes the incremental model update, regression parameters estimate, and item selection is presented in listing R3.1.

LinUCB is known to be a relatively simple yet efficient solution for dynamic use cases such as newsfeed personalization. The linearity assumption allows for a closed-form expression for the UCB rule, but this does not necessarily limit the expressiveness of the model because the features in $x_{t,a}$ can include nonlinear transformations. We conclude

---

Algorithm R3.1: LinUCB

for $t = 1, 2, \ldots$ **do**
    Compute context vectors $\mathbf{x}_{t,a}$ for all items

    for a in $a_1, \ldots, a_k$ **do**
        if a is new **do**
            $\mathbf{A}_a = \mathbf{I}_d$
            $\mathbf{r}_a = \mathbf{0}$
        end
        $\hat{\theta}_a = \mathbf{A}_a^{-1} \mathbf{r}_a$
    end

    $a_t = \underset{a}{\mathrm{argmax}} \left(\mathbf{x}_{t,a}^T \hat{\theta}_a + \alpha \sqrt{\mathbf{x}_{t,a}^T \mathbf{A}_a^{-1} \mathbf{x}_{t,a}} \right)$

    Recommend item a_t and observe reward r_t

    Update the model:
    $\mathbf{A}_{a_t} = \mathbf{A}_{a_t} + \mathbf{x}_{t,a_t} \mathbf{x}_{t,a_t}^T$
    $\mathbf{r}_{a_t} = \mathbf{r}_{a_t} + r_t \mathbf{x}_{t,a_t}$
end

---

this section with a proof for the upper confidence bound estimate R3.4 [Chu et al., 2011].

Estimating the Upper Confidence Bound in LinUCB

Let us consider the reward estimation error for item a at time t, and decompose it using the notation we introduced earlier, omitting subscripts a and t for the sake of clarity:

$$
\begin{aligned}
\hat{r} - \mathbf{x}^T \theta^* &= \mathbf{x}^T \hat{\theta} - \mathbf{x}^T \theta^* \\
&= \mathbf{x}^T \mathbf{A}^{-1} \mathbf{D}^T \mathbf{r} - \mathbf{x}^T \mathbf{A}^{-1} (\mathbf{D}^T \mathbf{D} + \mathbf{I}_d) \theta^* \\
&= \mathbf{x}^T \mathbf{A}^{-1} \mathbf{D}^T \mathbf{r} - \mathbf{x}^T \mathbf{A}^{-1} (\theta^* + \mathbf{D}^T \mathbf{D} \theta^*) \\
&= \mathbf{x}^T \mathbf{A}^{-1} \mathbf{D}^T (\mathbf{r} - \mathbf{D} \theta^*) - \mathbf{x}^T \mathbf{A}^{-1} \theta^*
\end{aligned} \tag{R3.6}
$$

Assuming that the coefficients are normalized so that $\|\theta^*\| \leqslant 1$, the magnitude of the error is then limited by the following:

$$
\left| \hat{r} - \mathbf{x}^T \theta^* \right| \leqslant \left| \mathbf{x}^T \mathbf{A}^{-1} \mathbf{D}^T (\mathbf{r} - \mathbf{D} \theta^*) \right| + \left\| \mathbf{A}^{-1} \mathbf{x} \right\| \tag{R3.7}
$$

The first term on the right-hand side of the above inequality corresponds to the error variance, and the second term is a nonrandom error bias. We can estimate the first term using Azuma's inequality, which states that for a sequence of finite random variables $y_1, y_2, \ldots$ such that

$$|y_i - y_{i-1}| \leqslant q_i \quad \text{and} \quad \mathbb{E}[y_i \mid y_1, \ldots, y_{i-1}] = y_{i-1} \quad \text{(R3.8)}$$

the probability that the i-th element diverges from the starting point by more than ε is bounded by the following:

$$p(|y_i - y_0| \geqslant \varepsilon) \leqslant 2 \exp\left(\frac{-\varepsilon^2}{2 \sum_{j=1}^{i} q_j^2}\right) \quad \text{(R3.9)}$$

Assuming that the samples in matrix $\mathbf{D}$ are statistically independent, we have $\mathbb{E}[\mathbf{r} - \mathbf{D}\theta^*] = 0$ and thus we can apply Azuma's inequality to the first term of the error, interpreting the vector of m error values as a sequence of random variables. Let us denote

$$s = \sqrt{\mathbf{x}^{\mathsf{T}} \mathbf{A}^{-1} \mathbf{x}} \quad \text{(R3.10)}$$

and then apply Azuma's inequality, setting the threshold to αs where α is a constant:

$$p\left(\left|\mathbf{x}^{\mathsf{T}} \mathbf{A}^{-1} \mathbf{D}^{\mathsf{T}} (\mathbf{r} - \mathbf{D}\theta^*)\right| \geqslant \alpha s\right)$$

$$\leqslant 2 \exp\left(-\frac{2\alpha^2 s^2}{\|\mathbf{D}\mathbf{A}^{-1}\mathbf{x}\|^2}\right) \quad \text{(R3.11)}$$

$$\leqslant 2 \exp\left(-2\alpha^2\right)$$

We do the last transition in the above using the following bound:

$$s^2 = \mathbf{x}^{\mathsf{T}} \mathbf{A}^{-1} \mathbf{x}$$

$$= \mathbf{x}^{\mathsf{T}} \mathbf{A}^{-1} \left(\mathbf{D}^{\mathsf{T}} \mathbf{D} + \mathbf{I}_d\right) \mathbf{A}^{-1} \mathbf{x}$$

$$\geqslant \mathbf{x}^{\mathsf{T}} \mathbf{A}^{-1} \mathbf{D}^{\mathsf{T}} \mathbf{D} \mathbf{A}^{-1} \mathbf{x} \quad \text{(R3.12)}$$

$$= \left\|\mathbf{D}\mathbf{A}^{-1}\mathbf{x}\right\|^2$$

Let us now denote the probability of the first error term exceeding the threshold as δ and solve R3.11 for α:

$$\delta = 2 \exp\left(-2\alpha^2\right) \quad \Rightarrow \quad \alpha = \sqrt{\frac{1}{2} \ln \frac{2}{\delta}} \quad \text{(R3.13)}$$

Consequently, we can guarantee the following bound for the first error term in expression R3.7 with probability at least $1 - \delta$:

$$\left| x^{\mathsf{T}} A^{-1} D^{\mathsf{T}} (r - D\theta^*) \right| \leqslant \alpha s \qquad (R3.14)$$

The second term in expression R3.7 can be bounded as follows:

$$\begin{aligned} \left\| A^{-1} x \right\| &= \sqrt{x^{\mathsf{T}} A^{-1} I_d A^{-1} x} \\ &\leqslant \sqrt{x^{\mathsf{T}} A^{-1} \left(D^{\mathsf{T}} D + I_d \right) A^{-1} x} \qquad (R3.15) \\ &= \sqrt{x^{\mathsf{T}} A^{-1} x} = s \end{aligned}$$

Inserting bounds R3.14 and R3.15 into expression R3.7, we get the overall error bound that holds true with probability $1 - \delta$:

$$\left| \hat{r} - x^{\mathsf{T}} \theta^* \right| \leqslant (1 + \alpha) s \qquad (R3.16)$$

This corresponds to bound R3.4 which we used earlier in the discussion of the LinUCB algorithm.

R3.2.4   *Evaluation and Bootstrapping*

Conceptually, the goal of LinUCB is to provide a plug-and-play personalization component that can learn efficiently from experience without pretraining on historical data or other prior knowledge. In practice, it is often unacceptable to deploy a freshly initialized agent directly to production and allow it to explore the environment doing random actions. We need a framework that allows for full or partial pretraining and preproduction performance evaluation.

One possible solution is to develop a simulator of the environment, so the agent can connect to it, receive simulated contexts, make recommendations, and observe simulated feedback. This can be used either to pretrain the agent and meaningfully initialize its coefficients θ or evaluate the agent's performance to get some guarantees before it is deployed to production. The main problem with this approach is the high level of effort associated with the development and maintenance of the simulator, which can erase the benefits of the reinforcement learning approach. The second challenge is that the simulator is usually implemented using some standard recommendation or propensity scoring model trained in a batch mode. This model can be better or worse than LinUCB, but it is likely to introduce its own bias. In practice, however, an auxiliary model or simulator can be a reasonable solution for boot-strapping a reinforcement learning agent.

The second possible solution is to use the counterfactual evaluation methods discussed in Section 3.5. This approach generally allows for evaluation of the agent's performance using a sample of historical data, but it requires the context information and action distributions to be properly logged. In practice, counterfactual evaluation is often an appropriate tool for validating the algorithm during the development and while doing preproduction quality checks. We implement a basic yet practical solution for counterfactual evaluation of the LinUCB agent in the next section, and continue to discuss this topic in recipe R4 (Next Best Action) in the context of a more generic reinforcement learning solution.

R3.3   PROTOTYPE

 The complete reference implementation for this section is available at https://bit.ly/3x7K0Dk

We develop a prototype of a LinUCB-based recommendation system using a simple simulator of an online store. Consider an online apparel store that sells raincoats and polo shirts, and 70 percent of its customers come from Seattle and the remaining 30 percent from Miami. All customers have to register by entering their age before they can see personalized offers, and their ages are uniformly distributed in the range between 18 and 80 years. Once a customer registers, the recommendation system shows either a raincoat or polo shirt (polo) offer, and the customer may or may not accept it. Each conversion (acceptance of a recommendation) is associated with a reward of one, so the expected reward value is numerically equal to the conversion probability.

We choose to use the following formula in the customer simulator to calculate the offer acceptance probability:

$$p(\text{conversion}) = 0.4 - 0.3 \times L$$
$$+ 0.00125 \times A$$
$$- 0.25 \times R \tag{R3.17}$$
$$+ 0.6 \times L \times R$$

where L is the location variable, equal to 0 for Seattle and 1 for Miami, A is age in years, and R is the recommended item equal to 0 for a raincoat and 1 for a polo. The following table shows conversion probabilities computed using formula R3.17 for several typical profiles suggesting that customers from Seattle are likely to respond to raincoat recommendations, while customers from Miami are more likely to respond to polo offers:

```
+---------------+----------+------------------------+------------------------+
| location (L)  | age (A)  |  recommended item (R)  | conversion probability |
|---------------+----------+------------------------+------------------------|
|  Seattle (0)  |    20    |             Polo (1)   |                 0.175  |
|  Seattle (0)  |    20    |         Raincoat (0)   |                 0.425  |
|  Seattle (0)  |    60    |             Polo (1)   |                 0.225  |
|  Seattle (0)  |    60    |         Raincoat (0)   |                 0.475  |
|    Miami (1)  |    20    |             Polo (1)   |                 0.475  |
|    Miami (1)  |    20    |         Raincoat (0)   |                 0.125  |
|    Miami (1)  |    60    |             Polo (1)   |                 0.525  |
|    Miami (1)  |    60    |         Raincoat (0)   |                 0.175  |
+---------------+----------+------------------------+------------------------+
```

We next implement the basic UCB agent described in Section 3.3.2 and the LinUCB agent specified in algorithm R3.1. For LinUCB, we use a four-dimensional context vector that includes the basic variables L, A and R specified above, and the interaction variable $L \times R$. Note that we have to add the interaction term because the dependency specified by formula R3.17 is nonlinear in the basic variables. Consequently, LinUCB is not able to learn an accurate model of the environment without auxiliary variables in the context. This illustrates the trade-off between the simplicity and expressiveness of LinUCB.

The performance of agents is evaluated using two strategies: direct comparison with the ground truth and counterfactual evaluation. For direct comparison, we connect a freshly initialized agent to the simulator. We then process 200 sequential recommendation requests recording the item recommended by the agent and the optimal item (ground truth) that maximizes the conversion probability R3.17 given the context at each time step. We repeat the process 500 times, estimate the accuracy of recommendations for each time step as the fraction of the agent's recommendations that matched the ground truth, and plot this metric in Figure R3.5 for both UCB and LinUCB.

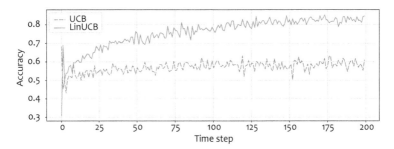

Figure R3.5: Average accuracy of UCB and LinUCB agents.

The UCB agent performs better than a random guess because it learns and exploits the global bias toward raincoats due to the majority of customers coming from Seattle. However, LinUCB achieves much better accuracy by leveraging the contextual information. We can also record the conversion rates for both algorithms, as shown in Figure R3.6. This confirms that LinUCB also outperforms UCB in terms of the primary performance metric.

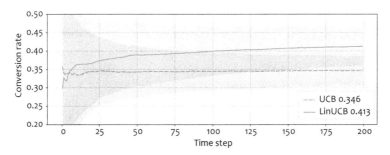

Figure R3.6: Average conversion rates of UCB and LinUCB agents. The width of the shaded areas is two standard deviations.

The last feature we implement in the prototype is the counterfactual evaluation. First, we connect a random or context-free UCB agent to the environment and collect samples that include context vectors, agent's actions, and rewards. The random agent recommends raincoats and polos with equal probabilities. Second, we use the collected samples to evaluate LinUCB performance using the algorithm from Section 3.5, and compare the estimated conversion rate for LinUCB with the simulation result presented in Figure R3.6. The estimates agree with the simulation results for samples collected both under a random and UCB policies, despite the UCB policy not satisfying the assumption about the uniform probability distribution over the items which we made in Section 3.5. (As we discussed earlier, UCB is biased toward the raincoats.)

R3.4   SUMMARY

- Traditional personalization methods such as look-alike modeling and collaborative filtering can be difficult to adapt to non-stationary environments or environments with high turnover of the content and users. The latter problem is known as the cold start problem.

- We can use multi-armed bandit algorithms to dynamically learn average popularities of different items and exploit this knowledge to maximize click-through rates or similar performance metrics. The advantage of this approach over the more basic methods such as A/B testing is a near-optimal balance between the number of impressions spent on environment exploration and the number of impressions exploited to earn rewards.

- The shortcoming of the basic multi-armed bandit algorithms is their inability to use the contextual information such as user and item profile features to personalize the recommendations. For this reason these algorithms are referred to as context-free.

- There are heuristics to combine the context-free bandits with personalization models trained in a batch mode.

- The UCB algorithm can be extended to calculate the action values, as well as its upper confidence bound, as a function of the context vector that can include user, item, and session features.

- The LinUCB algorithm makes an assumption that the action value function is linear in the context variables. This allows us to compute the upper confidence bound in a closed form. The nonlinear dependencies can be incorporated using proper feature design techniques.

- LinUCB is designed to operate in cold-start settings without pretraining, but it is often unacceptable to deploy a freshly initialized agent to production. The agent can be pretrained or evaluated using an environment simulator. The second option is to use counterfactual evaluation methods to ensure some performance guarantees.

NEXT BEST ACTION

Optimizing Marketing Actions Strategically Using Reinforcement Learning

---

In recipes R1 (Propensity Modeling) and R2 (Customer Feature Learning) we discussed how to estimate the propensity of a customer to a certain behavior. The models and techniques developed in these recipes predict the expected outcome, but they do not prescribe how this outcome can be improved using interventions such as advertisements or special offers. In practice, marketers and personalization systems can take specific actions based on the predictive scores using various heuristics, and this approach is generally feasible for environments with a relatively small number of scores and possible actions. However, the process can become unmanageable as the ecosystem of scoring models and marketing treatments evolves and becomes more sophisticated.

In recipe R3 (Dynamic Personalization), we took a step towards a prescriptive solution by developing an agent that not only learns the affinities between users and items, but also takes actions on its own. This solution is useful in environments that require autonomous decision-making, but it does not, of course, take into account all the considerations that a human marketer would when planning a personalization strategy or campaign. In this recipe, we examine the decision-making process more thoroughly and develop a more comprehensive prescriptive framework that helps a marketer or personalization system to take optimal actions.

R4.1   BUSINESS PROBLEM

We consider a marketing communications environment where a company interacts with their customers via one or several digital or physical touchpoints. We generally assume that the company can link individual interactions to customer identities by using loyalty cards, online account logins, and other mechanisms. However, we do not make any specific assumptions about the quality and efficiency of the identity resolution process so some customer profiles may be incomplete or inaccurate. For each interaction, the company chooses an action from the space of actions supported by a given touchpoint or chooses to take no action. Examples of actions include sending an email or mobile push notification, showing a special offer or recommendation on a website, or printing a coupon using an in-store printer. Some of these actions can be initiated by the company and executed at any time, whilst other actions can be taken only in certain situations in response to specific customer actions.

In parallel with the marketing interactions, the customer transacts with the company or interacts with products or services provided by the company. In many cases, these transactions and interactions are tightly coupled and synchronized with marketing actions. For example, a grocery store customer can get a discount coupon at checkout, that is at the end of one transaction, and redeem it by scanning the bar code during the next checkout, that is at the end of another transaction. In other cases, transactions and marketing actions run as two parallel flows. For example, a video game publisher could give away in-game perks to players, but track and optimize monthly-average engagement metrics instead of tracking how players interact with the perks. In either case, the business value of transactions or engagement needs to be quantified and eventually linked to the marketing actions to enable action optimization.

The environment described above is depicted in Figure R4.1. We assume that the interactions are occurring in discrete steps and denote a customer or user who interacts with the company time step t as u_t, marketing action as a_t, and the portion of the business value derived from or attributed to this interaction as r_t. We refer to these discrete portions of the value as *rewards*. We also assume that the actions are determined by a programmatic agent that has access to feature vectors **u** and **a** that represent the user and their action, respectively. These vectors can include manually designed aggregated features, event sequences, or features produced by upstream models such as Customer2Vec. We also assume that the user vector **u** can incorporate contextual information such as channel, touchpoint, or session features.

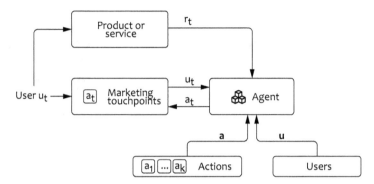

Figure R4.1: The main components of the environment with automated optimization of marketing communications or customer experiences.

The environment presented in Figure R4.1 is structurally similar to the setup we used in recipe R3 (Dynamic Personalization), but the problem we want to solve is substantially different. We elaborate on the main aspects of the problem statement in the next few sections.

R4.1.1   Objectives and Reward Design

A marketer needs to quantify the business value derived from the interactions with a customer in order to apply data-driven methods. The design of the value metrics is generally a complex problem that involves many considerations.

First, marketing activities are typically planned and executed in the context of a specific business objective, and this objective is the primary consideration for designing the reward metric in the framework we introduced above. The most typical top-level business objectives include the following:

ACQUISITION A marketing activity or campaign can be designed to target prospects rather than existing customers to drive new customer acquisitions. In this case, the reward metric can be set based on some activation event such as a registration, first conversion, or response.

GROWTH The company can target existing customers aiming to increase product consumption through up-sell, cross-sell, or subscription upgrades. For such an activity, the reward metric can be set proportional to some measure of product consumption or consumption uplift.

RETENTION The company can target customers who are at risk of churn, aiming to change their decision using retention offers or service improvements. The reward can be designed based on the account cancellation events or product consumption metrics.

REACTIVATION Finally, the company can target customers who have already churned, aiming to re-engage with them. The reward can be set based on the reactivation event such as a purchase.

The business objective alone, however, does not provide all the information needed to design the reward metrics and optimize actions. Two companies that seek the same business objective may approach the problem very differently, depending on their financial targets, product life cycle stage, and other factors. From the reward design perspective, many of these factors can be translated into the following considerations:

ENGAGEMENT VS MONETIZATION The reward metrics are often defined using relatively straightforward engagement metrics such as the number of clicks or online sessions per week. In some cases, this approach accurately captures the true goals of the company. For example, a social network can be focused on maximizing the frequency of user sessions, and optimize user notifications accordingly. At the end of the day, most social networks will be looking to maximize their profits that typically come from advertising, but the connection between user notifications and advertising profits can be so sophisticated that these two problems might need to be solved separately, by different teams, and at different stages of the company's business life cycle.

In other cases, the company might be looking to optimize a monetary metric such as profit, but use an engagement metric as a reasonable proxy. For example, it is common to optimize product recommendations and other elements of the user interface based on engagement metrics such as click-through rates, although the ultimate goal may be to increase conversions or order totals.

Finally, the reward can explicitly incorporate monetary metrics. This is often the case for optimizing marketing actions associated with significant costs such as discounts or retention packages. In such cases, the reward can be defined using customer lifetime value, that is the expenditure over a long period of time, or the lifetime value uplift.

SHORT-TERM VS LONG-TERM Both engagement and monetary metrics can be measured as immediate responses to the actions. For instance, it is common to measure the performance of online services such as product recommendations in terms of click-through rates and order totals. The immediate responses are relatively easy to track and optimize for, but these metrics are generally disconnected from the macro-level objectives of the company. In order to align with the macro-level goals, the reward is often measured over a period of time that can span months or even years. For example, a supermarket chain can design an offer personalization system to target customers who are likely to switch from a 6-pack to a 12-pack of soda for at least 3 months in response to the offer, but not customers who are likely to buy the 12-pack just once.

MYOPIC VS STRATEGIC Regardless of the time frame used for reward calculation (short-term or long-term), we can optimize each action in isolation or jointly optimize a sequence of actions. We refer to the former approach as *myopic optimization*, and to the latter approach as *strategic optimization*. The rationale behind strategic optimization is that the company is often interested in building strong customer relationships through multiple interactions, and thus each action should be considered in a strategic context that includes both previous and subsequent actions. This approach is more complex, but it is also more expressive because an action that is not optimal in terms of the immediate reward can be a gateway to a sequence of interactions with the optimal total gain.

The considerations discussed above, particularly the last one, suggest that we should look for a method that strategically optimizes sequences of actions with the goal of maximizing the return, that is the sum of rewards gained at individual interactions. This concept is illustrated in Figure R4.2. Individual rewards can, in turn, be defined based on engagement or monetary metrics which are, in turn, defined according to the business objective.

The concept of strategic optimization can be illustrated by the following example. In retail, particularly in the grocery and CPG sectors, it is common to do multistage promotion campaigns that are known to trigger more persistent and longer-term changes in customer shopping habits compared to one-off campaigns. A retailer can start by distributing personalized messages to customers announcing a promotional campaign. Each message states that a customer needs to buy at least k units of some product to unlock a discount coupon for the next purchase. This incentivizes customers to purchase the required

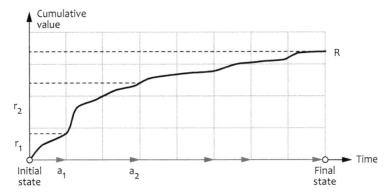

Figure R4.2: Strategic decision-making in marketing communications and customer experience management. R stands for the total return, that
is the sum of rewards r_t.

number of units to deliver incremental profits. The discount coupon
typically also includes some condition such as buy-k-get-one-free to
create an additional stretch during the second purchase. The entire
campaign flow is shown in Figure R4.3 where we emphasized that the
sequence of actions aims to drive the customer along a certain route,
preventing lost sales. All targeting and thresholding parameters in this
setup are interrelated, requiring a strategic approach to optimization.
Strategic optimization is relevant for many other industries that rely on
long-term customer relationships, such as telecom, video games, social
networks, and retail financial services.

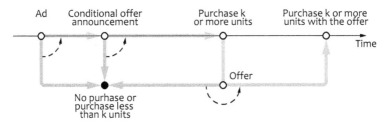

Figure R4.3: An example of a multistage campaign with several related actions.

R4.1.2   Action Design

A programmatic agent that manages marketing communications or
customer experiences generally needs to make several types of deci-

sions. First, the agent needs to assign messages, pieces of content, or offers to customers. In traditional marketing campaigns, the agent starts with a specific message or offer and determines the optimal audience to be targeted with this message. In many online scenarios, the agent starts with a specific user or session and determines the optimal banner, offer, or product recommendation to be presented to the given user in the given context. Both cases require the agent to evaluate possible pairs of user and action to determine the optimal action based on the evaluated score. If the number of actions is relatively small and each action is somewhat unique, an action can be represented by just its identifier a_t, and the agent would prescribe a specific offer or message to the execution system (touchpoint). Alternatively, an action can be a categorical or continuous variable such as the product brand, offer type, or offer amount. In this case, the agent prescribes the criteria that can be converted into the actual offer or message by the execution system.

The action design can incorporate more types of decisions such as which communication channel to use or what discount depth to offer. This can be modeled using either a one-dimensional action space where each element a_t is a cross-product of several different decisions (e.g. the action space includes all possible combinations of offer types and channels) or multidimensional action spaces where $\mathbf{a}_t$ is a vector. This topic is discussed more thoroughly later in this section.

The second category of decisions is related to the timing of communications: the agent generally needs to determine the optimal time for each action. For example, the end of the purchasing cycle of a given customer is often the optimal time to recommend a consumable product. The timing aspect is often incorporated into the above framework by adding a no-action element to the action space so the agent can choose not to intervene at any time step. The user state vector $\mathbf{u}_t$ should also include time-related or time-normalized features such as the time since last visit, to enable the agent to learn and use the optimal action cadence.

R4.1.3 *Modeling and Experimentation*

The problem of strategic action optimization as outlined above can be regarded as a modeling problem where we need to analyze available data, develop a model that captures how various actions influence the behavior of customers in various states, and use this model for decision-making. Although this approach is generally feasible, it requires a comprehensive dataset that covers all relevant actions and customer states. This basically means that one needs to test all actions or, at least, action types thoroughly in production, to collect data needed for modeling. The behavioral patterns captured in this data need to stay actual for the period of time required for operationalization. This approach also assumes that someone needs to design and build a model that is sophisticated enough to capture the complexity of customer behavior.

The alternative approach is to view action optimization as an experimentation problem. In this case, we can start without prior data, run multiple experiments to determine the best-performing actions, and then keep experimenting on an ongoing basis to accommodate any possible changes in the environment. The shortcomings of pure experimentation include the inability to generalize from the limited number of observations (the agent basically needs to test all possible actions for each user), and degradation of the customer experience and business performance due to continuous random testing.

We ideally want to combine the modeling and experimentation paradigms into one solution. This solution should operate in the previously unexplored environment in a similar way to an experimentation agent, but provide powerful generalization capabilities similar to traditional modeling. Achieving this flexibility, as well as performing the strategic decision planning we discussed earlier, are the two main goals of this recipe.

R4.2 SOLUTION OPTIONS

We can start to design a solution for the above problem statement with a review of propensity modeling introduced in recipe R1 (Propensity Modeling). Propensity modeling requires specifying the propensity score, and the design of this score is critically important for building a successful model and getting meaningful business results. In the recipe for propensity modeling referred to here, we used the scores constructed based on simple engagement metrics and events, but the monetary objectives and strategic considerations discussed in the previous sections can also be incorporated into the score design.

R4.2.1 *Advanced Score Design*

As an example, let us consider a company that builds a propensity model for online promotion targeting. For each individual customer, the company can either take no action, which we denote as a_0, or display a promotion, which we denote as a_1. The most basic solution is to use historical data from previous campaigns to identify customers with a high unconditional propensity to convert, that is to learn the mapping between customer feature vector $\mathbf{u}$ and the following score:

$$score(\mathbf{u}) = p(e \mid \mathbf{u}) \qquad (R4.1)$$

where e stands for the conversion event. This is feasible practically but it is a limited solution that can be improved in many ways. One possible improvement is to focus not on the probability of conversion, but on the total profit derived from the converted customer over a certain future time period, so the score is constructed to estimate the following value:

$$score(\mathbf{u}) = p(e \mid \mathbf{u}) \times LTV(\mathbf{u}) - C \qquad (R4.2)$$

where $LTV(\mathbf{u})$ is the expected revenue over a certain time period (e. g. six months) that can be estimated using some other model or rule, and C is the promotion cost.

The second common improvement is to focus on customers with the largest difference between the conversion probability, provided that they are offered with a promotion and the conversion probability without a promotion:

$$score(\mathbf{u}) = p(e \mid \mathbf{u}, a_1) - p(e \mid \mathbf{u}, a_0) \qquad (R4.3)$$

This approach is called *uplift modeling*, and it aims to reduce promotional costs by excluding customers who are likely to convert without a treatment. We can also combine uplift modeling with the LTV estimates to build a model that maximizes the LTV uplift which can be even more useful from the business perspective:

$$score(\mathbf{u}) = (p(e \mid \mathbf{u}, a_1) - p(e \mid \mathbf{u}, a_0)) \times LTV(\mathbf{u}) \qquad (R4.4)$$

The relationship between the above scores and time windows used to compute the corresponding training labels is shown in Figure R4.4. The label design techniques help put the modeling process into the context of long-term business objectives, but they do not provide a generic framework for strategic optimization and prescriptive action recommendations.

R4.2.2   *Conditional Propensities*

We can consider extending the basic propensity scoring framework to support more than two actions and more than one time interval by

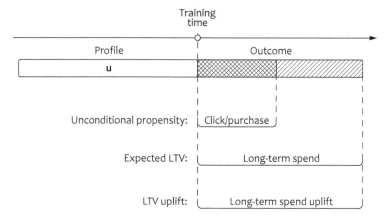

Figure R4.4: Aggregation windows used to compute target labels for myopic, strategic, and monetary objectives.

chaining multiple propensity models together. One way to implement this idea is to build an array of models that score the long-term value of a user conditional on them taking action a_i at step t:

$$M_{ti}: \quad score(\mathbf{u}_t, a_i) = LTV(\mathbf{u}_t \mid a_t = a_i) \tag{R4.5}$$

where M_{ti} is a dedicated model for time step t and action a_i. The overall layout of this solution is shown in Figure R4.5.

The model layer for the first step enables the evaluation of the value scores for each action allowed in this state. This layer can be viewed as a prescriptive model that can not only estimate the propensities or LTVs, but recommend the value-maximizing action. The subsequent actions can then be optimized using the next model layers.

The practical implementation of the above concept can be challenging for two reasons. First, the expression R4.5 assumes that the profile vector $\mathbf{u}_t$ includes the information about the actions related to the given user prior to step t to capture the impact of these actions. Second, it also assumes that the LTV is evaluated over the distribution of all subsequent actions to account for the particular communication strategy that we use. These two assumptions are challenging because a large number of possible action sequences include both the past and future interactions, requiring an impractically large number of samples to fit the LTV model. The problem is further aggravated by the fact that this design does not provide any experimentation capabilities that could assist with collecting the needed samples efficiently.

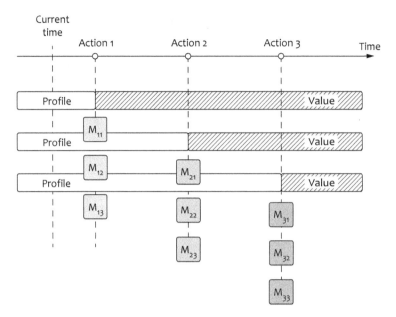

Figure R4.5: Chained propensity models for the next best action optimization.

R4.2.3 *Reinforcement Learning*

We can overcome the limitations of the naïve approach described above by recognizing that the problem can be formulated as a Markov decision process (MDP) introduced in Section 3.4.1. In fact, we already used the MDP terminology quite extensively when defining the business problem and the environment. We stated that the marketing automation agent interacts with a user in discrete steps, taking action a_t bounded to some discrete or continuous space at each step and receiving a reward r_t after each interaction. We also stated that the sum of rewards amounts to the total return that can, in particular, be equal to LTV, and that the agent aims to maximize it.

To complete the MDP formulation, we need to define the state s_t in a way that satisfies the Markov property, incorporating all the information that conditions the transition to the next state and the amount of the reward. The state vector can be constructed based on the user vector and should generally incorporate the history of past actions related to this user either as individual events or as aggregated features. The contextual information can be incorporated into both the state and action vectors. For example, the information about the channel (e.g.

touchpoint or device type) can be incorporated into the state when the agent responds to the user request as is the case in a recommender system, but it needs to be incorporated into the action when the agent chooses the channel as is the case in a notification campaign. Finally, we assume that the user behavior and all environmental factors are incorporated into transition function $p(s_{t+1}, r_t \mid s_t, a_t)$ which is unknown to the agent.

The MDP formulation of the next best action problem is illustrated by an example in Figure R4.6. This is a toy example with five discrete states, each of which has some semantic meaning. For example, all users who made only one purchase are considered to be in the *one timer* state. In practice, states are typically multidimensional real-valued vectors, although it is generally possible to analyze their semantic meaning using clustering or other statistical tools.

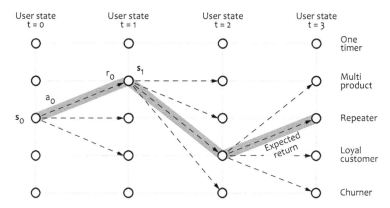

Figure R4.6: The next best action problem represented as a Markov decision process.

The main advantage of the MDP approach is that it unlocks the opportunity to apply a wide range of reinforcement learning algorithms to the next best action problem. The reinforcement learning algorithms, in turn, have several major advantages, such as the ability to produce prescriptive policies that can be integrated with the environment as self-contained decision automation components. It is particularly important that many reinforcement learning frameworks provide environment exploration, policy optimization, and counterfactual evaluation capabilities out of the box, and this functionality can often be used without substantial modifications of the framework itself.

R4.3   PROTOTYPE

    The complete reference implementation for this
section is available at https://bit.ly/3uaM37D

In this section, we develop a simple prototype that demonstrates how the reinforcement learning approach can be applied to the action optimization problem. We use the Fitted Q Iteration (FQI) algorithm from Section 3.4.4.4 to achieve strategic optimization, but skip over the exploration and operationalization aspects, which will be addressed later on in this recipe. Although the FQI approach is relatively simple, it can deliver substantial improvements compared to myopic optimization [Theocharous et al., 2015].

The overall layout of the prototype is shown in R4.7. We start with developing an environment simulator that can generate user trajectories with multistep interactions, learn the action value function from these data using FQI, analyze how the value estimates are distributed across the users, construct the ε-greedy policy, and evaluate it using counterfactual methods.

We develop a simulator of a digital commerce environment where users visit the website, make purchases, and receive special offers. We assume that at any time step a user can either take no action, visit the website without a purchase, or make a purchase. The default probabilities of these events are 0.90, 0.08, and 0.02, respectively, for all users. We also assume that the agent that manages the communications with the user can either make one of three available offers or make no offer at any time step, so we have a discrete action space with four elements. We denote the available offer options as a_1, a_2, and a_3. The agent we use to generate the input data makes exactly three offers to each user during the simulation time frame and draws these offers at random from the set of available options. For example, if, for some user, we make an offer a_1 and then, any time later, offer a_3, this user becomes more likely to make a purchase. That user's event probability distribution changes to 0.70 for no action, 0.08 for a visit, and 0.22 for a purchase. Any other combination of offers does not change the event probabilities.

A data sample generated using the above logic is visualized in Figure R4.8. The upper plate of the figure represents a matrix where each

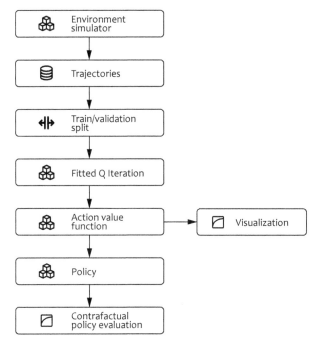

Figure R4.7: The implementation plan for the FQI-based prototype of strategic action optimization.

row corresponds to one user and each column corresponds to a time step. The lower plate shows the agent's actions, that is offers, for each customer. The agent distributes the offers in three waves that can be thought of as promotional campaigns, but the distribution times are randomized and thus differ across all users. We generate training and test sets comprised of 1000 users each.

FQI learns the action value function based on transition samples, so we cut each trajectory into a set of transitions as shown in Figure R4.9. The state vector s_t of a user at the moment of t-th action includes four features: the number of visits since the beginning of the trajectory up until the time of the action, and three time steps that correspond to the first exposures to offers a_1, a_2, and a_3, respectively. If the user has not yet been exposed to some of the offers, the corresponding time step features are set to null. The reward r_t is calculated as the total number of purchases between the time of the offer a_t and the next offer. Transition samples obtained from all users are combined into one unordered set that is used for FQI training.

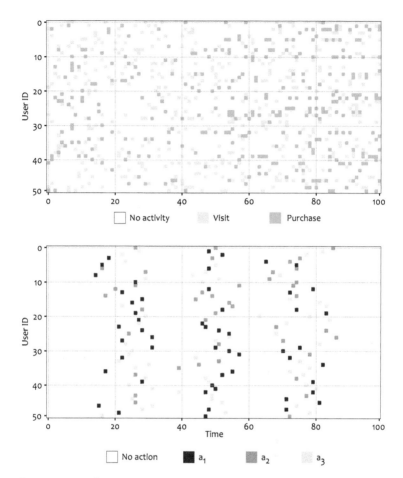

Figure R4.8: A data sample with user trajectories and corresponding actions. The trajectories have a fixed length of 100 time steps, a subset of 50 users is shown.

Once the trajectories are disjoined into individual transitions, we can apply a standard FQI implementation with an arbitrary approximator such as a random forest or neural network. The output of the FQI algorithm is the action value function $Q(\mathbf{s}_t, a_t)$ that estimates the expected sum of rewards after taking action a_t in state $\mathbf{s}_t$. We can analyze and validate the value function by plotting all states in the training or test set and color coding each state sample $\mathbf{s}$ according to the maximum value $\max_a Q(\mathbf{s}_t, a)$ achievable from this state. We have mentioned earlier that the states are four-dimensional vectors, so we project them

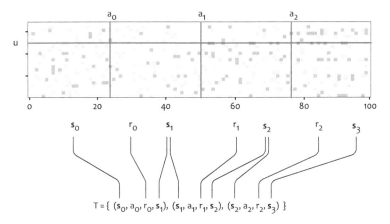

Figure R4.9: Cutting the trajectories into transitions.

onto a two-dimensional plane using t-SNE which also helps to cluster similar states together as apparent from Figure R4.10 where such a projection is presented. The tuples on the left-hand side of the figure are examples of the state vector features that represent the times of the first exposure to each of the three offer options. For example, the first user in the first segment was provided with offer a_1 at time step 28 and offer a_2 at time step 52, but did not get offer a_3 by the time the state was recorded. We can make several observations from this plot that are consistent with the design of the simulator:

- The users who got offer a_3 at early stages of the trajectory (Segment 3) have the lowest value. This agrees with the ground truth because getting a_3 before a_1 precludes the increase in the purchase probability.

- The users who received offer a_1 or a_1 followed by a_2 (Segments 1 and 2) have higher value because the agent is on track to unlock the correct combination of offers.

- The users who received offers a_1 during the first campaign and a_3 during the second campaign have the highest value.

The second way to visualize the value function is to plot the same state points but to color code them according to the prescribed actions, that is $\mathrm{argmax}_a Q(s_t, a)$, instead of the value magnitude. This visualization is presented in Figure R4.11. The model correctly recommends offer a_3 to segments 1 and 2 because it would immediately boost the probability of a purchase. Offer a_1 is recommended for segment 4 as the right first step, and it is also recommended for segments 3 and 5 as

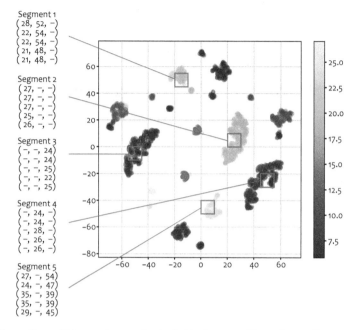

Segment 1
$\begin{pmatrix} 28, & 52, & - \\ 22, & 54, & - \\ 22, & 54, & - \\ 21, & 48, & - \\ 21, & 48, & - \end{pmatrix}$

Segment 2
$\begin{pmatrix} 27, & -, & - \\ 27, & -, & - \\ 27, & -, & - \\ 25, & -, & - \\ 26, & -, & - \end{pmatrix}$

Segment 3
$\begin{pmatrix} -, & -, & 24 \\ -, & -, & 24 \\ -, & -, & 25 \\ -, & -, & 22 \\ -, & -, & 25 \end{pmatrix}$

Segment 4
$\begin{pmatrix} -, & 24, & - \\ -, & 24, & - \\ -, & 28, & - \\ -, & 26, & - \\ -, & 26, & - \end{pmatrix}$

Segment 5
$\begin{pmatrix} 27, & -, & 54 \\ 24, & -, & 47 \\ 35, & -, & 39 \\ 35, & -, & 39 \\ 29, & -, & 45 \end{pmatrix}$

Figure R4.10: Value estimates for individual states. The color coding corresponds to the value magnitude.

a default action, but these segments are already finalized so the action choice is irrelevant.

The action value function produced by FQI can be used to construct an offer optimization policy that can be further integrated with the marketing automation software or online services. In practice, it is generally preferable and often required to evaluate the efficiency of the constructed policy before it is deployed in production. This can be done using the counterfactual evaluation methods discussed in Section 3.5. The training and test dataset were collected under a completely random baseline policy, and, assuming that this fact is known, we can use the importance sampling algorithm to evaluate the new policy. Let us illustrate this by defining the new policy using the ε-greedy approach as

$$\pi(a \mid s) = \begin{cases} 1 - \varepsilon, & \text{if } a = \underset{a}{\text{argmax }} Q(s, a) \\ \varepsilon/(k-1), & \text{otherwise} \end{cases} \tag{R4.6}$$

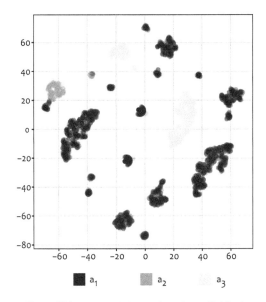

Figure R4.11: Value-maximizing actions for individual states.

where k is the cardinality of the action space. Our baseline policy is known to be

$$\beta(a \mid \mathbf{s}) = 1/k \tag{R4.7}$$

so we can estimate the return of a new policy based on a trajectory generated under the baseline policy as:

$$\hat{R}_\pi = R_\beta \prod_t \frac{\pi(a_t \mid \mathbf{s}_t)}{\beta(a_t \mid \mathbf{s}_t)} \tag{R4.8}$$

where $\mathbf{s}_t$ and a_t are the states and actions of the trajectory and R_β is the observed return of the trajectory. Averaging this estimate over a set of trajectories, we can evaluate the overall expected performance of a policy. This approach can be used, for instance, to answer the question of how the return depends on the policy parameter ε. The evaluation results for different values of ε are presented in Figure R4.12, and this plot agrees with the intuition that the policy performance degrades as the degree of experimentation increases.

Importance sampling and other counterfactual evaluation methods are the main tool for doing safety checks before a new policy is deployed in production. We discuss the role of policy evaluation in the context of an end-to-end reinforcement learning solution later in this recipe.

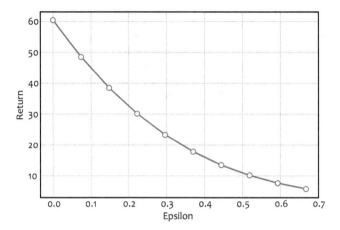

Figure R4.12: Counterfactual policy evaluation using importance sampling for different values of ϵ in the range from 0 to 2/3.

R4.4   CASE STUDY

We have seen in the previous section that FQI solves some parts of the next best action problem; namely, strategic optimization and prescriptive action recommendations. The prototype that we have developed, however, demonstrates only a subset of capabilities that can be enabled by the reinforcement learning approach. In this section, we walk through a real-world case study on the development of a reinforcement learning solution focusing on the system engineering and productization aspects. The approach discussed below is conceptually similar to the user experience optimization solution developed by Facebook for its social network platform [Gauci et al., 2019] and the optimization solution developed by Starbucks for its loyalty mobile app [Sokolowsky, 2019].

R4.4.1   *Business Problem*

We now consider the case of a company that develops video games and mobile applications. The company aims to improve user engagement and in-game monetization by means of personalized offers that are shown in the feeds of the mobile apps or in-game shops. Examples of such offers include game upgrades, virtual currency packs, and special deals in loyalty mobile apps.

From the business perspective, the objectives of the company closely match the framework we developed in the previous sections. Most applications created by the company assume long-term and intense interactions with each user, so the strategic optimization of the user engagement and experience is one of the main priorities. This goal naturally translates into the strategic optimization of promotion sequences using the Markov decision process formulation. The collections of offers are also frequently updated, making the cold start problem and dynamic experimentation relevant as well.

R4.4.2 *Solution Architecture*

From the engineering standpoint, the company seeks to automate the offer optimization process and to reduce the development and maintenance effort as much as possible. In general, the reinforcement learning approach has a very high potential for automation because the agent can learn from interactions with the environment requiring no pretraining. Moreover, we do not necessarily need to design a custom agent specifically for the offer personalization problem. It is possible to use an off-the-shelf implementation of some standard reinforcement learning algorithm. In light of this, it can be appealing to integrate the agent directly into the production environment, so it can execute the offer personalization decisions in real time and learn instantly from the feedback. Unfortunately it is challenging to implement and operate such a solution in practice because it provides no way to modify, retrain, or evaluate the agent separately from the production environment.

We can address the above problem by decoupling the agent from the application's backend services or video game servers as shown in Figure R4.13. In this architecture, the transactional applications are required to log the user interaction events in a certain format that includes the customer journey ID, sequence number of the event within this journey, state vector associated with the event, action taken by the agent, probabilities of other possible actions, and the reward. These logs are then used to iteratively train the agent:

- We start by collecting logs under the initial policy which can be random or rule-based.
- The logged states, actions, and rewards are used to train an arbitrary off-policy reinforcement learning algorithm: the log is replayed event by event simulating the actual interaction with the environment.

- The logged action probabilities are used for the counterfactual evaluation of the policy produced using the training process.

- If the evaluation results meet the quality and safety criteria, the new version of the policy is deployed to production, and the training cycle repeats.

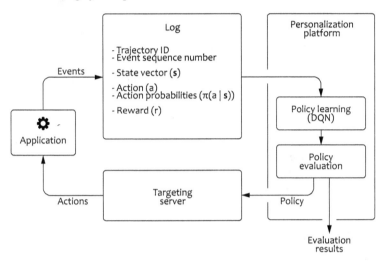

Figure R4.13: A high-level architecture of a reinforcement learning-based personalization platform and its integrations.

The design depicted in Figure R4.13 was implemented as a generic platform using off-the-shelf components. The platform supports several reinforcement learning algorithms that are borrowed from open-source libraries without modifications, and it is easy to switch between the algorithms. The platform also supports several methods for counterfactual evaluation, and provides generic interfaces for the analysis of the evaluation results. Finally, the targeting server depicted in Figure R4.13 is used as a generic deployment container for the trained policies that are exported from the platform as binary artifacts. The server processes offer personalization requests from the transactional applications, block certain policy decisions based on the business rules, and manage the A/B testing logic.

The solution described above takes a fundamentally different perspective on reinforcement learning compared to the basic FQI-based prototype. It uses reinforcement learning not just as an algorithm for the value function estimation, but as an end-to-end optimization machine that packages together exploration, learning, and evaluation capabilities. This platform is also generic, and, in principle, can be applied to arbitrary optimization problems in any domain, not only to personalization. Such versatility is one of the main advantages of reinforcement learning compared to the traditional data science methods such as propensity modeling.

R4.4.3 *Algorithms*

In principle, the platform can use any off-policy reinforcement learning algorithm. In practice, DQN proved itself to be a reasonable choice from the standpoints of performance and stability. One of the disadvantages of the DQN-based approach is that it requires the action space to be discrete and relatively small, so that all actions can be explicitly enumerated. In personalization applications, this assumption can sometimes be limiting because the number of available promotions or promotion-placement combinations can be relatively high. This problem can be alleviated by using actor-critic algorithms that support continuous action spaces, as we discussed in Section 3.4.6.1.

R4.4.4 *Design of Actions, States, and Rewards*

The reinforcement learning platform generally provides a high level of automation, but it still requires designing the action, states, and rewards as a part of the integration effort. In this section, we take a closer look at these details.

In the video games developed by the company, users can be presented with both individual offers and sets of offers to choose from, and the reinforcement learning platform supports both cases. For the sake of illustration, we focus on the case when the user is presented with one offer at a time. An example timeline that illustrates this scenario is shown in Figure R4.14. The agent makes the offer decisions sequentially, so that the user is first offered option a_1 and then the agent waits until the offer is either accepted (event a_1^c) or expires. The minimum time between the offers is limited to n_r days, and the agent switches to the inactive mode if the offer is accepted sooner. Once the offer is accepted or expires, the agent switches to the active mode, generates the next offer a_2, and the cycle repeats.

The action design can also be impacted by the cost of actions for the company. In this particular case, the offers such as in-game upgrades and virtual currency packs have the monetary cost of zero to the video game publisher, and this can result in learning a policy that abuses the incentives. The platform described above mitigates this issue by in-

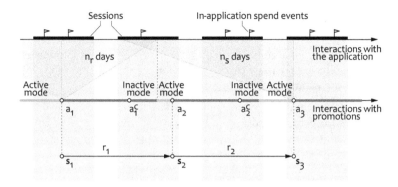

Figure R4.14: The design of the states (**s**), actions (**a**), and rewards (**r**).

cluding a no-action element into the action set, monitoring the uplift delivered by offers compared to the no-offer baseline, and imposing penalties that prevent the agent from learning an abusive policy. The uplift can be managed more directly for offers that are associated with non-zero monetary costs by factoring these costs into the reward design.

The platform supports several reward calculation methods including in-app revenue, virtual currency spend, and binary rewards (reward of one if the offer is accepted and zero otherwise). In all these cases, the reward is calculated based on time windows of n_r days after the action, and, consequently, the reward values are obtained with a delay of n_r days. To create a complete log that can be consumed by the reinforcement learning platform, the log records that are produced at the time of actions are stored in a buffer and later joined with the corresponding rewards.

The state features include a number of engagement metrics such as the duration of sessions, calendar and user demographic features. The engagement features are calculated over the fixed time window of n_s days before the action, as shown in Figure R4.14.

R4.5   SUMMARY

- Next best action solutions aim to prescribe marketing actions that deliver long-term customer engagement improvements.

- The main design considerations for next best action systems include business objectives such as customer acquisition or retention, engagement and monetization metrics, and the balance between myopic and strategic objectives.

- The additional considerations for the next best action solution design include dynamic experimentation capabilities and reduction of the engineering and operationalization effort.

- Strategic and prescriptive optimization can be partly achieved using propensity modeling. A more generic solution is provided by reinforcement learning where customer journeys are represented as Markov decision processes.

- The basic propensity modeling can be extended into a strategic optimization solution using Fitted Q Iteration.

- The reinforcement learning and counterfactual evaluation algorithms can be packaged into a generic platform that can be used for a wide range of enterprise applications including marketing and personalization. This approach helps to create highly automated solutions that provide strategic optimization, dynamic experimentation, and that reduce the engineering effort.

Part III

CONTENT INTELLIGENCE

The methods developed in the previous part aim to improve customer experience and the efficiency of marketing communications. This is achieved by extracting useful traits from the customer behavior data, evaluating the impact of possible actions such as promotions and advertisements based on these traits, and executing or recommending the actions that appear to be optimal. At the same time, we considered the actions, content assets, and other elements of the customer experience mainly as black boxes, so that each action or asset was represented by a discrete token or vector of arbitrary features. In many marketing use cases, however, actions and content assets are complex entities represented as collections of attributes, texts, or images. This part of the book focuses on methods that leverage this information to create advanced customer-facing functionality and to combine content data with behavioral data to improve the efficiency of customer analytics and personalization.

VISUAL SEARCH

Searching for Similar Items Using Custom-built Semantic Spaces

---

Many retailers and consumer goods manufacturers have large product catalogs that include hundreds of thousands or even millions of items. The business performance of their digital commerce systems depends directly on how efficiently customers can navigate through such catalogs and search for relevant items, so the quality of product discovery services is critically important.

The problem of product discovery can be approached from several different angles. One large group of methods is associated with *text retrieval* where a customer enters a query string, and products are matched and ranked based on the similarity between the query and the product's description and attributes. This approach works well for many applications, but it also has several major shortcomings. First, it can be difficult or impossible to create meaningful and unambiguous attributes and descriptions for certain categories of products. For example, art posters can have attributes such as style and dominating color, but this basic categorization is not sufficient for searching posters in large catalogs. Attempts to create more sophisticated categorizations are likely to fail because each person describes style and aesthetics in a different way. Second, some applications require searching for specific items that cannot be described unambiguously using attributes or words. For example, a customer might be looking to replace a broken porcelain saucer from an old dinnerware set, and the search criteria is a specific pattern that cannot be precisely specified in words or attributes. Third, some products have a complex system of attributes that requires the customer to know special terminology or perform precise measurements. For example, searching for a particular screw requires specifying multiple attributes such as head type, tip type, length, and pitch which can be a challenging problem for the average consumer. Finally, the quality of keyword search is determined by the quality of product descriptions and attributes, and setting these attributes accurately is often a challenging problem in itself.

The above challenges cannot be resolved within a framework that uses only product descriptions and attributes, and we need to incorporate additional sources of information about both products and the customer's search intention to address them. It is quite clear that product images are the most appropriate source of such information for all of the above use cases. In this recipe, we discuss how to build product discovery services that leverage product images to work around the limitations of the text retrieval approaches. It is also worth noting that although we focus on the product discovery use cases for the sake of specificity, the methods we develop are very generic and can be used in a wide range of applications that require assessing image similarity. For example, the same approaches are used in security systems for facial identification that requires matching a given image to one in an existing database of faces.

R5.1 BUSINESS PROBLEM

We focus on the problem of building a service for searching items in a catalog of images based on a query image (reference image) provided by a user. At a conceptual level, we want this service to evaluate some similarity measure between the query image and each of the catalog images, to rank catalog images based on this measure, and return the most similar items to the user. In more technical terms, this means that we need to construct a semantic space where the Euclidean distance between two points is a proper measure of similarity, map both the catalog and query images to points (embeddings) in this space, and then search for nearest neighbors of the query image, as illustrated in Figure R5.1. A list of these nearest neighbors sorted by the distance to the query is the search result.

In the above framework, the central problem is how to define the image similarity measure or, alternatively, construct the embedding space. The design of the similarity measure is heavily influenced by the business use case which can be illustrated by the following examples:

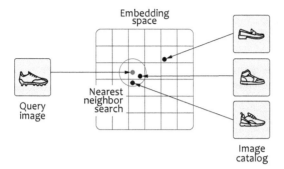

Figure R5.1: The concept of visual search.

- An online retailer that sells art prints and posters might use artistic style as a measure of similarity or, at least, one of the major signals for constructing the similarity function. For example, we can expect that the search results for a pencil drawing query image are mainly pencil drawings as well.

- An online retailer that sells shoes might want to use domain-specific attributes such as the heel height as dimensions of the semantic space. This retailer might also provide different search options such as search by color or heel height, and each of these options requires its own similarity function.

- A retailer that sells fasteners might want to identify one specific item that exactly matches the reference image provided by the customer. The exact match is defined based on domain-specific attributes such as the head type of a screw.

The second important group of problems that need to be addressed in many applications of visual search is related to the quality and complex structure of the images. For example, a customer can take a picture of a person wearing a shirt they like and use this picture as a query image in a visual search service of an online apparel store. This image is likely to include not only the shirt, but also a background, other garments the person wears, and other objects. In order to search for the shirt efficiently, it needs to be located in the image, separated from other objects, and mapped to an embedding. We refer to this task as *localization*.

In the next sections, we develop a toolkit for implementing several different similarity measures and we also discuss localization methods. This toolkit, however, demonstrates only a few major capabilities that can be implemented in a visual search service, and many other techniques can be used to improve the quality of the search results' ranking, as well as the ability to process images with complex structures.

R5.2   SOLUTION OPTIONS

The architecture of a visual search engine usually includes two major parts. The first part is an indexer that preprocesses catalog images, computes image embeddings, and creates an embedding index that can be used to search efficiently to find nearest neighbors for a given point in the embedding space in near real time. The second part is a query engine that preprocesses the query image, computes its embedding vector, and then looks up its nearest neighbors in the index. Since both the catalog and the query images need to be mapped to the same embedding space, the indexing and query processing pipelines generally use the same preprocessing and embedding models, although these pipelines are not necessarily identical.

We start by examining several design options for the query processing pipeline which are depicted in Figure R5.2. The first stage of the pipeline is the image preprocessing. In some applications such as an art poster search, the user explicitly searches for images similar to the query image, not for physical objects present in the image, so the preprocessing can be limited to a few basic operations such as brightness normalization. In many applications, however, the user searches for objects similar to the object depicted in the query image, and this object needs to be identified and isolated from the background. This problem can be approached in several different ways depending on the assumptions we can make about the number and semantic structure of objects in the image, and we discuss these options in Section R5.6.

Once the query image has been preprocessed, it needs to be mapped to a representation in a semantic space that can further be used for the nearest neighbors search. As we discussed in the previous section, the semantic space needs to be custom designed for every specific application, but there are several basic methods that we can use as starting points:

- One option is to use standard image classification models trained on generic image classification datasets. Such pretrained models are readily available in public repositories, and newly developed state-of-the-art solutions are constantly added. Although these models are usually pretrained on datasets with fairly generic classes such as "snail" and "ice cream", the image embeddings computed by certain layers of such models efficiently capture the

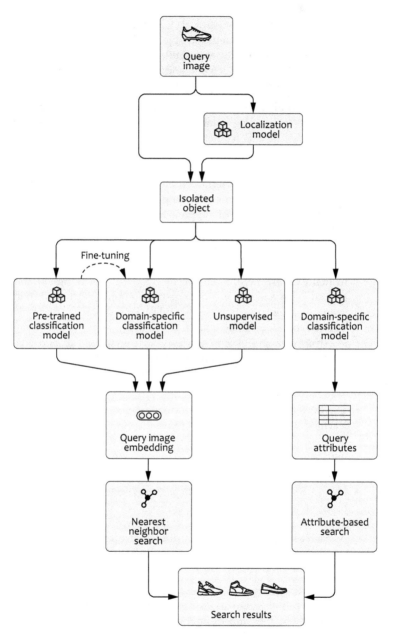

Figure R5.2: Several design options for the query processing pipeline.

information about the artistic style of the image and generic semantic features of the depicted objects. This phenomenon can be leveraged to compute useful similarity measures in the spaces constructed based on such embeddings. We discuss this strategy and build a corresponding prototype in Section R5.3.

- The second alternative is to train a domain-specific image classification model using a dataset with domain-specific labels. For example, an apparel retailer can create a dataset with labels such as "long sleeve dress" and "high heel sandals" and use it to train a custom classification model. This model can then be used in exactly the same way as pretrained models. We can tap into certain layers to extract image embeddings and use them to compute similarity measures. This approach, however, allows for aligning the embedding space with the dimensions prescribed by the domain-specific labels, and thus produces more relevant similarity measures.

  In many cases, the domain-specific model is not designed and trained from scratch, but obtained by retraining all or certain layers of a generic pretrained model. This process, commonly referred to as *fine-tuning*, reuses the ability of a pretrained model to extract meaningful semantic features from the image, and thus dramatically reduces the number of domain-specific samples that need to be created for training. We build a prototype for this approach in Section R5.4.

- The third option is to produce embeddings using representation learning models as discussed in Section 2.6. This approach can be used when the embeddings do not need to be discriminative with regard to specific classes of objects. We create a prototype of such a solution in Section R5.5.

- Finally, one or several domain-specific classification models can be used to map the query image to a set of attributes. In the above example of the apparel retailer, classification models can be used to explicitly estimate attributes such as product category, sleeve length, and heel height. These attributes can then be used to filter the product catalog or find the exact match.

The high-level design for these three options is shown in Figure R5.2. The design of an indexing pipeline generally matches the query pipeline. In the embedding-based approaches, the same pretrained or domain-specific models are used to compute embeddings for all images in the catalog, although certain preprocessing steps such as object localization might be excluded or configured differently. In the attribute-based approach, the attributes usually come directly from the catalog data, although computer vision models are sometimes used to enrich or validate the attributes [Pakhomova, 2017].

In the next sections, we discuss how to implement components for embedding computation and object localization, and create several prototypes that can be used jointly or separately to build a visual search service.

R5.3   SEARCH BY IMAGE STYLE

The first scenario we consider is searching by image style. We assume a catalog of art posters, pencil drawings, paintings, or other items of that kind, and users who search for items that are similar to the reference image in terms of artistic style. For example, we expect the service to return mostly cubist paintings for a query image in cubist style, and distinguish between the styles shown in Figure R5.3.

Cubist
painting

Impressionist
painting

Botanical
illustration

Figure R5.3: Examples of artistic styles we want the visual search service to be able to distinguish.

On the one hand, this is a challenging scenario because we need to define a measure of similarity for artistic styles. This problem obviously does not have a single unambiguous solution, but we can attempt to develop an approximation that is of practical use. On the other hand, we can assume that both catalog and query images contain only the artwork, so that no complex preprocessing and object localization is required.

R5.3.1 *Style Embeddings*

The artistic style can, to a certain extent, be characterized in terms of low-level image features such as the sharpness of edges and outlines, length of brushstrokes, and color intensity. We can attempt to build a model that extracts such style-related features from an image producing the corresponding embedding vector, and then measure the style similarity between two images by computing the distance between these embeddings.

In Section 2.5, we discussed that convolutional networks is a default choice for building image classification models, and a typical network architecture represents a deep stack of convolutional and pooling layers. We also discussed that most architectures start with an input of a relatively large dimensionality in terms of height and width, but only three channels (red, green, and blue). The dimensionality is then gradually decreased using pooling and the number of channels is simultaneously increased using convolution layers with multiple filters. Consequently, the input pixels are first mapped to a stack of smaller matrices, commonly referred to as *feature maps*, where each element is a convolution of multiple pixels, and these maps therefore capture the microstructure of the image. These feature maps are further transformed into progressively smaller maps by the downstream layers, and their elements thus capture the presence of more complex and spatially larger patterns in the image. We can expect that feature maps at certain stages of this process will capture the level of details that corresponds to the human perception of the artistic style, and we can then attempt to create style embeddings by fetching and post-processing certain feature maps from a regular image classification model.

The strategy outlined above can be directly implemented using off-the-shelf image classification models. For purposes of illustration, let us create a specific design based on the VGG19 model.

> **VGG Models**
>
> The VGG architecture was developed in 2014 by the Visual Geometry Group (VGG) at Oxford University [Simonyan and Zisserman, 2014]. The original paper describes several model configurations with different numbers of layers. The smallest configuration, known as VGG11, has 11 layers and 133 million parameters in total, and the largest configuration, known as VGG19, has 19 layers and 144 million parameters. These con-

figurations achieve different trade-offs between the accuracy and computational complexity.

The architecture of the VGG19 model is presented in Figure R5.4. The entire model is created using only four building blocks: convolution layers with 3×3 filters, max pooling layers with pool size 2×2, dense layers, and a softmax mapper. The input of the model is a 224×224 image with three channels. This input is processed by two convolution layers with 64 filters which produce 64 feature maps of size 224×224. These maps are then reduced using the pooling layer producing a 112×112 output, and this output is processed by two convolution layers with 128 filters. The output is then processed by three more blocks that consist of pooling and convolution layers which finally produce a stack of 512 small 7×7 feature maps, as shown in Figure R5.4. This stack is processed by two dense layers, each of which produces 4096-dimensional vectors, and then by the third dense layer that produces a 1000-dimensional vector. The final output is obtained by normalizing this vector into a vector of class probabilities using softmax. This reference design assumes that the model is trained on a dataset with 1000 classes, but an arbitrary number of classes can be supported by changing the dimensionality of the top dense layers.

VGG was the state-of-the-art architecture for image classification when it was introduced, but it was quickly surpassed by more advanced models that achieve both better accuracy and lower computational complexity with a smaller number of parameters. We choose to use the VGG model for the style embedding problem because it has relatively simple architecture which allows it to extract style-related embeddings in a relatively straightforward way. Most newer models that outperform VGG have more sophisticated architectures which makes this task more complex.

Assuming that we have a VGG19 model that was pretrained on an arbitrary, but sufficiently large and comprehensive image classification dataset, we can use it to extract style-related features for any given image and then construct a style embedding. A specific algorithm could be as follows:

1. The first step is to perform model inference for a given image and to capture the outputs (feature maps) produced by certain

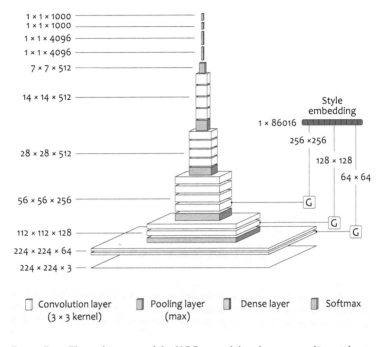

Figure R5.4: The architecture of the VGG19 model and corresponding style embeddings. Block G denotes the computation of the Gram matrix.

layers of the network. It is typical to use the first convolution layers from the third to the fifth lowest stages of the network, as shown on the right-hand side of Figure R5.4. We can control how the style is defined by changing the composition of layers. As discussed previously, the lower layers capture mainly small details, whereas the upper layers capture larger patterns, so we can, for instance, put more emphasis on brushstrokes by upweighting the lower layers.

2. The feature maps computed in the previous step can be postprocessed to amplify the style-related signals. One possible way to achieve this is to compute the Gram matrices of the extracted feature maps [Gatys et al., 2016]. In linear algebra, the Gram matrix of a set of vectors $x_1, \ldots, x_n$ is defined as a matrix of pairwise dot products whose entries are given by

$$g_{ij} = x_i \cdot x_j \qquad 1 \leqslant i, j \leqslant n \tag{R5.1}$$

The concept of the Gram matrix can be useful for extracting style-related signals because correlation patterns between the feature maps are known to be consistent with the visual styles. However, we need to extend the basic definition of the Gram matrix to support multiple channels. Assuming that the output x of a convolution layer is a batch of c feature maps (channels) each of which is a $n \times m$ matrix, we can define its Gram matrix as follows:

$$g_{ij} = \frac{1}{n \cdot m} \sum_{p,q} x_{pqi} \cdot x_{pqj} \qquad (R5.2)$$

indexes $1 \leqslant i,\ j \leqslant c$ iterate over channels, and indexes $1 \leqslant p \leqslant n$ and $1 \leqslant q \leqslant m$ iterate over the feature map height and width, respectively. In other words, the Gram matrix is a $c \times c$ matrix whose elements are the correlations between the feature maps (channels).

3. The final style embedding is obtained by reshaping all Gram matrices computed in the previous step into flat vectors and concatenating them as shown in Figure R5.4. Assuming that we selected three outputs with 64, 128, and 256 channels, respectively, the style vector will have 86016 dimensions ($64 \times 64 + 128 \times 128 + 256 \times 256$).

Once the embeddings are computed, the style-based similarity between two images can then be evaluated as the cosine distance between their embedding vectors. We prototype this design in the next section.

R5.3.2   *Prototype*

 The complete reference implementation for this section is available at https://bit.ly/3rM01vn

We consider a toy example of an art seller who has a collection of 32 cubist and impressionist paintings and wants to build a visual search service that enables customers to search for artworks based on the reference image. A subset of the collection is presented in Figure R5.5. We assume that this collection is unlabeled, so that the images are not explicitly tagged as "cubist" or "impressionist".

Our first step is to download the VGG19 model pretrained on the ImageNet dataset from a public repository. Although this model is trained

Figure R5.5: Examples of images used for style search.

on a dataset that has nothing to do with artworks, it produces meaning-ful feature maps for a wide range of imagery including photographs, drawings, and paintings. A pretrained model is an excellent solution for our scenario because it helps us to avoid building a large custom dataset needed for training a high-capacity model such as VGG19.

ImageNet and ILSVRC Datasets

ImageNet is a large public image database created primarily for computer vision and deep learning research [Deng et al., 2009]. It includes more than 14 million hand-annotated images categorized into more than 22,000 classes.

A subset of the ImageNet database with about 1.2 million images and 1,000 classes that was created for the annual ImageNet Large Scale Visual Recognition Challenge (ILSVRC) became a standard benchmark for image classification problems. The reference design of the VGG19 model presented in the previous section has a top layer with 1,000 classes because it is supposed to be trained and evaluated on the ILSVRC dataset.

The second step is to compute the style embeddings according to the algorithm described in the previous section. We perform the inference for all images in the collection, capture the outputs of the intermediate layers, compute the corresponding Gram matrices, and concatenate them into the style embedding vectors. We can analyze the embedding space by projecting these vectors to a two-dimensional plane using t-SNE, as shown in Figure R5.6. This visualization makes it apparent that images of different styles, namely cubist and impressionist, become linearly separable in the embedding space, which indicates that the embeddings we have constructed properly capture the human perception of the artistic style.

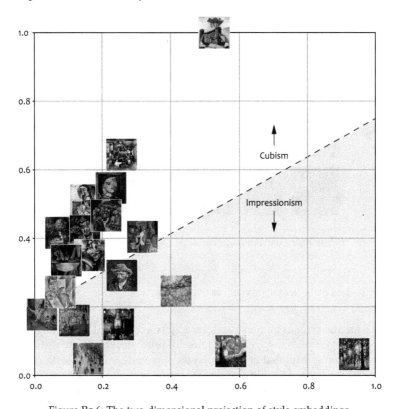

Figure R5.6: The two-dimensional projection of style embeddings.

The last step is to implement the actual image search in the space of style embeddings. In this small example, we can simply iterate over all artworks in the collection, compute cosine distances between an artwork's embedding and query image embedding, and return its nearest neighbors. Examples of top search results for two query images are presented in Figure R5.7. We can see that the service performs well, returning the artworks that match the style of the query. In real-world environments, catalogs can include hundreds of thousands of images, and we cannot usually compute cosine distances to all catalog images in real time. This challenge is usually solved by building special indexes that allow rapid searches for nearest neighbors of a given embedding.

Figure R5.7: Searching for nearest neighbors in the style space.

R5.4   SEARCH IN A CUSTOM SEMANTIC SPACE

The artistic style of an image can usually be recognized based on low-level image features such as sharpness of brushstrokes. These features are normally amplified at certain layers of generic image classification models, and we can build a reasonably good style search service using only a pretrained model. In many visual search applications, however, we need to use a customized similarity measure that is aligned with business goals and domain-specific requirements. We cannot usually specify this measure explicitly as a formula or rule, but we can provide examples of images that we consider to be similar or dissimilar. Such a dataset can then be used to learn a mapping to an embedding space where the images that are considered to be similar are clustered together, and images considered dissimilar are separated. In this section, we discuss how to implement this idea.

R5.4.1   *Custom Images Embeddings and Attributes*

A model trained on some generic dataset such as ImageNet learns a mapping to an embedding space where the classes of this dataset are linearly separable and then normalizes them into class probabilities using softmax. Consequently, the output of the top layer of the network is a good embedding for evaluating the similarity in terms of the classes of the training dataset. For instance, the top layer of a VGG network that is trained on the ImageNet dataset produces embeddings where ImageNext classes such as "banana" and "screw" are well separated, so that the distance between two images of a banana tends to be small, and the distance between the images of a banana and a screw tends to be large. This is generally aligned with what one would expect from a visual search service, but it is usually not sufficient for real-world applications. For example, a retailer that sells screws might need an embedding space where different types of screws are well separated.

In principle, we can solve the above problem by creating a large custom dataset of screw images labeled with head type, tip type, and other domain-specific attributes, and training a standard image classification model on this dataset from scratch. This approach, however, is impractical because millions of instances might be required for training a large network such as VGG or its successors. A more practical solution is to use a model pretrained on a generic dataset such as ImageNet to produce an intermediate embedding space (feature maps), and then redesign and retrain its top layers to map the intermediate space to the final domain-specific space. As we discussed in Chapter 2, this concept of adapting a model trained on one domain to a different domain is referred to as *transfer learning*.

The details of the transfer learning process are shown in Figure R5.8. We start with a pretrained model that can be used to produce image embeddings by capturing the outputs of the top layer of the network, as shown on the left-hand side of the figure. In the case where the model is pretrained on ImageNet, the embedding vector has 1,000 dimensions because there are 1,000 classes in ImageNet. The second step is to create a custom dataset of images with domain-specific labels, and to replace the pretrained top layers with a custom layer or stack of layers that produce embeddings and final outputs of the required dimensionality. For example, we might create a dataset with 10 different screw-head types and replace the top layer with a dense layer that produces a 10-dimensional output vector. This vector can then be used as an embedding and input to the softmax layer that produces the class labels. If we want the dimensionality of the embedding to be different from the number of classes, we can use a stack of two dense layers. For example, the first layer can produce a 100-dimensional vector that can be used as an embedding, and the second layer can map it to a vector with 10 dimensions to match the number of classes.

Once the structural adjustments of the network are made, we retrain it to align the output space with the semantic dimensions specified in our custom dataset. The retraining can be performed using a regular gradient descent algorithm that optimizes the entire network end to end, just like for training from scratch. The various layers of the network can be treated in one of three different ways:

TRAIN The parameters of the newly added or redesigned layers of the network are just randomly initialized, so these layers need to be trained from scratch. In particular, this applies to custom embedding and classification layers that replace the top layers of the pretrained network.

FREEZE The bottom layers of the pretrained network extract relatively low-level image features such as edges. The feature maps produced by these layers are suitable for most domains [Yosinski et al., 2014]. It is common to freeze the parameters of these layers, so that they are not modified during the training process.

FINE-TUNE Finally, the parameters of the intermediate layers can be initialized using the values from the pretrained model, but they are updated by the gradient descent procedure during the retraining. This helps to produce feature maps aligned with the domain-specific guidelines before these maps are fed into the classifier at the top of the network. This process of adjusting the pretrained parameters is known as *fine-tuning*.

In practice, we can use different combinations of the above three techniques depending on the domain, data availability, and computational capacity. We can consider our design option in terms of the following trade-offs:

- One extreme is to use the pretrained model as it is, to produce image embeddings. This could be a reasonable solution when our target domain is similar to the domain the model was pretrained on. It may also be the only choice when no custom datasets are available.

- The above baseline can be improved by creating and training a custom classifier on top of the network, but freezing all other layers. The top classifier often has a few thousand parameters, and it can thus be trained using far less data and computational resources than are needed to train the complete network with

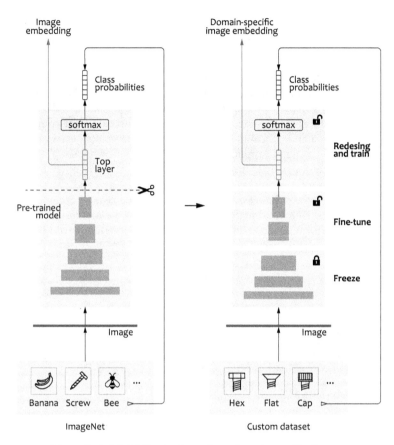

Figure R5.8: Model fine-tuning using a domain-specific dataset.

millions of parameters. However, this approach might not work well for target domains that are very different from the original domain of the pretrained model.

- The ability to accommodate for highly specific target domains can be improved by unfreezing and fine-tuning several pretrained layers under the top classifier. The more layers we fine-tune, the better we can accommodate to the new domain, but the training dataset also needs to be larger. The fine-tuning process, however, is sample-efficient because we start with pretrained parameters rather than randomly initialized values.

- Finally, the other extreme is to fine-tune all layers or train the entire network from scratch. This makes sense for highly specific domains, and it requires comprehensive custom datasets.

The fine-tuned models can be used in several different ways. One option is to build multiple classification models or one multihead model to estimate various domain-specific attributes and then use these attributes to filter the catalog. This may be a good solution for complex items and search applications that require the exact match [Isaev, 2019]. For example, a mobile application provided by a hardware shop can estimate attributes such as head type, tip type, length, and pitch, based on a picture of a screw, as illustrated in Figure R5.9, and search for exactly the same product or close substitutes. The second option is to capture image embeddings at the top layer of the classifier, and use them to perform nearest neighbor search similar to what we did in the solution for a style-based search.

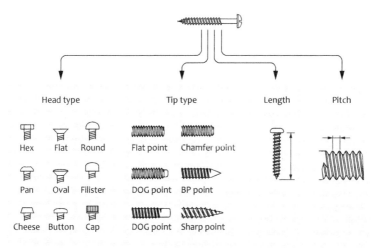

Figure R5.9: An example of attribute inference.

The design of the loss function used in the training process can be different for the above two strategies. If the goal is to build a regular classification model, then a regular loss function such as the categorical cross-entropy loss can be used. If the goal is to produce embeddings for nearest neighbor search, one should use custom losses for representation learning as discussed in Section 2.6.1, although regular loss functions can also produce meaningful but less optimal results.

R5.4.2 *Prototype*

 The complete reference implementation for this
section is available at https://bit.ly/3MuXhKJ

In this section, our goal is to implement a visual search service with
a domain-specific image similarity measure. We approach this problem
by fine-tuning a large image classification network to make it produce
domain-specific image embeddings, and then evaluate image similarities as cosine distances between these embedding vectors.

We consider the case of a clothing retailer that is looking to build
a visual search service that distinguishes clearly between clothing categories. Some of these categories, such as t-shirts, long sleeve shirts,
and dresses might not be easily distinguishable for a model pretrained
on a generic dataset, and fine-tuning is needed to produce high quality embeddings. For the prototyping purposes, we prepare a dataset
that contains about 2,700 clothing images of five classes: t-shirts, shoes,
long sleeves, dresses, and hats [Grigoriev, 2020]. Examples of these images with the corresponding class labels are presented in Figure R5.10.
We further split this dataset into training and test parts (75% and 25%,
respectively).

Next, we use an EfficientNet-B0 model pretrained on the ImageNet dataset as a baseline. The topmost convolutional layer of the
EfficientNet-B0 network produces an output with 1280 channels, each
of which is a 7×7 feature map, and this output is then fed into the
classifier. We remove the classifier for ImageNet, and replace it with a
stack of two dense layers followed by softmax. The first layer produces
a 32-dimensional vector which we can use as an embedding, and
the second layer maps it to a 5-dimensional vector that matches the
number of classes in our custom dataset.

We then freeze all layers of the network except the two newly added
dense layers on the top, and train it using a regular categorical cross-
entropy loss function on the training part of our dataset. The trained
model has relatively high accuracy, and we can use it to predict clothing categories based on the image. Examples of predictions for some
images from the test dataset are shown in Figure R5.11.

Figure R5.10: Examples of apparel images and their class labels.

EfficientNet Models

The EfficientNet architecture was proposed by Google Research in 2019 [Tan and Le, 2019]. EfficientNet was designed with a goal to optimize computational complexity and size of models, while achieving state-of-the-art accuracy on the standard benchmarks. The original paper describes eight configurations that provide different trade-offs between accuracy and complexity. The smallest configuration, referred to as EfficientNet-B0, has 5.3 million parameters, and the biggest, EfficientNet-B7, has 66 million parameters. All EfficientNet models, including EfficientNet-B0, achieve substantially higher accuracy than the VGG19 network despite having far fewer trainable parameters.

As we discussed previously, this fine-tuned network can either be used to explicitly predict the clothing categories that can be used as filters, or the outputs of its top layers can be used for nearest neighbor search. In the former case, the quality of the model can be assessed using accuracy metrics. In the latter case, we need to evaluate the quality of the embedding space. One of most basic ways of assessing the

Figure R5.11: Class probabilities for some of the test images.

embeddings is to inspect their low-dimensional projection and analyze how well the classes are separated and how well our domain-specific notion of similarity is approximated by the Euclidean distance. So we compute 32-dimensional embeddings for all images in the test dataset using the fine-tuned model, project these vectors on a two-dimensional plane using t-SNE, and visualize the result in Figure R5.12. The clothing classes are clearly separated in this space, and the distances are aligned with the intuition that dresses, long sleeves, and t-shirts are close to each other, but shoes and hats are somewhat isolated from them.

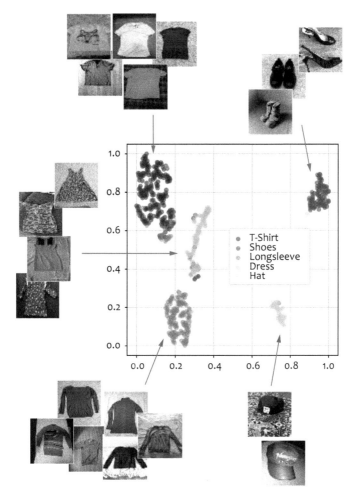

Figure R5.12: Visualization of the t-SNE projection of the clothing image embeddings. Each cluster of embeddings is annotated with a few image examples.

R5.5   UNSUPERVISED EMBEDDING LEARNING

 The complete reference implementation for this section is available at https://bit.ly/3EIiCxi

Embedding learning using supervised models offers many advantages including the high discriminative power of the produced embeddings regarding the domain classes, the ability to leverage pretrained models, and the flexibility to customize the distance metric to track style, object class, or some other characteristic. These capabilities result in the supervised approach being commonly used in practice, generally allowing good results to be achieved in a wide range of applications. The supervised approach, however, requires either that images in a given application are consistent with the dataset used for model pretraining or that a labeled custom dataset trains an application-specific model. These requirements might be impracticable for certain applications, particularly ones with highly specialized types of imagery such as that from industrial sensors or satellites. In some of these applications, unsupervised representation learning methods can be considered as alternatives to the supervised approach.

The unsupervised feature learning from a collection of images is a challenging problem, and we can expect the unsupervised methods to produce embeddings of a lower quality than the supervised ones. However, we can achieve reasonably good results using advanced representation learning methods discussed in Section 2.6. In this section, we build a prototype that demonstrates how the variational autoencoder introduced in Section 2.6.2.4 can be applied to the visual search tasks.

We use the Fashion-MNIST dataset that contains clothing images of 10 different classes, as shown in Figure R5.13. We do not need the class labels to train the autoencoder model, so we do the basic preprocessing and prepare a dataset that contains only 60,000 unlabeled grayscale images.

Fashion-MNIST Dataset

Fashion-MNIST is a dataset of clothing images open-sourced by a fashion retailer Zalando in 2017 [Xiao et al., 2017]. The dataset consists of small 28×28 grayscale images, each of which is associated with a label from 10 classes such as "dress" or "sandal". The dataset includes 60,000 training images and 10,000 test images.

We then implement a variational autoencoder with the encoding subnetwork that consists of two stacked convolution layers and a decoding subnetwork that consists of two upconvolution layers. The encoding

T-shirt/top	
Trouser	
Pullover	
Dress	
Coat	
Sandal	
Shirt	
Sneaker	
Bag	
Ankle boot	

Figure R5.13: Example images from the Fashion-MNIST dataset.

and decoding subnetworks have symmetrical (mirrored) layer parameters in terms of filter sizes and strides, as shown in Figure R5.14. The overall architecture is similar to the reference design in Figure 2.51, except that the dense layers are replaced with two-dimensional convolution layers. The autoencoder is then trained using the ELBO loss.

We configure the model in a way that embeddings are two-dimensional, that is they are drawn from the bivariate normal distribution. This greatly facilitates the visualization of the manifold. We can simply traverse a two-dimensional grid spanned over the semantic space, and decode each point into an image of the same size as the training images. The result of such a visualization is shown in Figure R5.15. This inspection confirms that the variational autoencoder has learned a regular continuous embedding space that is aligned with the image classes, although the training process did not have access to the ground truth labels. It is also evident that the decoder is

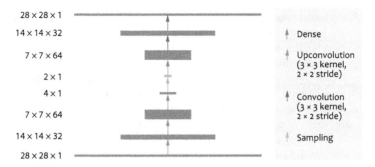

$28 \times 28 \times 1$		
$14 \times 14 \times 32$		Dense
$7 \times 7 \times 64$		Upconvolution (3×3 kernel, 2×2 stride)
2×1		
4×1		Convolution (3×3 kernel, 2×2 stride)
$7 \times 7 \times 64$		
$14 \times 14 \times 32$		Sampling
$28 \times 28 \times 1$		

Figure R5.14: Architecture of the variational autoencoder for learning two-dimensional embeddings for the Fashion-MNIST images.

able to reconstruct the original images quite accurately, although each image is represented using only two real numbers.

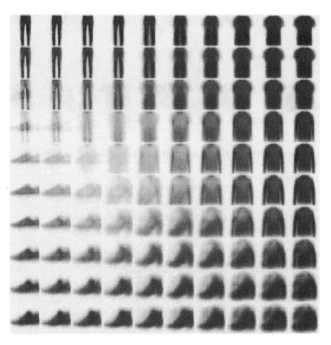

Figure R5.15: The manifold learned using the variational autoencoder based on the Fashion-MNIST dataset. We use a two-dimensional semantic space to simplify the visualization, and pick 100 points from this space using a square 10 × 10 grid centered around the origin. Each point is then decoded into a 28 × 28 image.

The trained model can be used to map images to embeddings and perform searches in the embedding space. Since we use the variational autoencoder, the encoding network produces two two-dimensional vectors which are interpreted as the mean and variance vectors of the bivariate normal distribution. Consequently, we compute the mean vectors for each image in the collection to create the search index. A search request is carried out by computing the mean vector for the query image and looking up the nearest neighbors in the index. Example search results for a couple of query images are presented in Figure R5.16. We can see that the solution is able to produce meaningful results that are aligned with our intuitive expectations, but it is generally more prone to issues and artifacts than supervised solutions.

Figure R5.16: Searching for nearest neighbors in the embedding space produced the autoencoder.

R5.6   OBJECT LOCALIZATION AND SEGMENTATION

The visual search solutions developed in the previous two sections compute embeddings for entire images on the assumption that each image contains only the object of interest such as an artwork or garment on a smooth background. The networks we used to compute the embeddings tend to amplify the characteristic features of objects in the feature maps they produce, so the network can to some extent separate objects from the background. This capability, however, might not be sufficient for producing proper embeddings based on images with noisy backgrounds or containing multiple objects. In such cases, we might need to use special techniques to locate and separate the objects that can further be used as inputs for the visual search pipeline.

The problem of object localization and separation can be approached in several different ways depending on assumptions we make about the structure of the query image. In the field of computer vision, there are four standard problem formulations and, consequently, four types of solutions that we can potentially use for our purposes:

OBJECT LOCALIZATION If we can assume that only one instance of the object of interest is present in the image, and our goal is to separate it from the background, we can attempt to build a model that estimates the coordinates and size of the object. More specifically, the model can output the tuple (c, x, y, w, h) where c is the object class, x and y are the coordinates of the center point of the object, and w and h are the width and height of the object. The rectangle specified by the coordinates, width, and height is commonly referred to as a *bounding box*. This approach, illustrated in Figure R5.17 (a), can be used to roughly separate the object from the background, but this separation is imperfect for objects with a non-rectangular shape or a diagonal orientation.

OBJECT DETECTION If we cannot make an assumption that the image contains only one object instance, we might need to build a model that produces a set of labeled bounding boxes as shown in Figure R5.17 (b). This is a far more complex task than the localization of a single object.

SEMANTIC SEGMENTATION Since the bounding box approach does not provide a perfect solution for separating objects from their background, we can attempt to build a model that assigns a class label to individual pixels of the image, as illustrated in Figure R5.17 (c). The output of such a model is a matrix of the same size as the input image, and each element of this matrix is a class label. The objects can then be separated from the background by selecting pixels of the same class. The limitation of this approach is that the model does not differentiate between object instances. If the image contains multiple overlapping or non-overlapping instances of the same class, all objects will be lumped together in a single mask.

INSTANCE SEGMENTATION Finally, we can attempt to combine object detection with semantic segmentation and build a model that produces pixel-level masks for individual objects in the image, as shown in Figure R5.17 (d).

In this section, we focus on the semantic segmentation approach and build a model for separating objects from their background. This solution works well for many visual search applications, except ones that deal with complex multi-object input images which require instance segmentation.

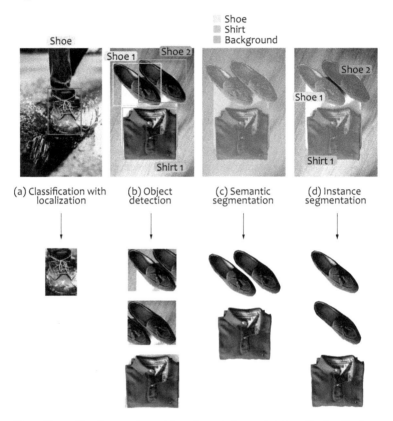

Figure R5.17: The four main problem formulations related to the localization task.

R5.6.1   *Semantic Segmentation*

The problem of semantic segmentation requires building a model that assigns a class label to each pixel of the input image. Conceptually, this means that we need to build a network that consumes $n \times m$ image and produces $n \times m \times k$ tensor where k is the number of classes. The values of this tensor should be softmax-normalized along the last dimension, so it can be interpreted as an $n \times m$ matrix of k-dimensional class probability vectors. This network can then be trained using a dataset where the training labels are $n \times m$ matrices of ground truth pixel-level class annotations, as illustrated in Figure R5.18. This setup has a lot of similarities with a regular image classification problem, but evaluation metrics, loss function, and network design need to be adapted to deal with matrices of class labels instead of a single label.

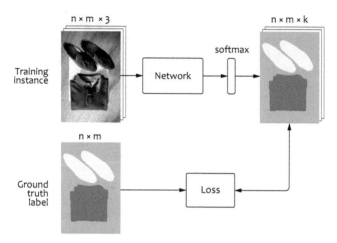

Figure R5.18: Training of a semantic segmentation network.

R5.6.1.1   Evaluation Metrics

Since the segmentation model produces an array of class probability vectors that can be compared element-wise to the corresponding pixel-level class labels, the network can be trained using a standard classification loss function such as categorical cross-entropy. In the context of segmentation tasks, this evaluation metric is commonly referred to as the *pixel accuracy*. Pixel accuracy, however, can be misleading when classes are imbalanced. For example, about 90% of the image presented in Figure R5.17 (a) is background, and only 10% of the image area is an object (shoe). Consequently, a baseline model that annotates all pixels of the image as background would reach the classification accuracy of about 90% in this case.

The above problem can be minimized by measuring the percent overlap between the ground truth and predicted masks. This metric is known as the *intersection over union* (IoU) or the *Jaccard index*. For each individual class, the mask can be represented simply as a set of pixel positions that are labeled with this class, and the IoU metric can be defined as the number of pixels in common between the ground truth and predicted masks divided by the total number of distinct pixel positions present in both masks:

$$\text{IoU} = \frac{|\text{ Ground truth} \cap \text{Predicted }|}{|\text{ Ground truth} \cup \text{Predicted }|} \tag{R5.3}$$

In the above example of the shoe image, the IoU score of the constant-output baseline model that annotates all pixels as background will be $0\% = 0\%/10\%$ for the shoe class and $10\% = 10\%/100\%$ for the background class. The IoU is calculated for each class separately and then averaged over all classes to provide the total IoU score.

R5.6.1.2 *Network Design*

The network design for segmentation can employ the autoencoder concepts discussed in Section 2.6.2. The input image is first processed by a contracting subnetwork to produce a large number of relatively small feature maps, and these feature maps are then upscaled by an expanding subnetwork to produce the output that matches the size of the input image but has only k channels. One of the best known architectures that uses this approach is U-Net. We discuss the U-Net architecture in detail below, and prototype it in the next section.

U-Net Model

The U-Net model was proposed in 2015 in the context of biomedical applications [Ronneberger et al., 2015]. U-Net is basically a convolutional autoencoder that consists of the encoder and decoder parts, as illustrated in Figure R5.19.

The encoder part represents a stack of convolution layers with 3×3 filters and 2×2 max pooling layers. The first block of convolution layers, denoted as E1 in Figure R5.19, has 64 channels. In the second block (E2), the size of the feature maps is reduced by half using max pooling, but the number of channels doubles to 128. This process repeats, and the number of channels subsequently doubles three more times in blocks E3, E4, and E5, so that the final output of the encoder has 1024 layers.

The decoder part represents a stack of convolution and upconvolution layers. The final output of the encoder with 1024 channels is first processed by an upconvolution layer with 512 output channels that doubles the size of the feature maps. This output is then concatenated with the 512-channel output of the block E4, producing a 1024-channel tensor. The goal of admixing the partially encoded representation from one of the previous layers is to provide the necessary detail that facilitates the reconstructions of accurate segmentation boundaries. This technique is known as *skip connection* because it allows the information to bypass certain layers. The result of the concatenation is then processed by a regular convolution layer with 512 output filters. This process repeats in decoder blocks D2, D3, and D4, and the number of channels subsequently decreases to 64, while the size of the feature maps increases to match the size of the input image. The output of the last decoder block D4 is post-processed by a 1×1 convolution layer to produce a mask with as many channels as output classes. This mask is then normalized using a softmax layer to produce the final output.

R5.6.2   *Prototype*

The complete reference implementation for this section is available at https://bit.ly/3xPXEeQ

In this section, we build a prototype of a semantic segmentation network using the U-Net architecture. This type of solution is typically used in visual search applications to remove the background and isolate the query object, so that more accurate similarity measures can be computed. This solution can also be used to separate different classes of objects (e.g. clothes and shoes in a fashion image) to search for them separately.

We use a clothing co-parsing (CCP) dataset that includes more than a thousand fashion images with pixel-level annotations [Yang et al., 2013]. The original dataset contains 59 object classes, but for the sake of simplicity, we remap the annotations to just four classes: background, clothes, skin, and hair. Several example images and the corresponding pixel-level annotations (segmentation masks) are presented in Figure R5.20. We further split the preprocessed dataset into train and test subsets.

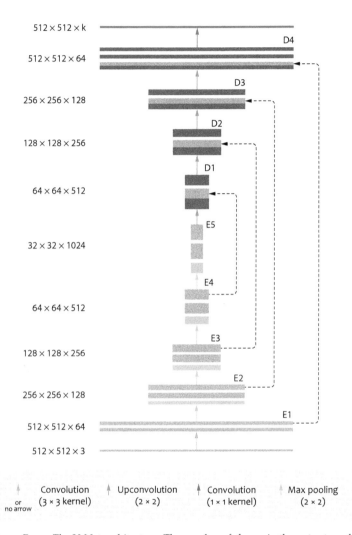

Figure R5.19: The U-Net architecture. The number of classes in the output mask is denoted as k.

Next, we train the U-Net model from scratch using only 750 instances from the training set. Although this is a very limited dataset, we can obtain a reasonably good solution using these data alone without pretraining. However, we have to use standard data augmentation techniques to achieve acceptable results.

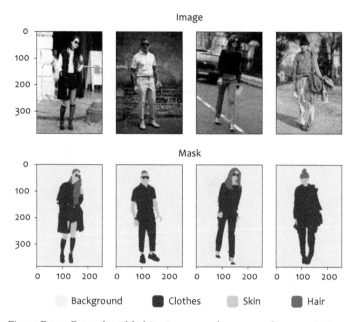

Figure R5.20: Examples of fashion images and corresponding annotations.

Finally, we evaluate the trained network on the test dataset. A few examples of input images and the corresponding predicted and ground truth segmentation masks are presented in Figure R5.21. The predicted masks can then be used to separate clothing objects and compute embeddings for visual search. This basic prototype can be further improved by increasing the number of clothing classes and separating individual garments instead of lumping all clothing objects together into a single mask.

R5.7 SUMMARY

- Visual search services enable users to retrieve relevant entities from a collection based on the query image.
- The relevancy is approximated by a similarity measure which can be evaluated as a distance in an embedding space or distance between vectors of numerical and categorical attributes inferred from images. In both cases, the distance measure needs to be designed based on a particular domain and application.

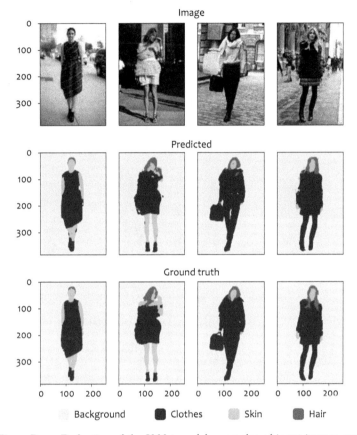

Figure R5.21: Evaluation of the U-Net model: examples of input images, predicted masks, and ground truth masks.

- The embedding space can be constructed based on feature maps produced by computer vision models. It is common to use the output of the top layer of the model as an image embedding vector, but it is also common to assemble embedding vectors using outputs of multiple intermediate layers or their transformations.

- In some applications, it is sufficient to use feature maps that describe the small-scale structure of the image. Such feature maps can be obtained using general-purpose models pretrained on common computer vision datasets.

- Some applications need to differentiate properly between domain-specific classes or use a custom measure of similarity. A custom similarity measure can rarely be specified explicitly, but we can learn a custom embedding function by training a new model or fine-tuning a pretrained model on domain-specific examples.

- The fine-tuning process aims to adapt a model trained on one domain to another domain. Some parameters of a pretrained model can be frozen, some parameters can be updated by the gradient descent, and parameters of newly added layers need to be learned from scratch.

- Unsupervised embedding learning can be used as an alternative to supervised methods in certain applications. It is generally challenging to obtain consistent results with unsupervised methods even using powerful methods such as variational autoencoders.

- Images that contain multiple objects or large background areas need to locate and separate objects of interest before embeddings can be computed. This can be done using object localization, object detection, semantic segmentation, or instance segmentation models depending on the assumptions about the image structure.

- Semantic segmentation models can produce pixel-level masks for individual classes of objects. Such models can be implemented using convolutional autoencoders.

Recipe

6

PRODUCT RECOMMENDATIONS

Recommending Products Based on Textual, Visual, and Graph Data

---

In recipe R5 (Visual Search), we discussed the problem of searching for the most relevant items based on a query image provided by a user. We assumed that the query image is the only source of information about the search intent of the user, and no other information is available about the user and the context of their search. Consequently, we used various image similarity measures as proxy measures of relevancy, and relied on content data (images) to identify relevant items. Furthermore, we have developed a comprehensive toolkit for user experience personalization based on behavioral and demographic information in recipes R1–R4. Unlike search services, these methods use the similarity of behavioral patterns as a proxy measure of relevancy, and do not require either content data to be available, or search intent to be explicitly expressed as a query.

In this section, we explore how these two groups of methods can be combined, so that the resulting service can leverage both behavioral and content data to provide users with the most relevant recommendations on items such as products, offers, articles, or videos. We also discuss how such hybrid solutions can operate on a large scale, handling millions of items, billions of personalization requests, and newly registered users.

We consider the case of a digital service that creates a personalized user experience by selecting one or several items from a collection of available items. For example, a digital commerce platform can provide a user with a short list of recommended products, selecting them from the full catalog. A streaming service can recommend the next movie to watch by selecting it from a comprehensive movie database, and a media platform can personalize newsfeeds by selecting the most relevant stories from all available news. This functionality is particularly important in applications where the number of available items is very large, often in the millions, and users might not be able to discover relevant products or content without a service that recommends items to them automatically.

The development of an industrial recommendation system requires incorporating multiple considerations including the business use case, end user representation, data availability, performance goals, and evaluation strategy. In the next section, we discuss the recommendation environment at a high level, and then delve deeper into the individual aspects of the problem.

R6.1.1   *High-level Environment Overview*

We assume that the service has access to user profiles that can include static attributes such as demographic data, account preferences, and history of events, as illustrated in Figure R6.1. We further assume that some of these events such as product page views, purchases, and submissions of customer ratings can be associated with specific items. Consequently, each user can be linked to a set of items they interacted with, and, conversely, each item can be linked to a set of users. We also assume that each interaction between a user and an item contains enough information to compute one or several *feedback* variables that characterize the intensity of the interaction. The feedback variables can be unary (e.g. purchase or no purchase), binary (e.g. like or dislike), ordinal (e.g. customer rating from 1 to 5), or continuous (e.g. time on a product page).

The number of interaction events for an individual user can vary greatly depending on whether we can track the user's identity across multiple interaction sessions or not. For example, an online service can personalize recommendations for logged-in users based on the events in their current and previous sessions, but recommendations for un-

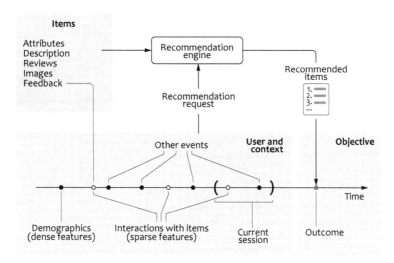

Figure R6.1: Main inputs and outputs of a recommendation engine.

known users might need to be personalized based only on their current session. The number of events associated with each item can also vary depending on the popularity and novelty of the item. In practice, the fraction of user-item pairs for which any feedback information is available is typically very small compared to the total number of possible user-item pairs. This property is commonly referred to as *sparsity* of the feedback data.

The second major source of the information that can be leveraged by a recommendation service is the item data. This generally includes categorical and numerical item attributes, human-readable descriptions, customer reviews, images, and videos. We do not make any specific assumptions about the format, availability, and quality of the item data, and expect the recommendation engine to be able of digesting any mix of structured features, texts, and images. In practice, the item data are often noisy, and the ability to reconcile the information from multiple heterogeneous sources is an important requirement of a recommendation engine. For instance, a retailer can consolidate product data feeds from hundreds of suppliers, merchandisers, and content writers, and the final result may include various inconsistencies in attribute values due to differences in nomenclatures, as well as inconsistencies between attributes and product images.

A recommendation engine leverages the user and item information to create an ordered list of recommended items, these items are presented to the user, and the engine observes the *outcome*. The outcome can include interaction events for individual items from the recommended list and additional metrics that can be used to evaluate the quality of recommendations. The interaction events, in turn, are assumed to be associated with the feedback variables. These events are then added to the event histories of the corresponding users and items, and can be leveraged by the engine to improve subsequent recommendation decisions.

R6.1.2   *Environment Types*

The environment specification provided in the previous section is fairly generic, and it is challenging to design a recommendation engine that supports all mentioned types of input and feedback data in one step. In order to facilitate the design process and break it into a sequence of simpler tasks, we will distinguish between several particular cases of the environment. First, we can categorize the environments based on the feedback type:

CONTINUOUS/ORDINAL FEEDBACK In some applications, we are interested in predicting the strength of the customer feedback on items that we can possibly recommend. For example, an online video-sharing service might need to predict watching times for recommended videos to differentiate between truly relevant recommendations and clickbait videos. Movie recommendation services often aim to predict ordinal user ratings given to the movies.

UNARY FEEDBACK In many other applications, we might need to identify only the items a given user is likely to interact with. In this case, the feedback variable can be considered unary – the user either interacts with a specific item or does not. We also do not need the event records to contain any feedback data explicitly; the presence of an event for a certain pair of user and item is interpreted as feedback of 1, and absence is interpreted as 0.

The second important characteristic of the environment that influences the design of the recommendation engine is the type and availability of the user and item data. We will distinguish between the following scenarios:

ONLY FEEDBACK One of the most basic options is to assume that we do not have any content or user information and observe only event tuples (u, v, g_{uv}, t) that consist of the user identifier u, item identifier v, feedback variable g_{uv}, and timestamp t. In this scenario, we can make recommendations only by capturing interaction patterns that are common across the users. This setup is commonly referred to as *collaborative filtering*.

FEEDBACK AND CONTENT The second option is to assume that we have access to both feedback data and item content data, so that each observation can be represented as (u, x_v, g_{uv}, t) where x_v is a structure that represents item features such as human-readable descriptions, product attributes, and images. In this case, user interaction histories can be analyzed individually, and recommendations can be made based on item features that are typical for a given user. The analysis of interaction patterns that are common across the users is optional. We refer to the problem of making recommendations based predominantly on the item data as *content-based filtering*.

FEEDBACK, CONTENT, AND USER The most general setup includes the feedback, content, and user data, so that observations (x_u, x_v, g_{uv}, t) include both user features x_u and item features x_v. We call this setup a *hybrid* recommendation environment.

In this recipe, we aim to develop solutions that can work efficiently in hybrid environments, but we will design them in stages, starting with simpler content-based and collaborative filtering formulations and then add hybrid capabilities on top.

R6.1.3   *Evaluation and Optimization Metrics*

The primary goal of a recommendation engine is to achieve the best possible outcomes, and the design of recommendation models is driven by the metrics that we choose for measuring the quality of the outcomes. The design of such metrics is an important part of the environment specification, and we dedicate this section to a discussion of how the quality of recommendations can be evaluated based on historical data and how the actual outcomes can be evaluated in production.

The environment model described in the previous sections does not assume that a user had been provided with recommendations at any time before the current session. Consequently, the user-item interactions recorded in the event history did not necessarily occur in response to past recommendations, but rather occurred naturally as a part of a normal user activity such as website browsing. This means that a recommendation engine cannot establish a direct link between the actions (recommendations) and outcomes, but can only optimize some proxy measure that gauges the relevancy of recommendations to the user or expected business outcome. Since this proxy measure cannot be used to reliably evaluate the true impact of recommendations, the development of a recommendation solution usually includes the following steps:

- The first step is to specify a set of proxy metrics for training a recommendation model offline based on the available historical data. This set usually includes a primary metric that is used as a loss function, and multiple secondary metrics that are used to evaluate the quality of recommendations from different perspectives.

- The second step is to establish one or several baselines that can be compared to the newly developed solution, both offline using the metrics defined in the previous step and online using A/B testing in production. One of the commonly used baselines is a simple algorithm called *most popular items*. It ranks all items by the number of purchases, views, clicks, or some other statistics, and recommends the same top items to all users without any personalization. In many real-world projects, new recommendation algorithms are developed to replace legacy solutions, and thus legacy systems or models are used as baselines.

- The new solution is developed and evaluated offline using the previously defined metrics and baselines.

- Finally, the new solution is compared to the baselines in production using A/B testing. The metrics collected during the online evaluation may be substantially different from the metrics used for offline evaluation.

The design of both offline and online metrics can vary significantly depending on the application, business goals, and available data. In the next two sections, we discuss several common techniques that can be used as starting points for building a specific solution.

R6.1.3.1   *Offline Evaluation: Basic Metrics*

The final output of a recommendation engine is an ordered list of items. This output is typically obtained by scoring all candidate items and ranking them according to the scores. The scoring model, in turn, is usually trained to estimate one of the feedback variables such as a customer rating, time on a product page, or probability of a click on a specific item. Consequently, we can evaluate the quality of a recommendation model either by comparing the individual feedback predictions to the ground truth or by comparing the entire lists of recommendations to the ground truth. Let us examine these two options separately.

The accuracy of individual feedback predictions is typically evaluated using regular regression and classification metrics. Assuming that we have a dataset that consists of (u_i, v_i, g_i, t_i) tuples where u_i is a user, v_i is an item, g_i is a feedback value, and t_i is a timestamp of the corresponding interaction event, we first split this dataset into training and test sets. This can be done at random, but it is also common to group all samples by user, sort each group by timestamp, and use all-but-latest samples for training, holding the latest samples in each group for testing, as shown in Figure R6.2.

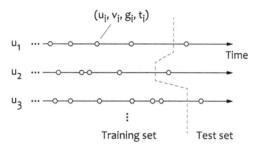

Figure R6.2: Creating training and test sets for model development and offline evaluation.

The recommendation model can then be trained and evaluated using losses and metrics that match the type of the feedback variable:

CONTINUOUS FEEDBACK Assuming that we use a continuous or ordinal feedback variable such as a video watch time or customer rating, the model can be trained and evaluated using regular regression loss functions and metrics. For example, we can use the MSE loss and evaluate the accuracy of the model on the training set in terms of MSE as

$$\text{MSE} = \frac{1}{|T|} \sum_{i \in T} (\hat{g}_i - g_i)^2 \qquad \text{(R6.1)}$$

where T is the test set, and $\hat{g}_i$ is the predicted feedback value for the i-th sample.

UNARY FEEDBACK In the case of a unary feedback variable such as a 'click' or 'like' flag, the problem reduces to a multinomial classification problem; the model needs to predict item v_i based on user u_i for each sample. The output of such a model is a probability vector $(p_1, \ldots, p_m)$ where m is the total number of items, j-th entry corresponds to the probability of interaction with item v_j, and all entries add up to one. In this case, the model can be trained using a regular classification loss such as a categorical cross-entropy and evaluated using standard classification metrics such as the area under curve (AUC).

The two options described above can be viewed as two different frameworks for building recommendation models, and we discuss how to use each of them later in this recipe.

The point metrics such as MSE and ROC AUC help to evaluate the accuracy of scores that are used to rank the items, but not the integral quality of the recommendations eventually presented to the user. This integral quality can be assessed by comparing the list of recommended items to the ground truth, that is an ordered list of items that are assumed to be relevant for a given user. One possible way of creating such a list is to select the most recent items from the user's interaction history and rank them in the same order as they were interacted with, as shown in Figure R6.3. In other words, we assume the interaction order to be a proxy for relevancy, so that the user interacts with the most relevant items first.

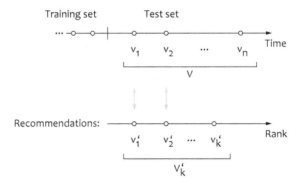

Figure R6.3: Creating a test set for offline evaluation of ranking metrics.

Assuming that we have a ground truth list $V = (v_1, \ldots, v_n)$ and a recommended list $V'_k = (v'_1, \ldots, v'_k)$ for individual users, we can evaluate the quality of recommendations using several metrics including the following [He et al., 2015]:

HIT RATIO The *hit ratio* is the percentage of the ground truth items that appear in the recommended list:

$$HR(k) = \frac{1}{n} | V'_k \cap V | = \frac{1}{n} \sum_{i=1}^{n} q_i \qquad (R6.2)$$

where q_i is equal to one if item v_i is in set V'_k and zero other-wise. The hit ratio is a function of the cut-off value k because we can generally increase the number of hits by increasing the number of recommended items. Two recommendation models can be compared in terms of their hit ratios computed for some fixed value of k and averaged across all users in the test set.

MEAN AVERAGE PRECISION The hit ratio quantifies the complete-ness of recommendations compared to the ground truth. The complementary metric is the *precision* of recommendations, i.e. the percentage of relevant items in the recommended list:

$$\text{precision}(k) = \frac{1}{k} \sum_{i=1}^{k} r_i \qquad (R6.3)$$

where r_i is equal to one if item v'_i is in set V and zero otherwise. The overall performance of a recommendation model is usually assessed using *mean average precision* or MAP which is obtained by averaging precision values across all cut-off values up to k and all users:

$$\text{MAP}(k) = \frac{1}{|U|} \sum_{u \in U} \frac{1}{k} \sum_{i=1}^{k} \text{precision}_u(i) \qquad (R6.4)$$

where U are the users in the test set. Similar to the hit ratio, the precision and MAP metrics are also the functions of the number of recommended items k.

DISCOUNTED CUMULATIVE GAIN The MAP metric does not account for the positions of the ground truth items in the recommended list. In practice, the probability that a user will review a certain item in the recommended list decreases exponentially as a func-tion of the position of the item in the list. We can account for this phenomenon using metrics that assign higher weights to the hits at the top of the list. One specific example of such a metric is the *normalized discounted cumulative gain* (NDCG) defined as follows:

$$\text{NDCG}(k) = c_k \sum_{i=1}^{k} \frac{2^{r_i} - 1}{\log_2(i+1)} \qquad (R6.5)$$

where c_k is the normalization factor that ensures that the perfect ranking has the value of one.

The list-wise measures like MAP and NDCG are not directly differ-entiable, so they cannot be used straightforwardly as loss functions. A number of loss functions exist that aim to approximate MAP and

NDCG [Lan et al., 2014], but it is more common to train recommendation models using point losses like MSE and to use list-wise metrics only for the evaluation of the results.

R6.1.3.2   *Offline Evaluation: Advanced Techniques*

All metrics discussed in the previous section evaluate how well a recommendation model captures the interaction and feedback patterns and predicts the future interactions between users and items. Although this capability is essential for producing relevant recommendations, the reliance on regular patterns tends to constrain the diversity of recommendations and the ability to provide the user with non-trivial suggestions. This aspect can be monitored using specialized metrics such as diversity (average distance between recommended items in some semantic space), serendipity (percentage of recommended items that do not coincide with recommendations produced by some simple baseline algorithm), and catalog coverage (percentage of items that are never recommended to any users).

In most practical applications, however, the generic quantitative metrics are not sufficient to adequately assess the quality of recommendations, and domain-specific and subjective tests play an important role in the model development process. For example, a developer of a movie recommendation service should preferably pick several typical user profiles such as *fans of the Marvel universe* or *comedy fans*, and assess the quality of recommendations using domain-specific rules, focus group, or manual subjective checks.

R6.1.3.3   *Online Evaluation*

The models developed and evaluated offline are then compared to the baselines using A/B testing in production. The online evaluation metrics are usually designed to track the actual business gains, and the uplifts in the click-through rate and conversion rate are the most common choices. These metrics are consistent with model training using unary feedback labels as discussed in the previous section.

The second aspect of online evaluation is the tracking of performance metrics such as the latency (response time) and throughput. These metrics are particularly important for the near real-time scenarios where the latency has a major impact on the user experience. Performance considerations can significantly influence the design of a recommendation engine, and we discuss these implications in detail in the next section.

R6.2   SOLUTION OPTIONS

In the environment specification presented in Section R6.1.1, we outlined a number of challenges that need to be addressed in the design of a recommendation engine including the scalability by the number of users and items, sparsity and noisiness of the feedback data, diversity of the user and item data, and complexity of behavioral patterns. We then discussed several quality metrics and loss measures that can guide the design, training, and evaluation of a recommendation model. In this section, we aim to combine these two perspectives into one framework and develop several specific solutions using deep learning methods.

R6.2.1   *System Architecture*

Scalability and latency requirements are the main factors that shape the system architecture of recommendation engines. Many recommendation algorithms perform well on a small scale, but fail in environments with millions of items, strict latency constraints, and sparse feedback data. One common approach that helps to alleviate these challenges is precomputed recommendations: the engine can create recommendation lists for all known users in the background, save them to the operational database (index), and fetch individual lists in real time to serve recommendation requests. This solution can help to work around latency constraints in certain applications. However, it has major disadvantages such as the inability to incorporate the real-time context and anonymous users, as well as high computational loads associated with regular recomputing of recommendations for the entire customer base.

The basic solution with fully precomputed recommendations can be improved using a two-layer architecture that uses one model or algorithm to retrieve a few hundreds or thousands of *candidate* items from the catalog. The second model would then *rank* these candidates to produce the final recommendation list with tens of items, as shown in Figure R6.4. These two models can have similar designs, but would use different input features and parameters to achieve different trade-offs between performance and quality. The two-layer architecture helps to manage the balance between the real-time and background computations more efficiently. For example, the candidate retrieval algorithm can rely heavily on precomputed values and human-defined rules, meanwhile the ranking algorithm can perform scoring in real time to account for the current context and in-session user actions. The methods that we develop in the next sections can be used to build both the candidate retrieval and ranking algorithms.

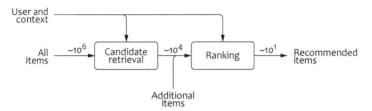

Figure R6.4: The two-layer architecture recommendation service.

The second advantage of the two-layer architecture is the modularity. In many environments, recommendations are shown to the user in multiple contexts, each of which can be associated with unique business requirements and constraints. For example, an online retailer can display recommendations on the landing page, catalog pages, product pages, as well as send recommendations in emails. The two-layer architecture helps to handle this complexity because the candidate retrieval layer can include multiple recommendation algorithms, and the ranking layer can include multiple use case-specific services that mix the outputs of the retrieval algorithms and perform the final ranking of the candidate items. This way, the two-layer approach helps to reuse the recommendation algorithms across multiple use cases and customize business logic for each use case.

R6.2.2   *Model Architecture*

Let us now develop several basic design principles that can be used to create scalable and robust retrieval and ranking models. As we discussed in Section R6.1.1, a recommendation model can be built to predict different types of feedback variables including continuous and unary. We consider these two cases separately starting with the continuous feedback.

R6.2.2.1   *Continuous Feedback*

Assuming a continuous feedback variable, we can build an arbitrary regression model f that estimates the feedback g_{uv} for user u and item v based on their feature vectors x_u and x_v, respectively:

$$\hat{g}_{uv} = f(x_u, x_v) \tag{R6.6}$$

This model can then be used to score all items for a given user, and create a recommendation list by selecting items with the highest scores. The main shortcoming with this approach is high computational complexity because the number of scoring operations grows linearly with the number of items in the catalog, and each scoring requires evaluating the model.

We can attempt to improve the computational efficiency of the above approach by embedding users and items into a semantic space where the feedback can be estimated based on the distances between the embedding vectors. Assuming that we can precompute the embeddings efficiently, this approach offers two major benefits: first, we can replace the evaluation of arbitrary models with the basic vector operations; and second, we can replace the exhaustive scoring of all items by the nearest neighbor search in the embedding space, which can be done efficiently using specialized indexing techniques [Liu et al., 2004].

To better understand the embedding-based approach, let us first consider a simplified scenario where we have only the feedback variables and item embeddings. The item embeddings are assumed to be computed based on the content data such as attributes, human-readable descriptions, and images. Let us assume that we make recommendations to user u, and this user has already interacted with a set of items $v_1^u, \ldots, v_n^u$ producing the corresponding feedback variables $g_{uv_1}, \ldots, g_{uv_n}$. We then can estimate the expected feedback for arbitrary item v as a weighted average of known feedbacks using the distances in the semantic space as weights:

$$\hat{g}_{uv} = \sum_{j=1}^{n} \left(1 - \frac{1}{2} \left\| \mathbf{z}_{v_j^u} - \mathbf{z}_v \right\|^2 \right) \cdot g_{uv_j} \tag{R6.7}$$

where $\mathbf{z}_v$ is the embedding of item v, and the embeddings are assumed to be normalized so that $\mathbf{z}^T \mathbf{z} = 1$. In other words, the contribution of item v_j^u into the feedback estimate for item v is proportional to its proximity to v in the embedding space.

We can further simplify this expression using the following identity that works for any pair of normalized vectors $\mathbf{p}$ and $\mathbf{q}$ such that $\mathbf{p}^T \mathbf{p} = \mathbf{q}^T \mathbf{q} = 1$:

$$\frac{1}{2} \left\| \mathbf{p} - \mathbf{q} \right\|^2 = \frac{1}{2} \left(\mathbf{p}^T \mathbf{p} + \mathbf{q}^T \mathbf{q} - 2 \mathbf{p}^T \mathbf{q} \right) = 1 - \mathbf{p}^T \mathbf{q} \tag{R6.8}$$

Consequently, we can rewrite the feedback estimate using the dot product similarity instead of the Euclidean distance[1]:

$$\hat{g}_{uv} = \sum_{j=1}^{n} \mathbf{z}_{v_j^u}^T \cdot \mathbf{z}_v \cdot g_{uv_j} \qquad (\text{R6.9})$$

This approach, commonly referred to as the *item-based approach*, allows us to replace the evaluation of an arbitrary regression model with the dot product, but still provides the flexibility to incorporate arbitrary item data. In particular, we can implement pure content-based filtering by computing embeddings $\mathbf{z}$ for each item independently based on its content such as attributes, texts, and images. Alternatively, we can implement pure collaborative filtering by constructing item embeddings based on the common behavioral patterns across the users. However, this simplistic solution has several shortcomings related to the limited generalization ability of a simple weighted sum model. In particular, it works only for users with sufficiently large interaction histories so that the sum in expression R6.9 can be evaluated, and this sum is sensitive to outliers in the feedback data.

A more general solution can be obtained by mapping both users and items to the same semantic space and estimating the expected feedback using the distance between user and item embeddings. Using the reverse relationship between the distance and dot product given in expression R6.8, we can estimate the expected feedback as

$$\hat{g}_{uv} = \mathbf{z}_u^T \cdot \mathbf{z}_v \qquad (\text{R6.10})$$

where $\mathbf{z}_u$ and $\mathbf{z}_v$ are the user and item embeddings, respectively. This design is often referred to as the feedback *factorization* because the feedback is decomposed into a product of embeddings. It is worth noting that expression R6.9 can also be interpreted as a product of item and user embeddings. We can make this fact more apparent by rewriting the expression as follows:

$$\hat{g}_{uv} = \mathbf{z}_v^T \cdot \sum_{j=1}^{n} \mathbf{z}_{v_j^u} \cdot g_{uv_j} \qquad (\text{R6.11})$$

It can be seen that the sum on the right-hand side can be interpreted as a user embedding which is computed as a weighted average of the corresponding item embeddings.

The general factorization solution R6.10 resolves several shortcomings of the item-based solution R6.9. First, common behavioral patterns

---

1 See Section 2.3.4 for a more general discussion of the entity interaction models.

and feedbacks of the given user are captured in the user embedding, eliminating the direct dependency on the individual feedback values and thus making the solution more robust to noises and data sparsity. Second, user embeddings enable us to incorporate arbitrary user data including event history and profile attributes. Finally, the top items to be recommended to the given user can be identified using the nearest neighbor search. (We need to find the nearest neighbors of z_u among all item embeddings z_v.) The item-based and feedback factorization designs are compared side by side in Figure R6.5.

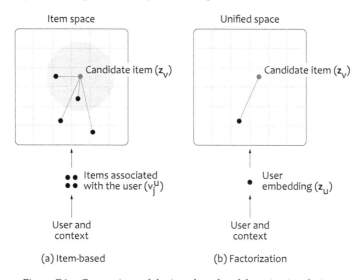

Figure R6.5: Comparison of the item-based and factorization designs.

The three approaches described above can be used to achieve different trade-offs between precomputing and real-time contextualization. The real-time scoring using an arbitrary regression model can incorporate real-time user, context, and item data at the expense of high computational complexity. In the two-layer architecture that was introduced in the previous section, this approach is most suitable for the ranking stage. The content-based similarity scoring can be used in applications with limited or highly dynamic user data where it may be challenging to precompute user embeddings, whereas it may be easier to map a user, session, or context to a collection of items. In particular, this approach can be used to produce non-personalized recommendations based, for example, on the currently browsed page or product. Finally, the feedback factorization approach allows us to reduce the recommendation problem to real-time nearest neighbor search, but this requires both user and item embeddings to be precomputed. In the two-layer architecture, both retrieval and ranking models can leverage the factorization concepts.

R6.2.2.2   *Unary Feedback*

The three design options given by expressions R6.6, R6.9, and R6.10 can be adapted to the case of the unary feedback. We can do this consistently by reformulating the feedback prediction problems into *interaction prediction*. For example, the most general solution that matches expressions R6.6 can be obtained by building a classification model f that estimates interaction probabilities for individual items based on a user feature vector:

$$(p_{u1}, \ldots, p_{um}) = f(\mathbf{x}_u) \tag{R6.12}$$

where p_{uj} is the probability that user u will interact with item v_j, all p_{uj} sum up to one, and m is the total number of items. In this design, the user feature vector is assumed to incorporate the interaction history including features of the items that the user interacted with. The recommended list can then be created by selecting items with the highest interaction probabilities.

The item-based solution analogous to expression R6.9 can be obtained by evaluating the similarity scores in the semantic space based on the historical interactions of the user, and using these scores as unnormalized interaction probabilities. More specifically, we can evaluate the following score for each item in the catalog, and create the final recommended list by selecting the items with the highest scores:

$$s_{ui} = \sum_j \mathbf{z}_{v_j^u}^{\mathsf{T}} \cdot \mathbf{z}_{v_i}, \quad i = 1, \ldots, m \tag{R6.13}$$

Finally, the general factorization solution is identical to expression R6.10 except that the product of embeddings is interpreted as unnormalized interaction probability, not the feedback estimate:

$$s_{ui} = \mathbf{z}_u^{\mathsf{T}} \cdot \mathbf{z}_{v_i}, \quad i = 1, \ldots, m \tag{R6.14}$$

Similar to the continuous feedback case, the recommended list can be created by locating the nearest neighbors of the user embedding $\mathbf{z}_u$ among all items.

The above designs provide a high-level idea of how recommendations can be created using regression and classification models, and

scalability and robustness can be improved by reducing the problem
to vector operations in semantic spaces. However, this is just a conceptual framework that does not specify how the appropriate embeddings
can be computed and what model architectures should be used. We
build specific solutions that address these questions in the next sections, starting with relatively basic methods and gradually increasing
the complexity.

R6.3   FEEDBACK PREDICTION MODELS

Our first step is to design a recommendation model that predicts the
continuous feedback and ranks the items accordingly. We start by developing a solution for the pure collaborative filtering problem introduced in Section R6.1.2, and then extend it to the hybrid setup.

R6.3.1   *Basic Factorization*

 The complete reference implementation for this
section is available at https://bit.ly/3vaMAaq

In the pure collaborative filtering problem, we observe tuples
(u, v, g_{uv}, t) where u is the user identifier, v is the item identifier, g_{uv}
is the corresponding feedback, and t is the observation timestamp.
For the sake of simplicity, let us ignore the timestamps, and assume
that the input dataset is merely a collection of tuples (u, v, g_{uv}) where
the feedback is continuous. We further assume that the feedbacks are
known only for a small subset of all possible user-item pairs, and our
goal is to build a model that predicts the feedback g_{uv} for an arbitrary
pair of user u and item v.

The most straightforward solution is to map user and item identifiers to one-hot vectors, concatenate them, and fit an arbitrary regression model to approximate common user-item interaction patterns.
The shortcoming of this approach is that the number of input features
grows linearly with the number of users and items making the problem intractable for many standard regression methods. We can work
around this issue by learning dense embeddings instead of sparse one-
hot encodings, and estimating the feedback as a product of embed-

dings based on the result R6.10. The user and item embeddings z_u and z_v can be learned using the embedding lookup approach, so that we start with random vectors and update them using stochastic gradient descent (SGD) to minimize the feedback prediction error. More specifically, we can set the goal of minimizing the prediction MSE over the training samples [Koren et al., 2009]:

$$\text{MSE} = \sum_{(u,v)} \left(g_{uv} - z_u^T z_v\right)^2 + \lambda \|z_u\|^2 + \lambda \|z_v\|^2 \qquad (R6.15)$$

where (u,v) iterate over all tuples in the training set, and λ is a regularization coefficient. Calculating the gradients over z_u and z_v, we obtain the following update rules:

$$z_u \leftarrow z_u + \alpha(\varepsilon_{uv} z_v - \lambda z_u)$$
$$z_v \leftarrow z_v + \alpha(\varepsilon_{uv} z_u - \lambda z_v) \qquad (R6.16)$$

where α is the learning rate, and ε_{uv} is the feedback prediction error. The complete SGD algorithm that learns user and item embeddings is presented in box R6.1. In practice, we can run this procedure on a regular basis to catch up with the ongoing feedback data and, as we discussed earlier, index the user and item embeddings in a data structure that supports efficient nearest neighbor search. The recommendations for a given user can then be precomputed or computed in near real time by finding nearest neighbors of the user's embedding among all item embeddings.

Let us consider a small numerical example that illustrates the factorization solution. We use a dataset with 10 users and 10 items presented in Figure R6.6 as a matrix. Each row of this matrix corresponds to a user, each column corresponds to an item, and the elements are the feedback values on a scale from 1 to 5. The feedback values are known only for a subset of user-item pairs, and our goal is to predict (impute) the unknown feedbacks. For the sake of illustration, the dataset is constructed in a way that there are two categories of items (bakery products and fruits) and two cohorts of users (bakery-lovers and fruit-lovers) that strongly correlate, so that bakery-lovers provide strong positive feedback on the bakery products, and fruit-lovers provide positive feedback on fruits. This pattern is visible in Figure R6.6.

We use algorithm R6.1 to compute two-dimensional user and item embeddings based on the known feedback values, and then predict the missed values to obtain a complete feedback matrix presented in Figure R6.7. We can see that the embeddings correctly capture the four-block structure assumed in the input matrix.

Algorithm R6.1: Factorization Using SGD

parameters:
   k – embedding dimensionality
   n – total number of users
   m – total number of items
   t – number of training iterations
   α – learning rate
   λ – regularization coefficient

initialization:
   $z_{u_1}, \ldots, z_{u_n}$ – random k-dimensional user embeddings
   $z_{v_1}, \ldots, z_{v_m}$ – random k-dimensional item embeddings

for $i = 1, 2, \ldots, t$ **do**
   randomly sample (u, v, g_{uv}) from the training dataset
   $\varepsilon_{uv} = g_{uv} - z_u^T z_v$
   $z_u \leftarrow z_u + \alpha(\varepsilon_{uv} z_v - \lambda z_u)$
   $z_v \leftarrow z_v + \alpha(\varepsilon_{uv} z_u - \lambda z_v)$
end

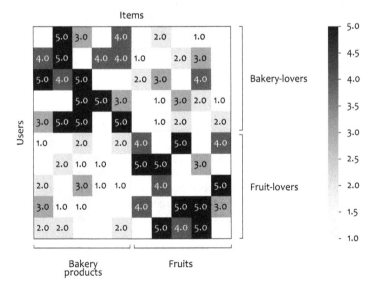

Figure R6.6: An example of an interaction matrix.

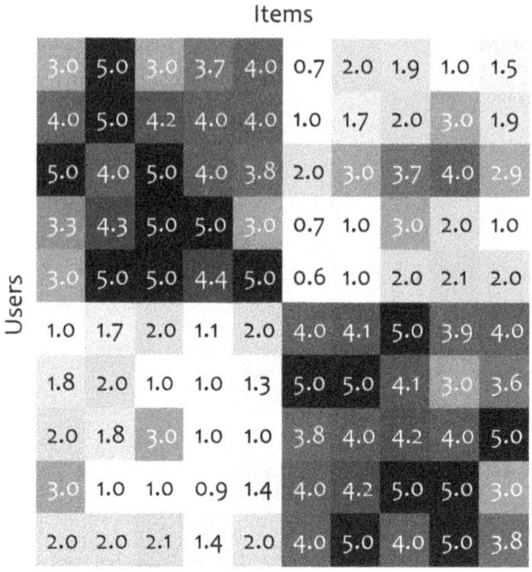

Figure R6.7: A reconstruction of the matrix from Figure R6.6 using the embeddings computed with the SGD algorithm. We use two-dimensional embeddings for both users and items.

The factorization approach is highly robust to sparse and noisy data, has relatively low computational complexity, and can be horizontally scaled using distributed versions of the SGD algorithm. These properties make factorization-based recommendation models widely popular in enterprise applications, and many extensions of the basic procedure R6.1 exist, that enhance accuracy, incorporate additional data sources, and improve computational properties.

R6.3.2   *Neural Collaborative Filtering*

Although the factorization design is powerful, it does not provide an extensible framework that can be used to incorporate arbitrary data or change the semantics of the embedding space. Any such extensions of the basic algorithm need to manually redesign the optimization problem and solve it using general mathematical methods such as SGD. In this section, we explore how a more flexible and comprehensive framework can be created by establishing a link between factorization and neural networks.

We can start with an observation that the factorization algorithm developed in the previous section can be implemented as a simple neural network presented in Figure R6.8 (a). This network consists of two standard embedding lookup units and a linear dot product layer that outputs the feedback estimate. Assuming that the network is trained using some variant of the SGD algorithm, the process is essentially equivalent to algorithm R6.1. Once the network is trained, the user and item embeddings can be extracted from the lookup units and used as we discussed previously. In particular, we can apply this solution to the example in Figure R6.6 and impute the missing feedback values obtaining a result similar to what is presented in Figure R6.7. Alternatively, the trained network can be evaluated directly to estimate the feedback for a specific user-item pair.

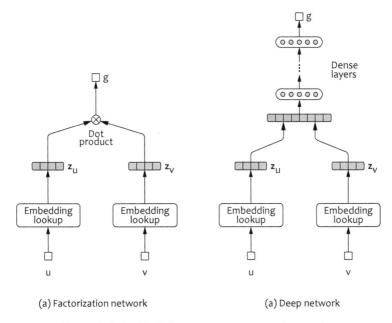

Figure R6.8: Feedback factorization using neural networks.

This perspective provides a much more flexible and comprehensive framework than the original factorization approach. First, we can arbitrarily change the capacity of the model by replacing the dot product layer with more complex designs, as illustrated in the example in Figure R6.8 (b). The neural network models for solving the collaborative filtering problem are collectively referred to as *neural collaborating filtering* (NCF) models. Second, the neural approach enables us to incorporate arbitrary data and signals, as well as to build complex architectures that use multiple subnetworks (towers) to process different types of data. We use these techniques to create a hybrid recommender in the next section.

R6.3.3 *Case Study*

 The complete reference implementation for this
section is available at `https://bit.ly/3rOo8JH`

In this section, we build an NCF-based movie recommendation
model using the MovieLens 20M dataset (see the box below for more
details about the MovieLens datasets). This dataset includes three
tables. The first one contains ratings for user-movie pairs and the
corresponding timestamps:

```
Ratings: 20000263 rows x 4 columns
+-----------+-----------+---------+------------+
|  user_id  |  item_id  |  rating | timestamp  |
+-----------+-----------+---------+------------|
|        1 |         2 |     3.5 | 1112486... |
|        1 |        29 |     3.5 | 1112484... |
|        1 |       112 |     3.5 | 1094785... |
|        1 |       151 |     4   | 1094785... |
|        1 |       223 |     4   | 1112485... |
+-----------+-----------+---------+------------+
```

> **MovieLens Datasets**
>
> MovieLens is a movie recommendation website run by
> GroupLens, a research lab at the University of Minnesota
> [Harper and Konstan, 2015]. GroupLens Research has
> collected and made available several datasets from the Movie-
> Lens site. These datasets have similar structures containing
> movie ratings, movie tags or genres, and user attributes, but
> they differ in size providing from 100K to 25M movie ratings.
> MovieLens datasets are among the most commonly used
> benchmarks for recommendation systems.
>
> In this section, we use the MovieLens 20M dataset that contains
> 20,000,263 ratings for 27,278 movies created by 138,493 users, as
> well as 465,564 movie tags. All users selected to be included in
> this dataset had rated at least 20 movies.

The second table contains movie titles and genres, and each movie
can be associated with more than one genre:

```
Movies: 27278 rows x 3 columns
+----------+-------------------------+----------------------------------+
|  item_id | title                   | genres                           |
+----------+-------------------------+----------------------------------|
|        1 | Toy Story (1995)        | Adventure|Animation|Childre...   |
|        2 | Jumanji (1995)          | Adventure|Children|Fantasy       |
|        3 | Grumpier Old Men (1995) | Comedy|Romance                   |
|        4 | Waiting to Exhale (1995)| Comedy|Drama|Romance             |
|        5 | Father of the Bride ... | Comedy                           |
|        6 | Heat (1995)             | Action|Crime|Thriller            |
+----------+-------------------------+----------------------------------+
```

Finally, the third table contains movie tags created by the users and the corresponding timestamps:

```
Tags: 465564 rows x 4 columns
+----------+----------+------------------+------------+
|  user_id |  item_id | tag              |  timestamp |
+----------+----------+------------------+------------|
|       18 |     4141 | Mark Waters      | 1240597180 |
|       65 |      208 | dark hero        | 1368150078 |
|       65 |      353 | dark hero        | 1368150079 |
|       65 |      521 | noir thriller    | 1368149983 |
|       65 |      592 | dark hero        | 1368150078 |
|       65 |      668 | bollywood        | 1368149876 |
|       65 |      898 | screwball comedy | 1368150160 |
+----------+----------+------------------+------------+
```

We preprocess the original dataset, removing movies with a small number of tags and concatenating all tags for each movie into a whitespace-separated string. This preprocessed dataset is then split into training and test sets, and we use them to train and evaluate two NCF models. The first one is a basic factorization network that follows the architecture presented in Figure R6.8 (a). This model is trained using only the rating data, and tag strings are ignored.

The second model is a hybrid solution that uses both the rating and tag data. This model extends the basic factorization network with a third tower that processes the tag data, as shown in Figure R6.9. The tag processing tower uses a pretrained NLP model from a public repository to map each tag string to a 384-dimensional embedding vector. The NLP model is based on the transformer design discussed in Section 2.4.7, and it interprets each tag string as a sentence. The embedding produced by the NLP model is resized using a dense layer to match the size of the identifier-based item embedding produced using the lookup table, and these two vectors are summed to create the hybrid item embedding. Finally, the movie rating is estimated using the dot product unit just as in the basic factorization network.

The rating estimation error achieved by the hybrid model is lower than the error achieved by the basic factorization model with the same

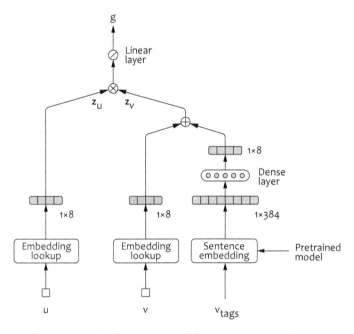

Figure R6.9: A hybrid NCF network for movie recommendations.

dimensionality of user and item embeddings. In many real-world settings, hybrid solutions achieve considerable improvement over models that use only behavioral or content data.

R6.4   INTERACTION PREDICTION MODELS

The networks developed in the previous sections are designed to estimate continuous feedback. In the case of unary feedback, we can reduce the recommendation problem to the interaction prediction problem. The recommendation model needs to identify items with the highest probability of being interacted with by the user. We have previously established that, in a general case, this approach can be implemented using a classification model that estimates the probability vector for the entire collection of items (expression R6.12). In particular, this estimate can be computed efficiently using the factorization design (expression R6.14). In this section, we discuss the details of the factorization-based approach using a recommendation system developed by YouTube as an illustrative example [Covington et al., 2016].

The solution developed by YouTube follows the two-tier architecture introduced in Section R6.2.1. It thus includes two parts: a candidate generation model that suggests hundreds of recommendations for each user and a ranking model that selects a few of the most relevant candidates. The models have similar architectures, and we focus on the candidate generation part for the sake of specificity. The candidate generation model is a classification model that estimates the probability that user u will watch video v_i at time t, as follows:

$$p(\text{watch video } v_i \text{ at time } t \mid u) = \frac{\exp(z_{v_i}^T z_u)}{\sum_{j \in V} \exp(z_{v_j}^T z_u)} \qquad (R6.17)$$

where V is the corpus of videos, z_v is the embedding of video v, and z_u is the embedding of the user at time t. Thus, learning user and video embeddings is at the core of the problem. This learning is done using the architecture shown in Figure R6.10.

The network consumes several inputs. The first is the user's watching history. This is a variable-length sequence $(v_1, \ldots, v_{t-1})$ of watched video IDs, each of which is mapped to a dense video watching embedding. Then, the embeddings are simply averaged into one fixed-length watching history embedding. The second input is the user's search history. Search queries are tokenized into unigrams and bigrams and then mapped to dense search token embeddings, which are also averaged to create a search history embedding. Finally, demographic and geolocation features are added. The resulting vectors are concatenated and passed through a basic four-layer network to produce user embeddings, z_u. Finally, user embeddings are normalized into class probabilities (i.e. the probabilities of individual videos) using softmax, and this output is used to train the network using the actual video watches v_t as targets. More specifically, the multinomial distribution over videos v is computed as

$$p(v) = \text{softmax}(z_u^T W) \qquad (R6.18)$$

where z_u is a d-dimensional user embedding produced by the previous layers, and W is d $\times$ m matrix of learnable parameters, m is the total number of videos (classes), and $p(v)$ is represented as an m-dimensional stochastic vector. This equation matches expression R6.17 assuming that the j-th column of matrix W is interpreted as video embeddings z_{v_j}. In other words, the design trick R6.18 ensures that each element of the probability vector $p(v)$ is decomposed into a product of two vectors that are associated with a specific user and specific video, and can thus be interpreted as user and item embeddings. Consequently, the network presented in Figure R6.10 is capable of learning

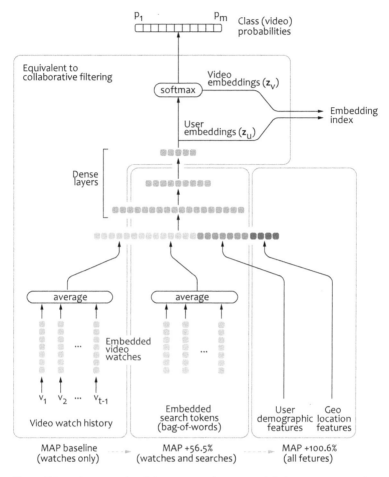

Figure R6.10: An example of the item prediction model that incorporates behavior history, search query history, demographic, and content details. The network uses the softmax trick to produce user and item embeddings.

both user and item embeddings. These embeddings can then be saved to the operational index and used for real-time generation of the video recommendation candidates in accordance with equation R6.17.

Note that if one removes all inputs but watching history and all network layers but one dense layer, then the resulting network will be similar to the basic collaborative filtering. YouTube reported that adding search embeddings improves accuracy by 56.5% compared to watching history only, and the complete set of features delivers close to 100.6% improvement.

R6.5   SEQUENCE MODELS

The fundamental limitation of the solutions developed in the previous sections is the reliance on the aggregated features, so that the order of the interaction events is ignored. In many real-world applications, however, the order and timing of events is important for understanding and predicting user behavior. For example, it may be typical for users to purchase accessories soon after buying a smartphone, but purchasing accessories before or long after buying a smartphone may be less common. The order and timing of events is particularly important in applications with short interaction histories. The most common example is session-based recommendations where the user interaction history is limited to the current web session [Liu et al., 2018].

We can attempt to improve the quality of recommendations by capturing the evolution of users' interests over time and the dynamic context in which the recommendations are made using sequence models. We already used this approach to solve several customer analytics problems in recipes R1 (Propensity Modeling) and R2 (Customer Feature Learning), and we explore how these ideas can be applied to the product recommendation problem in this section. The sequence-aware recommendation models are particularly efficient for use in cases with limited user histories such as session-based recommendations, but they can also be used as a generic alternative to the factorization models discussed in the previous sections.

R6.5.1   *Behavior Sequence Transformer*

Since the recommendation problem can usually be reduced to regression or classification tasks using the techniques introduced earlier, we can apply a wide range of standard sequence models including RNNs and transformers to predict the feedback variables and score items. In this section, we discuss a transformer-based solution called *behavior sequence transformer* (BST) that was adopted by companies such as Alibaba and Scribd [Kang and McAuley, 2018; Chen et al., 2019; Mistry, 2021].

The transformer is a generic component that can be used to build different types of recommendation models. So, for the sake of specificity, we start with examining one particular design for the unary feedback prediction and then discuss its alternatives and variations [Chen et al., 2019]. The high-level model architecture is shown in Figure R6.11.

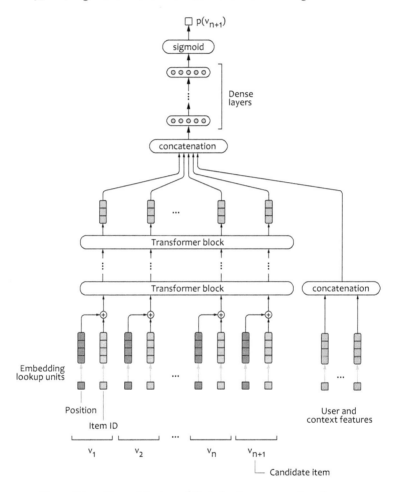

Figure R6.11: The architecture of the behavior sequence transformer.

This model is designed to estimate the probability that user u with interaction history $(v_1, \ldots, v_n)$ will interact with a given item v_{n+1}. We create the input for the transformer block by mapping each item in the interaction history, as well as the evaluated item v_{n+1}, to an embedding, and adding a position embedding as we discussed in Section 2.4.7. This sequence of embeddings is then processed by a stack of standard transformer blocks, and the outputs' vectors are concatenated to each other, as well as to additional user and context features. The output of the concatenation operations is then processed by a stack of dense layers with a sigmoid mapping on the top to produce the final interaction probability estimate $p(v_{n+1})$.

The model is trained as a binary classification model using a dataset where each sample consists of the input structure x that comprises the interaction sequence $(v_1, \ldots, v_{n+1})$ along with other user and context features, and target label $y \in \{0, 1\}$ that is equal to one when the user interacted with item v_{n+1} and is zero otherwise. Consequently, the training can be guided using the binary cross-entropy loss function:

$$L(D) = - \sum_{(x,y) \in D} (y \log p(x) + (1 - y) \log(1 - p(x))) \qquad (R6.19)$$

where D is the training set and $p(x)$ is the estimated probability of the interaction with the last item in the sequence comprised in x. The recommendations for a user with interaction history $(v_1, \ldots, v_n)$ are then produced by evaluating multiple candidate items v_{n+1} and selecting the items with the highest probability scores.

The original BST network estimates the interaction probabilities for individual candidate items specified as a part of the model input. This is, however, only one possible option, and we can use any of the sequence-to-value and sequence-to-sequence designs discussed in Section 2.4. In particular, we can simply switch from unary to continuous feedback values by replacing the sigmoid head in the above model with a linear layer. We can also switch from individual item scoring to the item prediction layout introduced in the previous section by replacing the sigmoid head with a softmax head and removing the candidate item from the inputs. The resulting model will output the vector of probabilities for all candidate items based on the input sequence $(v_1, \ldots, v_n)$.

R6.5.2   *Case Study*

   The complete reference implementation for this section is available at https://bit.ly/39h28AZ

We conclude the discussion of the behavior sequence transformer with a demonstration of how this design can be applied to the Movie-Lens 1M dataset. This dataset consists of three tables: users, movies, and ratings. The user table includes user ID and several demographic features such as sex, age group, and occupation. The movie table includes movie ID, title, and genre tags. There are eighteen genre tags such as *drama* and *western* in total, and each movie can be associated with multiple genres. Finally, the ratings table includes about one million records, each of which consists of a user ID, movie ID, an integer rating value from 1 to 5, and a timestamp.

The BST model requires user-item interactions to be represented as event sequences, so we start with reshaping the original dataset into sequences of movie IDs and corresponding ratings. For each user, we choose to generate multiple samples with event sequences of a fixed length using a sliding window that moves along the complete event history. This process is illustrated in the lower part of Figure R6.12 where we use a sliding window of size four and a stride of two. We then map each movie ID in the sequence to an embedding vector, concatenate this with the corresponding genre flags, add position embeddings, and multiply the result by the corresponding rating to incorporate the feedback level. The resulting sequence of embeddings is then processed by the transformer block. The outputs of the transformer are concatenated with the user feature embeddings and mapped to the final target movie rating estimate using the dense layers.

This prototype demonstrates how the sequential modeling approach can be applied to a relatively complex dataset that includes user features, item attributes, and ratings. The solution can be further improved by using more advanced sequential models such as bidirectional transformers [Sun et al., 2019].

R6.6   GRAPH MODELS

In the previous sections, we discussed that the data generated by a typical recommendation environment can be represented in several different ways, including rating matrices and sequences of interaction events. The third option that we can explore is a graph representation. This is a promising alternative because interactions between users and items can naturally be modeled as graphs, and additional entities such as user groups or user-defined item collections can be incorporated. This flexibility is a major advantage over the previously discussed approaches that often require the model to be redesigned from the ground up when the input structure changes.

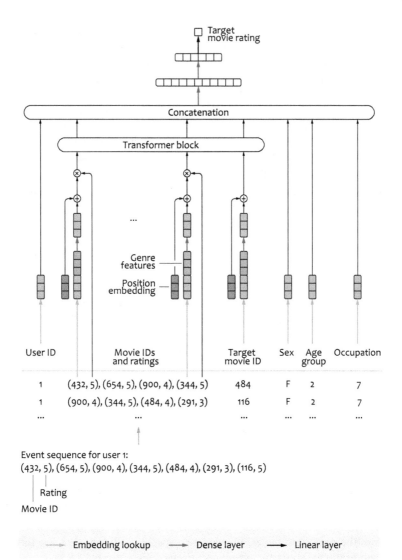

User ID	Movie IDs and ratings	Target movie ID	Sex	Age group	Occupation
1	(432, 5), (654, 5), (900, 4), (344, 5)	484	F	2	7
1	(900, 4), (344, 5), (484, 4), (291, 3)	116	F	2	7
...	...	...	...	...	...

Event sequence for user 1:
(432, 5), (654, 5), (900, 4), (344, 5), (484, 4), (291, 3), (116, 5)

Rating

Movie ID

Figure R6.12: The BST model for the MovieLens 1M dataset.

The data produced by a recommendation environment can be converted to a graphical representation using several different strategies
including the following:

BIPARTITE GRAPH The most common option is to use a bipartite
graph where users and items are modeled as nodes and inter-

actions are modeled as edges. The continuous feedback data is typically incorporated as edge weights, so that the graph is specified as $G = (U \cup V, E)$ where U is a set of user nodes, V is a set of item nodes, E is a set of edges each of which is a tuple (u, g_{uv}, v) where u is a user node, v is an item node, and g_{uv} is the corresponding feedback value. This layout is illustrated in Figure R6.13 (a). Assuming this representation, the recommendation problem can be solved by learning node embedding and then leveraging the standard scoring techniques discussed in the previous sections.

ITEM GRAPH The alternative option is to build a graph that includes only the item nodes. We can specify this graph as $G = (V, E)$ where V is the set of item nodes and E is the set of edges where each edge (v_i, g_{v_i, v_j}, v_j) captures the strength of association g_{v_i, v_j} between nodes v_i and v_j. The strength of association can be specified, for example, as the number of users who purchased both items. This layout is shown in Figure R6.13 (b). We can use this approach to learn item embeddings and make recommendations by searching nearest neighbors in the embedding space.

DIRECTED ITEM GRAPH The two methods described above assume that a single graph is built for all users and items, so that the learned node embeddings capture the global interaction patterns. The alternative approach is to build an item graph for an individual user or even a session, and predict the next item that the user will interact with based on this graph [Wu et al., 2019]. This basically reduces the recommendation problem to the graph classification task. The user-level and session-level representations are more granular than the global interaction graph, and this can be leveraged to capture more detailed information. For example, we can use a directed graph to capture the sequence of interactions, as illustrated in Figure R6.13.

In the next sections, we develop two specific solutions that use the item graph and bipartite graph approaches, respectively.

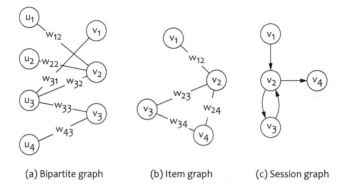

| (a) Bipartite graph | (b) Item graph | (c) Session graph |

Figure R6.13: Different options for representing interaction data as a graph.

R6.6.1   *Case Study: Recommendations Using Node2Vec*

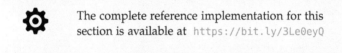

The complete reference implementation for this section is available at `https://bit.ly/3Le0eyQ`

We start by developing a basic solution that uses the Node2Vec algorithm introduced in Section 2.7.2.3 to learn node embeddings from the item graph, and then make recommendations by searching nearest neighbors in this embedding space. Similar to the previous sections, we use one of the MovieLens datasets that includes about 100,000 movie ratings. We build the item graph based on this dataset as follows:

- The original dataset consists of tuples (u, v, g_{uv}) where u is the user identifier, v is the item identifier, and g_{uv} is the corresponding rating made on a scale from 1 to 5. We keep only the records with the highest positive feedback ($g_{uv} = 5$) and filter out all other records, so that the preprocessed dataset is simply a collection of (u, v) tuples which can be interpreted as positive associations between the corresponding users and items.

- Next, we build a graph where each node represents an item (movie), and an edge between items v_i and v_j is created when at least one user exists who provided a positive feedback on both items, that is, the dataset contains tuples (u, v_i) and (u, v_j) for some user u.

- Finally, we assign weights to the edges to capture the strength of the item-to-item associations. We choose to compute the weight for the edge between nodes v_i and v_j using the following measure:

$$w_{v_i,v_j} = \log \frac{q(v_i, v_j)}{q(v_i)q(v_j)} \qquad \text{(R6.20)}$$

where $q(v_i)$ is the number of users who provided the feedback on item v_j, and $q(v_i, v_j)$ is the number of users who provided the feedback on both items v_i and v_j. This measure can be viewed as the mutual information between the items in the sense that the numerator corresponds to the joint probability of the feedback, and the denominator corresponds to the probability of the feedback assuming the independence between the items. A small part of the resulting graph is shown in Figure R6.14.

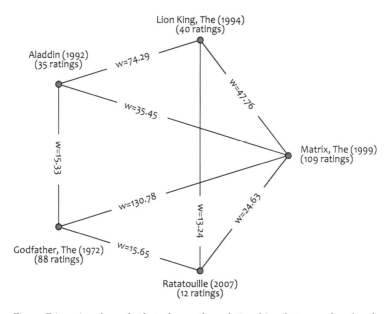

Figure R6.14: A subgraph that shows the relationships between five hand-picked movies. We show only the edges between the subgraph nodes, and each node has many other links to the nodes outside of this subgraph. On average, each item is linked to about 60 other items.

Once the graph is constructed, we can apply the Node2Vec algorithm. We use the standard Node2Vec algorithm specified in Section 2.7.2.3, but we modify the random walk routine to account for the edge weights. More specifically, we change rule 2.104 that controls the transition probabilities as follows[1]:

$$p(v, v'') \propto \begin{cases} w_{v,\, v''}/p, & \text{if } d(v, v'') = 0 \\ w_{v,\, v''}, & \text{if } d(v, v'') = 1 \\ w_{v,\, v''}/q, & \text{if } d(v, v'') = 2 \end{cases} \qquad \text{(R6.21)}$$

In other words, we make the random walk process biased towards the edges with relatively high weights. Once the random walks are performed, we follow the standard Node2Vec process. We first generate the training samples using negative sampling, and then train the dot product network to learn the node embeddings.

The node embeddings can be used to serve recommendation requests in many different ways. The first possible use case is to make non-personalized recommendations, for example, on a product detail page, by searching the nearest neighbors of a given item. Let us use this simple scenario to validate that the embedding space has a reasonable structure, and look up the nearest neighbors of five popular movies which were already used for illustrative purposes in Figure R6.14:

```
Matrix, The (1999):
- Lord of the Rings: The Fellowship of the Ring, The (2001)
- Lord of the Rings: The Return of the King, The (2003)
- Star Wars: Episode V - The Empire Strikes Back (1980)
- Star Wars: Episode VI - Return of the Jedi (1983)

Godfather, The (1972):
- Godfather: Part II, The (1974)
- Apocalypse Now (1979)
- Fargo (1996)
- Star Wars: Episode V - The Empire Strikes Back (1980)

Lion King, The (1994):
- Jurassic Park (1993)
- Aladdin (1992)
- Apollo 13 (1995)
- Braveheart (1995)

Aladdin (1992):
- Lion King, The (1994)
- Apollo 13 (1995)
- Beauty and the Beast (1991)
- Jurassic Park (1993)

Ratatouille (2007):
- Up (2009)
- Monsters, Inc. (2001)
- Guardians of the Galaxy (2014)
- Casino Royale (2006)
```

---

1 See Section 2.7.2.3 for the notation details.

We can see that most recommendations are aligned with the intuitive expectations based on the movie genres, although certain items look somewhat questionable. The second typical use case is to produce personalized recommendations using the item-based framework specified by expressions R6.9 and R6.13 where the items are scored based on the average distance to the items in the interaction history of a user. This solution can be categorized as pure collaborative filtering because the item embeddings produced by the Node2Vec algorithm capture nothing but the interaction patterns.

R6.6.2   *Recommendations Using GNNs*

In the previous section, we managed to replace the feedback prediction problem with the problem of learning the manifold of positive feedbacks, and it enabled us to successfully apply the unsupervised Node2Vec algorithm. In most cases, however, it is more convenient to follow the standard feedback prediction formulation and use the supervised modeling approach. The graph neural networks (GNNs) introduced in Section 2.7.3 provides a generic solution for this problem. In this section, we discuss a basic GNN recommendation model, known as *graph convolutional matrix completion* (GC-MC), that learns item and user embeddings in a supervised way [van den Berg et al., 2017]. A variant of this model was successfully productized by Pinterest at the scale of several billions of nodes [Ying et al., 2018].

Let us consider a recommendation environment where we observe interactions between users and items as tuples (u, v, g_{uv}) where u is the user identifier, v is the item identifier, and g_{uv} is a discrete feedback variable that takes values from the set of valid feedback levels $\{1, \ldots, R\}$. We also assume that users and items are associated with k-dimensional feature vectors which we denote as x_u and x_v, respectively.

We can represent the user-item interaction histories as R bipartite graphs $G_1, \ldots, G_R$ where graph G_r has an edge between user u and item v if, and only if, we observed the feedback $g_{uv} = r$. In other words, we represent multiple feedback levels as multiple layers, each of which is an unweighted graph. This enables us to apply the standard message passing framework defined in Section 2.7.3.1.

Conceptually, our goal is to develop a network that consists of an encoding part that maps users and items to embedding vectors z_u and z_v, respectively, and a decoding part that reconstructs feedback values g_{uv} based on these embeddings.

We specify the encoder using the standard message passing framework with several modifications that are needed to accommodate for multiple graph layers. The flow is symmetrical for user and item embeddings, so let us focus on the user embeddings first. For each user u, we start with aggregating messages from the adjacent item nodes as follows:

$$\mathbf{m}_{u,r} = \sum_{v \in N_r(u)} \frac{1}{c_{uv}} \mathbf{W}_r \mathbf{x}_v, \qquad 1 \leqslant r \leqslant R \tag{R6.22}$$

where index r iterates over all graph layers, $N_r(u)$ are the neighbors of u in graph G_r, and $\mathbf{W}_r$ is the matrix of learnable parameters for layer r. The normalization factor c_{uv} is used to remove the bias toward high-degree nodes, and we can specify it as follows:

$$c_{uv} = \sqrt{|N_r(u)| \cdot |N_r(v)|} \tag{R6.23}$$

The message vectors are then aggregated across the layers for each user as follows:

$$\mathbf{m}_u = a(\phi(\mathbf{m}_{u,1}, \ldots, \mathbf{m}_{u,R})) \tag{R6.24}$$

where ϕ is the aggregation operation such as averaging or concatenation, and a is the element-wise activation function such the sigmoid or ReLu. The final user embeddings are produced using a standard dense layer applied to the aggregated messages:

$$\mathbf{z}_u = a(\mathbf{W}\mathbf{m}_u) \tag{R6.25}$$

where $\mathbf{W}$ is the matrix of learnable parameters. The flow for item embeddings $\mathbf{z}_v$ is completely symmetrical, and parameter matrices $\mathbf{W}$ can be shared between users and items. This flow is illustrated in Figure R6.15. We can stack multiple message passing layers on top of each other by inserting embeddings $\mathbf{z}$ produced by the previous layer instead of the node feature vectors $\mathbf{x}$ in expression R6.22. In practice, however, the number of message passing layers is usually small: a one-layer network is sufficient for many real-world problems, and two layers will be sufficient for graphs with billions of nodes [van den Berg et al., 2017; Ying et al., 2018].

The decoding part of the network reconstructs the feedback values based on the user and item embeddings. We choose to model the user-item interaction using a bilinear layer, and start by computing the following scores:

$$s(u, v, r) = \mathbf{z}_u^\top \mathbf{Q}_r \mathbf{z}_v, \qquad 1 \leqslant r \leqslant R \tag{R6.26}$$

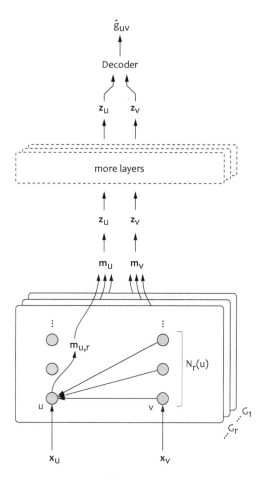

Figure R6.15: The architecture of the GC-MC model for feedback prediction.

where $\mathbf{Q}_r$ is a d × d matrix of learnable parameters assuming that the embedding vectors are d-dimensional. The probability that the feedback for user u and item v takes a specific value r is then estimated using softmax over the feedback values:

$$p(g_{uv} = r) = \operatorname*{softmax}_r s(u,v,r) = \frac{\exp(s(u,v,r))}{\sum_{\rho=1}^{R} \exp(s(u,v,\rho))} \qquad (R6.27)$$

These probabilities enable us to estimate the expected value of the feedback as follows:

$$\hat{g}_{uv} = \mathbb{E}\left[r \mid z_u, z_v\right] = \sum_{r=1}^{R} r \cdot p(g_{uv} = r) \tag{R6.28}$$

The complete network comprised of the encoding and decoding parts can then be trained using the standard categorical cross-entropy loss:

$$L(D) = -\sum_{u,v \in D} \sum_{r=1}^{R} \mathbb{I}(g_{uv} = r) \cdot \log p(g_{uv} = r) \tag{R6.29}$$

where D is the training dataset, and $\mathbb{I}$ is the indicator function that is equal to one when its argument is true and zero otherwise. Finally, the actual recommendations can be produced based on the estimated scores $\hat{g}_{uv}$ using the standard ranking techniques.

The GNN-based solution described above provides a powerful framework for building recommendation engines. First, it can be applied in pure collaborating filtering and hybrid environments because the user and item embeddings can incorporate both the structural information and entity features. Second, graph-based recommendation models generally achieve performance competitive with other approaches including the designs that we discussed in the previous sections of this recipe. Finally, the GNN approach is very flexible both in terms of scalability and expressiveness, so it can be applied to very large graphs that represent the entire user population, graphs with domain-specific entities such as user-defined item collections, and to small graphs that represent, for example, individual web-browsing sessions.

R6.7   EXTENSIONS AND VARIATIONS

The methods developed in the previous sections can be viewed as generic building blocks for estimating the feedback, predicting user-item interactions, and evaluating item similarities based on historical feedback data, entity features, event sequences, or interaction graphs. These methods can be modified and combined in many different ways to solve real-world recommendation problems. For example, we can produce nonpersonalized recommendations for product detail pages based on the distances in item embedding space, create recommendations for known customers based on their purchase histories, and recommend items to unknown (anonymous) customers based on their web sessions.

In this recipe, however, we assumed a basic B2C environment where the only goal is to create a list of relevant recommendations. This formulation is sufficient for a wide range of applications, but the functionality of a recommendation solution is not always limited to the item ranking. One typical example are B2B recommendation systems that are created by CPG, manufacturing, and other companies alike for their B2B digital commerce platforms. The users of such platforms are wholesale buyers who typically place recurrent orders with a large number of items and large quantities. The recommendation systems can provide features that facilitate this process by recommending not only items, but also the corresponding number of units, or recommending complete orders that can be placed with one click. This often requires involving not only the recommendation algorithms discussed in this section, but also demand forecasting methods which we discuss in other recipes.

In both B2C and B2B scenarios, the final list of recommendations can be the subject of various constraints that are applied on top of the output produced by the core recommendation algorithm. For example, a B2B recommendation system that suggests complete orders can make adjustments to fill up the shipping boxes or containers efficiently.

R6.8 SUMMARY

- The basic recommendation problem is to create an ordered list of items for a specific user and context in a way that the probability of desirable outcomes is maximized. In most environments, the desirable outcome is defined in terms of the probability of interaction with the recommended items or the magnitude of the feedback measured on some scale.

- The input of a recommendation system can be any combination of the user profile data and events, item data, user-item interaction events, and context data.

- A recommendation model is usually trained to optimize the accuracy of the interaction or feedback predictions, but multiple secondary metrics can be used in the offline evaluation to control the quality of recommendations. The overall efficiency of the recommendation solution is measured using online evaluation.

- Recommendation engines are commonly built using a two-layer architecture that consists of candidate retrieval and ranking algorithms.

- The interaction and feedback prediction problems can be solved by scoring individual items using arbitrary classification and regression models, but this approach is not always optimal from the computational standpoint. The alternative solution is to search for the nearest neighbors in the space of user and item embeddings.

- User and item embeddings suitable for the nearest neighbor search can be obtained using shallow and deep neural networks that predict the interaction probability or feedback using a dot product layer. Such networks can use item attributes, content embeddings, and user profile attributes as inputs.

- The order of interaction events can be accounted for using sequence models such as transformers. This approach is a powerful alternative to factorization networks with aggregated features.

- Interactions between user and items can naturally be represented as graphs, and thus the graph learning methods can be applied to learn user and item embeddings. This approach can be implemented using both unsupervised methods such as Node2Vec and supervised GNNs.

- The overall functional scope of a recommendation solution is often broader than just producing lists of recommended items. In both B2C and B2B environments, it can include quantity recommendations, one-click order recommendations, and various constraint-based optimizations.

Part IV

REVENUE AND INVENTORY MANAGEMENT

In the previous parts, we were mainly focused on the efficient usage of marketing resources such as budgets, campaigns, customer attention, and screen time. We generally assumed that customer engagement and conversion rates can be improved using personalized services, relevant and timely information, and valuable deals, and that the cost of these offerings to the company needs to be factored into the resource optimization problems. However, we did not discuss how to quantitatively assess the impact of pricing parameters on the demand, and how this assessment can be used to improve the overall financial performance of the company. In this part, we explore the relationship between prices, discounts, revenues, and profits more thoroughly and develop decision support tools and optimization components that help to efficiently manage the demand using pricing levers.

The demand modeling capabilities are the foundation of another large area of enterprise AI which is related to supply chain management and inventory optimization. We discuss how the operations in this area can be improved using forecasting, simulation, and optimization techniques.

7

PRICE AND PROMOTION OPTIMIZATION

Decision Support Tools and Optimization Models for Price Management

---

Pricing decisions are critically important for virtually all businesses because even small price changes can have a major impact on profitability and other key financial metrics. The idea to optimize prices using data-driven methods looks attractive because one can expect this approach to provide optimality guarantees and, in some sense, ensure that the company does not lose profits because of suboptimal pricing decisions. Secondly, pricing decisions are relatively easy to implement compared to other means, such as marketing campaigns or supply chain optimization, that the company can use to improve its profitability. One can therefore expect to achieve a high level of automation across both decision-making and decision operationalization processes.

The above considerations, as well as many other facts from economic theory and empirical studies, provide a strong argument for automated data-driven price management. Nevertheless, the practical implementation of these concepts is often challenging owing to the limited availability of data, complexity of demand patterns, sophisticated pricing structures, and other issues. This mismatch makes price management one of the most controversial areas of enterprise data science. In this recipe, we investigate some aspects of this problem and develop a few models and tools that help to improve certain pricing decisions. We focus mainly on the practical tasks and use cases providing only a basic overview of the fundamental models for price and demand analysis developed in economic theory.

R7.1   BUSINESS PROBLEM

Price management requires making many decisions at different levels of granularity, ranging from long-term strategic planning at the level of the entire company to personalized real-time decisions at the level of individual customers and specific moments in time. Some of these decisions require a lot of human judgment and can be supported only to a limited extent by data analytics, other decisions can be improved by combining advanced analytics with expert judgment, and certain decisions can be completely automated using programmatic agents.

In this section, we review the main stages of the price management process at a high level and discuss the functionality of possible decision support and automation tools for each stage. This analysis aims to identify specific problems that can be tackled using statistical methods and set a proper context for the development of specific solutions.

R7.1.1   *Price Management Process*

Price management processes vary significantly across companies depending on the industry, distribution channels, products, and other factors. In most cases, however, the process includes the development of a pricing structure and positioning, strategic analysis, regular planning, execution, and measurement. This reference process and some common activities associated with each step are shown in Figure R7.1. We discuss these steps one by one in the next subsections and then review the variations across industries.

R7.1.2   *Revenue Model*

The pricing model is generally inseparable from the overall business model of the company, and some pricing decisions need to be made in the early stages of the business or product life cycle. More concretely, the business model of a company usually includes a revenue model that specifies which revenue sources to pursue, what value to offer, who pays for this value, and how the value is priced, and this is the point where price management originates.

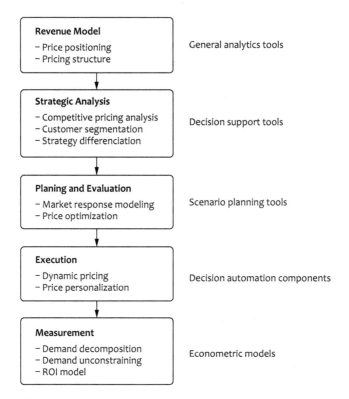

Figure R7.1: The main steps of the reference price management process and examples of specific activities in each of the stages. The typical level of automation for each step is shown on the right-hand side.

One category of fundamental pricing decisions is price positioning of a company, product line, or individual product. It is common to distinguish between luxury, premium, medium, low, and ultra-low price positions, and each of these positions has extensive implications on the business strategy in general and the price management approach in particular.

A company that pursues a luxury position typically makes heavy investments into brand awareness, the quality of their product or service, and limits production to relatively small volumes. The prices for luxury products are usually set to multiples of already-expensive premium alternatives to cover the costs associated with promotion, high quality, and limited production, as well as to communicate their value and exclusivity. Price setting for luxury goods requires deep understanding of the industry and close coordination with the setting of production limits.

In contrast, a company that pursues a low-price position would generally focus on sustainable cost minimization, limited assortment, product simplification, and large volumes. Price setting in this position usually follows the every day low price (EDLP) model with fewer special offers and discounts compared to the premium and medium positions.

Another large category of top-level pricing decisions is related to the design of the pricing structure. A software or media company, for instance, might need to choose between selling subscriptions and selling perpetual licenses. This choice has major implications on business sustainability, sales and marketing processes, and even organizational structure. In each of these two approaches, the pricing structure is further elaborated down to specific product packages, price tiers, and bundles.

The top-level decisions described above are usually supported by data analytics, and specific scenarios (business plans) are evaluated quantitatively to prove the feasibility of the approach and determine the key numerical parameters. This stage of the analysis can sometimes benefit from advanced statistical methods as well, but this approach generally requires a large set of comparable historical cases to be available. This may be feasible, for instance, for a large manufacturing company that can determine the price structure and positioning for a new product in a data-driven way based on the extensive portfolio of comparable products. In many other cases, the initial top-level analysis is done using conventional methods, but more nuanced details of the pricing structure and strategy are fine-tuned using decision support tools once the feedback data becomes available. This second level of the analysis is more relevant for the purposes of this recipe, and we discuss it more deeply in the next section.

R7.1.3   *Strategic Analysis*

Assuming that the price position and structure guidelines are shaped out, and certain market response data is available, we can plan and evaluate more specific scenarios using data-driven methods. The market response data can be obtained by executing *some* initial strategy, which can be viewed as experimentation, or collecting public or private data about similar businesses, products, and competitors. In this section, we review several analytical capabilities that can support strategic pricing decisions. Some of these capabilities can be implemented using basic data aggregation, but others require more advanced modeling techniques that will be discussed in the solution part of this recipe.

R7.1.3.1 *Price Strategy Differentiation by Product*

We first consider the problem of the price strategy differentiation across the products or services offered by the company. Let us assume a retailer that has a specific price position and a price structure that can include multiple elements such as regular prices, discounts, and special offers. Our goal is to determine the optimal pricing guidelines for individual products or product categories, although we are not looking to assign specific values to the price elements at this stage of the analysis. For example, we can determine that some products should be priced using the EDLP approach, but others would be better managed using the high-low pricing (also abbreviated as 'Hi-Lo' pricing) which alternates between regular and promotional prices.

This problem can be approached using the value maps introduced in Chapter 1. One common choice is to analyze products in the space of metrics that characterize the importance of a product to business and customers, as illustrated in Figure R7.2. The most basic measures that can be used to quantify the importance are the profit (importance to the business) and sales volume or revenue (importance to customers). However, more advanced metrics – such as number of online searches, number of shopping baskets, market share, and costs of switching between providers – can be used to measure the product's importance and consumer price perception.

The resulting space then can typically be divided into four areas that can potentially use different price strategies and guidelines:

KEY VALUE ITEMS The items with high value to both business and customers are often referred to as the key value items (KVIs)[1]. Customers generally remember market-average prices on KVIs, so these items play a central role in shaping customers' price perception of the seller. Consequently, KVIs are usually priced based on competitive pricing considerations, and setting the price points above the competitors' can negatively impact the pricing image of the seller.

PRIORITY ITEMS Certain high-volume items can have relatively low margins, but drive incremental shopping trips and cross-selling. Retailers commonly use price segmentation and personalization

---

1 This is just one of many KVI definitions. The term KVI is used broadly in many different contexts, and there are many different methodologies for determining and managing KVIs.

Figure R7.2: An example of a product value map spanned on financial metrics. Each point represents one entity such as an SKU, product, product group, category, or department.

techniques such as promotions to manage the trade-off between volume and margins for such items, and sometimes sell certain items at a loss just to drive incremental traffic.

FILLER ITEMS Slow-moving items that complement the main assortment can be priced mainly based on internal economics, for example, to maintain the target margin. These items also aim to improve customers' perception of the assortment.

TAIL ITEMS The items with low value to both business and customers, commonly referred to as 'tail' items, are also used to improve the perception of the assortment. These items are often differentiated across different locations and priced based on internal economics.

The above methodology facilitates the decomposition of the top-level pricing structures and positions into more specific strategies such as Hi-Lo promotions, and in the next section we will discuss how the parameters of these strategies can be set.

The analysis in the space of basic metrics such as volume and margin, however, is not the only option, and we can construct other useful spaces using more complex scores. For instance, the volume-margin space is not necessarily optimal for the KVI analysis because the volume and margin metrics are not directly linked to price perception and sensitivity. In practice, it may be better to develop more advanced scores that incorporate several metrics and to identify KVIs by ranking products according to these scores. For example, variants of the following algorithm are commonly used to identify KVIs in business verticals with frequently purchased items:

1. Identify bargain items that represent good value for the money (e.g. a 32 oz. yogurt product is a good value for the money, compared with a 6 oz. product).

2. Identify price-sensitive customers who mostly buy the bargain items.

3. Estimate the percentage of price-sensitive customers who buy the item. This value corresponds to ratio $C/(B + C)$ in Figure R7.3.

4. Estimate what percentage of all customers who buy the item are price-sensitive. This value corresponds to ratio $C/(A + C)$ in Figure R7.3.

5. Calculate the KVI score for frequently purchased items as

$$\text{score} = \alpha \cdot \frac{C}{B + C} + \beta \cdot \frac{C}{A + C} \tag{R7.1}$$

where α and β are the hyperparameters.

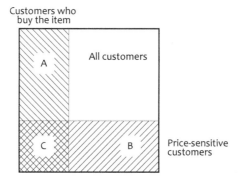

Figure R7.3: Customer cohorts for the product value analysis.

An example of the product value map constructed using the above algorithm is presented in Figure R7.4. The items are categorized as background, foreground, and KVIs based on the score defined by expression R7.1, and specialized pricing strategies can be set for each of these categories.

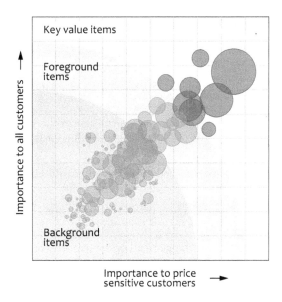

Figure R7.4: An example of a product value map spanned on the behavioral metrics. Each circle represents one entity such as a SKU, product, or category, and the radius of a circle is proportional to the sales volume of the entity.

The KVI analysis is mainly focused on managing pricing decisions against reference competitors' prices. However, an analysis in the space of advanced metrics can help differentiate between other aspects of the pricing strategy. In many verticals, price managers must balance between competing based only on regular prices and promoting products using special offers and discounts. This type of decision can be supported by a statistical analysis that quantifies regular-price and promoted-price elasticities, that is the sensitivity of demand to the changes in the corresponding pricing elements. We will discuss how these elasticities can be estimated later in this recipe, but assuming that such estimates are available, we can assign products to the following four pricing strategies:

EDLP For products and categories with relatively low promoted-price elasticities, promotion dollars can be redirected to the regular price.

HI-LO For products that are more sensitive to promoted-price than regular-price changes, fewer, but deeper, discounts can be offered.

HYBRID For products that are sensitive to both regular and promotion prices, a hybrid pricing strategy that optimizes the balance between regular prices and promoted-prices can be used.

MARGIN Products with low sensitivity to both regular-price and promoted-price changes can benefit from limits on promotion volume, as well as better price discipline.

This approach is illustrated in Figure R7.5. In addition to the customer response analysis, the choice between EDLP and Hi-Lo strategies also can be supported by the following insights:

MARKET SHARE Small brands will generally employ a Hi-Lo strategy to compete against stronger brands.

PRODUCT LIFE STAGE The Hi-Lo strategy is advantageous for new products with high levels of innovation and strong marketing support, while EDLP is generally more suitable for mature products.

SEASONALITY Products with seasonal demand spikes are likely to benefit from the Hi-Lo strategy.

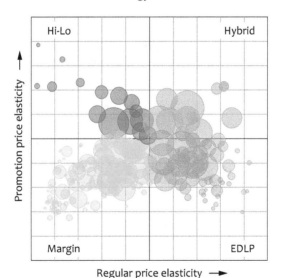

Figure R7.5: An example of a product value map spanned on elasticity metrics. Each circle represents one entity, and the radius of a circle corresponds to the sales volume.

R7.1.3.2   *Price Strategy Differentiation by Client*

The price differentiation techniques presented in the previous section are geared mainly towards retailers and direct-to-consumer businesses. These techniques can be applied in some B2B environments as well. For instance, a manufacturer of consumer packaged goods would use similar methods to manage manufacturer-sponsored promotions executed through its retail partner network. At the same time, many B2B and subscription-based businesses have complex pricing structures that are customized for each client. This requires the functionality for client-level pricing strategy differentiation to be provided by the decision support tools.

An example of a value map for the client-level strategy analysis is depicted in Figure R7.6. This map plots individual client entities in the space of simple metrics: the total client revenue for a period of time such as one year and the average discount amount provided to this client. In general, the value of a client, which we measure in terms of revenue, should be consistent with the discount, so the clients, ideally, should be concentrated along the diagonal line highlighted in the figure. This particular example, however, indicates that a number of clients with relatively low value are getting disproportionally large discounts, suggesting mismanagement. These cases might need to be investigated and pricing policies may need to be fixed.

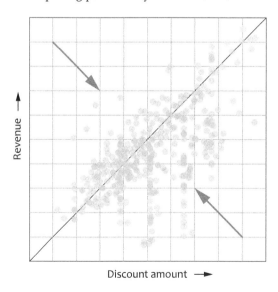

Figure R7.6: An example of a client value map. Each point represents one client.

The above method can be viewed as a simple client segmentation technique. We essentially grouped customers into different revenue buckets and validated that the corresponding discount policies are properly differentiated across the segments. We can, of course, use more advanced methods both to define the segments and to differentiate the strategies across them in both B2C and B2B environments. The segments are commonly defined using geolocation qualifiers such as country, state, region, or individual store; demographic properties such as income level; and various statistical scores discussed in recipes R1–R4 such as a lifetime value and propensity to churn. The previously described analytical techniques can then be applied at the level of individual segments. For example, a retailer can segment its brick-and-mortar stores based on the median income or average price elasticity in the corresponding locations, and then tune the product pricing strategies at the level of location zones using the tools described in the previous section.

The above approach is applicable in environments with relatively small numbers of segments, so that a meaningful strategic analysis can be performed for each of them. However, there is quite a broad range of scenarios that require the use of a large number of small segments or, ultimately, treating each customer as a stand-alone segment. This can be done to increase the efficiency of price differentiation, to work around data limitations, or to deal with complex and dynamic environments. These scenarios cannot be solved using methods and tools devised for strategic analytics, but need to be addressed using decision automation components which we discuss later in this recipe.

R7.1.3.3 *Competitive Pricing Analysis*

Competitor pricing is one of the main considerations for price setting, and pricing managers usually put a major effort into the analysis of how the value and price of the products they manage compare to those of competitors. Competitor pricing considerations are generally incorporated into all stages of the price management process. At the positioning level, the main focus is typically on the price-to-value relationship, so that a given product or service can be strategically priced below, in line, or above that of the competition depending on the relative value of its features. At the strategic analysis level, the choice of a pricing strategy is generally influenced by the strategies of competitors, and a pricing manager should justify why they take a similar or different approach compared to competitors. Statistical methods, however, enable us to go beyond the informal or qualitative comparison with competitors.

One technique that can be useful at the level of strategic analysis is the estimation of competitor price elasticities. Competitors' prices are commonly obtained by scraping the values from digital commerce systems and other web resources, but many retailers additionally provide the information about the inventory availability in online and brick-and-mortar stores, as illustrated in Figure R7.7. This information can be displayed as the number of stocked units or just binary indicators (available or not available). In either case, one can record the history of price, promotion, and inventory changes, and then estimate the efficiency of promotion campaigns executed by competitors, that is the acceleration or deceleration of the demand induced by price changes, through elasticity analysis.

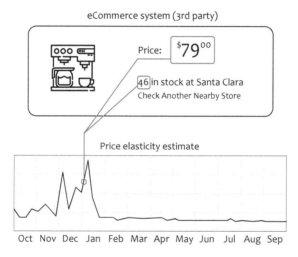

Figure R7.7: Estimating competitor price elasticity using web scraping.

At the lower levels of the price management process, competitor prices are usually incorporated into the demand models as one of the factors that influences the demand. We discuss this aspect in the next sections.

R7.1.4   *Planning and Evaluation*

The planning and evaluation stage of the price management process is focused on determining specific pricing parameters for the price strategies and structures selected in the previous steps. The planning process is more specific than the strategic analysis, and it usually provides more opportunities for statistical modeling and mathematical optimization, although it is not supposed to be completely automated. In this section, we discuss some of the planning activities and then review the design of the corresponding tools for decision support and optimization.

R7.1.4.1 *Planning Process*

For the sake of specificity, let us consider a typical planning process used by large retailers. The process generally starts with setting up a financial goal such as increasing sales by 5% over the previous year's figure, or achieving a specific target of $20 billion in sales and $8 billion in margin. Once the goal has been set, multiple teams build a specific plan for achieving the targets. This process, known as the *plan-to-sell process*, is often led by a merchandising team, with assortment planning, inventory, pricing and marketing teams helping the merchants to manage their respective processes. The plan-to-sell process is generally focused on developing two groups of assets: a buy plan that specifies what to buy, and a pricing plan that specifies how to sell, as shown in Figure R7.8.

Figure R7.8: The plan-to-sell process.

The merchandising team first develops the buy plan. This plan typically specifies the composition of the buy (what items, sizes, colors, and brands to carry), size of the buy (how many units of each item), and the life cycle of the buy (replenishment periodicity or seasonal cycles). Once the merchandising team has established the initial buying strategy, the pricing plan is then developed to specify how the merchandise will be sold. The pricing plan can initially be drafted using rough price optimization models at the level of categories and geographic regions, ignoring some of the inventory constraints. The buy and pricing plans are then iteratively reviewed and adjusted. For example, if the original buy plan does not have enough units to achieve the financial goals after exhausting all the pricing options, this information needs to be fed back, and the buy plan needs to be adjusted accordingly. As the retailer proceeds to execution, the pricing plan is regularly re-evaluated to incorporate ongoing sales data and other signals.

The price-to-sell process needs to account for supply and operational constraints which can be different for different types of products. From that perspective, it is common to differentiate between price-to-sell strategies for seasonal and replenishable items:

SEASONAL ITEMS Retailers typically purchase seasonal items such as apparel collections upfront and then optimize pricing to sell the limited purchased stock by the end of the season. A plan for seasonal products includes both an in-season promotion pricing plan and a post-season clearance markdown pricing, and the pricing goal for the seasonal plan is to achieve maximum sales revenues for the entire item life cycle or entire season. From the tooling standpoint, this involves long-term demand forecasting and inventory-constrained optimization.

REPLENISHABLE ITEMS For replenishable items such as toiletries, since inventory can be replenished and there are no constraints for the inventory ownership, the goal is to optimize profit for every selling period. Consequently, a pricing plan for replenishable items is usually much simpler than for seasonal items. From the tooling perspective, the problem boils down to price response modeling and unconstrained optimization.

We discuss the functionality of the tools that can support the price-to-sell process for both seasonal and replenishable items in the next section, and develop statistical and optimization models that back these tools in the solution sections.

R7.1.4.2 *Pricing Scenario Evaluation*

In order to create a pricing plan, we need to evaluate specific pricing scenarios. A scenario generally includes the following components:

VARIABLES Each product or service is associated with a price waterfall that generally includes multiple positive and negative elements. For example, the final price of a product can be computed by a retailer as

$$\text{out-the-door price} = \text{cost} + \text{markup} - \text{markdown}$$

In this expression, the markup and markdown components can be varied separately, and they can have different impacts on the demand, depending on how they are communicated to the customers. For example, a retailer can communicate only the out-the-door price in the case of the EDLP strategy, but emphasize the markdowns in the case of the Hi-Lo approach.

OBJECTIVES Scenario evaluation assumes that some performance metrics are estimated based on the input variables. In the most basic case, we can estimate the expected revenue or profit for an individual product over a certain time interval given specific pricing parameters. In practice, this approach is often imperfect or misleading because of significant cross-product and cross-interval effects, and a meaningful result can only be obtained through the evaluation of the total profit or revenue for a group of related products given all their pricing parameters.

CONSTRAINTS Finally, we often need to account for supply constraints such as inventory levels and lead times; the lack of coordination between inventory and pricing can result in out of stock events and lost revenues. Ideally, inventory and pricing parameters should be optimized jointly to achieve maximum returns, but, in practice, it is not always possible to do it this way. For example, seasonal items discussed in the previous section are typically purchased based on high-level demand estimates, and then only the pricing parameters are adjusted during the season to track the changes. In this recipe, we assume that supply constraints are fixed, and we can only optimize pricing parameters. A more general approach that involves both inventory and price decision optimization is discussed in recipe R9 (Inventory Optimization).

In order to evaluate a scenario, we need to estimate the performance metrics based on the pricing variables and constraints. As we stated earlier, such an evaluation often requires taking the following cross-product and cross-interval effects into account:

CANNIBALIZATION Comparable and substitutable products compete for the same demand, and aggressive pricing on one product can cause it to *cannibalize* the demand on the alternatives. For example, a manufacturer of power tools is likely to observe that promotions of drill kits cannibalize the demand on drills sold separately.

HALO The positive correlation between the demands on complementary products is referred to as the *halo effect*. For example, promotion of cordless drills is likely to increase sales of the corresponding batteries and other accessories. In some cases, a company can promote certain products exclusively to create halos and drive sales of other, more profitable items.

PULL-FORWARD Aggressive pricing on a product can drive an immediate revenue uplift at the expense of future revenues. A typical example is consumable goods such as toothbrushes – temporary promotions can entice a customer to purchase and stockpile multiple product units, but then this customer is likely to stop making any purchases until these units are consumed. This phenomenon is known as the *pull-forward* or *stockpiling effect*.

In practice, these effects can dramatically increase the complexity of evaluation because a large number of pricing variables need to be evaluated jointly.

An illustrative example of a tool that helps to evaluate pricing scenarios according to the above principles and guidelines is presented in Figure R7.9. In this example, we address the problem of the price promotion evaluation for a single product. The tool takes the promotion time frame (start and end dates) and promotion depth as input parameters, and then uses long-term demand and revenue forecasting models to evaluate the impact of this promotion on the product and category performance. The upper chart visualizes how the demand changes depending on the promotion depth or, alternatively, the out-the-door price. The spread between the demand forecasts that correspond to the minimum and maximum allowed prices characterizes the price elasticity of demand. For many products, the elasticity changes over time, and pricing managers can examine this plot to determine the optimal time frame for a promotion. For example, the price elasticity is usually higher during the holiday season compared to other times of the year.

The middle and lower charts visualize the cumulative product and category revenue, respectively. These charts help to analyze how the cross-product and temporal effects impact the business performance in the short and long runs. In particular, the cannibalization effect is highlighted in the middle and lower charts of Figure R7.9: the revenue of the promoted product increases during the promotion period compared to the baseline, but the overall category revenue decreases because of cannibalization. The middle chart of Figure R7.9 illustrates the analysis of the pull-forward effect: the promoted product is expected to get a revenue uplift during the campaign, but the long-term forecast shows the performance degradation compared to the baseline.

The example in Figure R7.9 demonstrates the use of predictive models for detailed price planning and evaluation. These models can further be combined with optimization algorithms to search for optimal pricing parameters such as promotion depth and date ranges. However, the optimization use cases can be more complex than just the setting of pricing points. Advanced examples include the detection of loss-driving promotions in manually created promotion calendars and

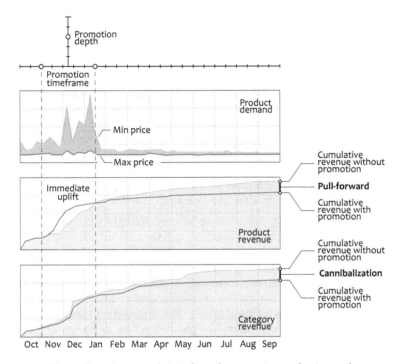

Figure R7.9: An example interface of a promotion evaluation tool.

the generation of new promotion suggestions. Similar to the forecasting problems, the main challenge in optimization is cross-product and temporal dependencies that require jointly optimizing multiple pricing variables.

R7.1.5 *Execution*

The planning framework described in the previous section aims to produce a pricing plan for a relatively distant horizon. Once the initial plan is finalized, and the seller proceeds to its execution, the discrepancy between the plan and actual results would typically emerge. For example, a retailer can observe that the actual sales rate for a seasonal product is lower than planned and recognize the risk of high liquidation losses. The usual approach to managing the execution phase is the continuous re-evaluation of the pricing scenarios based on the ongoing inventory and sales data and adjustment of the pricing parameters. In other words, the seller can dynamically change pricing variables to accelerate or decelerate the demand to meet the constraints and achieve the objectives.

The traditional approach to planning and execution, however, assumes the availability of historical data, a relatively static environment, and a fairly small number of pricing decisions. These assumptions hold true in many traditional environments, but there are a number of use cases, mainly related to digital channels, that cannot be efficiently solved using the planning framework alone. Such use cases require developing components that autonomously make decisions during the execution phase, often in real time and on a large scale. We collectively refer to this class of methods as *algorithmic pricing*. The main challenges that algorithmic pricing aims to address are as follows:

- First, historical sales data can be very limited in many environments. In practice, it is common to have only 10-20% of the catalog items sufficiently covered by historical data, and the remaining items are either new, have never been on promotion, or have data gaps because of technical or process issues. These limitations can be partly addressed using specialized demand forecasting techniques discussed later in this recipe, but, in general, pricing actions cannot always be planned for all items in advance, and some prices need to be automatically managed based on the near real-time market feedback.

- Second, prices need to be continuously adjusted in dynamic environments. For instance, many large retailers such as Amazon, Walmart, and Best Buy have adopted algorithmic price management which has resulted in frequent, often intra-day, price changes in their e-commerce systems. A retailer that operates in such an environment can use statistical analysis to estimate the impact of competitor price changes and design a proper price setting policy, but the implementation of this policy requires to develop near real-time decision-making components to respond automatically to competitor moves.

- Finally, price segmentation and personalization can sharply increase the number of pricing decisions. In an extreme case, the number of decisions can be as high as the number of customer-product combinations, and these decisions can only be made using decision automation components. The ability to differentiate pricing based on the willingness of individual customers to pay, and to capture the corresponding revenues, is one of the main advantages of algorithmic price management.

Algorithmic pricing plays an important role in modern price management environments, so we dedicate recipe R8 (Dynamic Pricing) to a more detailed discussion of the above problems and to the development of the corresponding solutions.

R7.1.6 *Measurement*

The primary goal of the measurement stage is to analyze the impact of the pricing actions that were planned and executed in the previous stages. Although it is the last step in our reference price management process, the ability to perform credible and accurate measurements of the results is the foundation and precursor of the entire process. In practice, the measurement capabilities should always be established before the optimization and execution take place.

Price management is an activity that is associated with financial gains and losses, and thus it generally makes sense to measure the impact of pricing actions using *return on investment* (ROI) concepts. As a starting point, let us define the *net marketing contribution* as

$$c = q \times p \times m - e \tag{R7.2}$$

where q is the volume sold, p is price, m is margin percentage, and e stands for marketing and sales expenses. The margin and expenses can be further decomposed into regular prices, markups, discounts, and other components according to the pricing and cost structures of the company. The *pricing ROI* can then be defined as

$$\text{ROI} = \frac{\text{uplift}(c)}{e_0} \times 100\% = \frac{c_a - c_b}{e_0} \times 100\% \tag{R7.3}$$

where c_b and c_a denote the contributions before and after a certain price change, respectively, and e_0 is the cost of planning and implementing the change. For instance, the ROI of a promotional campaign is commonly defined and measured as

$$\text{Promotion ROI} = \frac{(q_a - q_b) \times p \times m - e}{e} \times 100\% \tag{R7.4}$$

where subscripts b and a denote the values before and after the change, respectively, and e is the total cost of promotions. The practically useful ROI definitions, however, are usually more complex than the basic concept outlined in expression R7.3 because one needs to incorporate a wider range of business and econometric considerations. We examine some of these extensions in the next two sections.

R7.1.6.1 *Performance Metrics*

It is common practice to use several metrics that provide different perspectives on the gains and losses [Ruggiero and Haedt, 2014]. The following examples illustrate the process of breaking down the overall ROI into more granular measures, although the specific design is heavily influenced by the industry, business model, and sales channels:

BY PRICE Instead of tracking the overall contribution uplift, we can isolate the portion of revenue growth or loss attributable to a change in price as follows:

$$\text{uplift(price)} = (p_a - p_b) \times q_A \qquad\qquad (R7.5)$$

where p stands for price, q for volume, and subscripts a and b are used as defined in the previous section. This metric can be computed at different levels of aggregation such as product, category, client account, or business unit, and it helps to gauge how well the price change is received by sales channels and customers.

BY VOLUME Alternatively, the portion of revenue growth or loss attributable to a change in volume can be tracked as

$$\text{uplift(volume)} = (q_a - q_b) \times p_b \qquad\qquad (R7.6)$$

This metric isolates the impact of a change on longer-term consumption patterns. Similar to the price uplift, volume uplift can be calculated at various levels of aggregation.

BY PRODUCT Pricing actions can make customers switch between products or vendors, and some actions are specifically designed to drive cross-sell. The impact of pricing on the product portfolio can be measured as the portion of revenue attributable to the change in nonrepeating sales. Assuming a certain scope such as a regional or business account, we denote the set of all items with nonzero sales during the current period but without sales in the previous period as P_+ (added products), and all items without sales in the current period but nonzero sales in the previous period as P_- (removed products). The uplift by product can then be measured as the difference between the revenues associated with these two sets:

$$\text{uplift(product)} = \text{revenue}(P_+) - \text{revenue}(P_-) \qquad (R7.7)$$

This metrics, also known as *product churn*, helps to relate pricing actions with product penetration, sustainability of demand, and cross-sell potential.

The design of these metrics is mainly driven by business consider-ations and rarely involves complex statistical methods. The accurate estimation of these metrics, however, is not a trivial problem but one that often requires advanced mathematical apparatus, as we discuss in the next section.

R7.1.6.2   *Demand Decomposition*

The metrics presented above assume that we can accurately calculate the change in volume or revenue associated with a certain entity such as a product category and specific pricing action. Although this as-sumption can seemingly be satisfied using only the basic accounting methods, in practice it can be challenging to accurately estimate these values. As an illustrative example, let us consider a manufacturer that initially offered only one product a in a certain category, and then launched a second product b. The contribution uplift for this setup can be defined as

$$\text{uplift}(c) = q_b \times m_b - q_{a \to b} \times m_b \tag{R7.8}$$

where q_b is volume for the new product, m_a and m_b are margins for new and existing products, respectively, and $q_{a \to b}$ is the volume cannibalized by the new product from existing products. The evalu-ation of this expression can be complicated for several reasons. First, the estimation of the cannibalization term is likely to require statistical analysis, and it can be blocked by insufficient data variability in the collected samples.

Second, the estimation of volume q_b can also be complicated by out of stock events. To measure the success of a new product, we should calculate the uplift using the true demand values rather than the inventory-constrained sales numbers. This leads to the problem of *demand unconstraining*, that is the estimation of the true demand based on the sales data obtained under a limited supply. This task is impor-tant not only for measurement purposes, but for all other steps of the price management process, as well as inventory management. The rea-son for this is that making the forecasts and decisions based on partly observed demand is likely to produce suboptimal results. As we dis-cuss in the solution section, the demand unconstraining problem can be tackled using several different statistical methods.

Finally, we might be interested not only to estimate the total uplift delivered by the new product, but to determine which part of it comes from the market expansion, and which part comes from customers who are switching from competitors. Similar to demand unconstraining, this insight helps to properly analyze the success of the product.

The above examples demonstrate that even a seemingly simple scenario with two products can require decomposing the observed sales numbers into multiple components such as cannibalization, unrealized demand attributed to out of stock events, and market expansion to perform accurate and meaningful measurements. In real-world environments with multiple related products, competition, and other factors it is almost impossible to precisely measure the true positive or negative impact of a specific pricing action, but it is usually possible to avoid misleading results by making proper corrections.

R7.2   SOLUTION OPTIONS

In the above sections, we reviewed the typical problems that a price manager needs to solve at the different stages of the planning and execution cycle. Some of these problems are challenging to solve using advanced analytics, some can be solved more efficiently using decision support tools, and some require advanced decision automation. The problems that can benefit from machine learning and optimization appear at different stages of the price management process, but we can identify the set of basic capabilities that are needed to implement the functional designs described in the previous sections and transition from the business problem definitions to solution development:

MARKET RESPONSE MODELING Most planning activities require evaluating how the target market or its segments will respond to pricing actions and changes. The response can be estimated in terms of basic metrics such as volume or more complex ROI models that account for factors such as cannibalization and halo.

DEMAND FORECASTING Planning and execution steps often require not only estimating the aggregated market response, but also forecasting the demand, revenue, or profit as time series under different pricing scenarios. This task can be viewed as a generalization of the basic response modeling.

SALES DATA IMPUTATION Data limitations is one of the main challenges in price management, especially in B2B environments. These limitations can impair the response modeling and forecasting accuracy and validity. This problem can tackled using auxiliary models for *imputing* missed or invalid values in the observed data. The most common use cases include sales data imputation based on product similarity and demand unconstraining.

PRICE OPTIMIZATION Response and forecasting models enable the development of optimization models and the search for revenue or profit-maximizing pricing parameters under various constraints.

These tasks will be the main focus of the solution part of this recipe. We start by reviewing the basic market response models offered by traditional econometrics and chaining them together to capture multiple factors and effects. Then we discuss a more generic solution that uses time-series models to capture a wider range of factors as well as the dynamics of the market. After that, we review the imputation methods that help to apply market response models in settings with limited data availability. Finally, we discuss price optimization using traditional numerical methods and reinforcement learning techniques.

R7.3   MARKET RESPONSE MODELING

Market response on a price change is a sum of individual customer responses, and thus the response function can be derived from a probabilistic model of a customer. Let us first assume that each customer makes a yes-no purchasing decision based on the offered price. This is typically the case for services and durable products. A consumer can, for instance, decide between buying a car from a certain dealer or competitor, but buying two or more cars is not common even if an excellent price is offered. We can further assume that each customer has a maximum price they are willing to pay for a given product or service and we denote the distribution of such prices over the target market as $w(p)$. The aggregation of individual customer responses into the total market response is illustrated in Figure R7.10: the upper plots show the maximum acceptable prices for 16 customers that are drawn from the uniform distribution in the range from 0 to 100, and the lower plot is the sum of these step functions that corresponds to the total market demand.

In a more general case, customers can buy variable quantities of a product at different prices rather than make yes-no decisions. This is typical for consumable products such as groceries. Individual customer responses in this case are arbitrary functions of the price rather than step functions. An example of variable quantity responses is presented in Figure R7.11: each customer's response is a linear function specified by the intercept and slope coefficients drawn from two different uni-

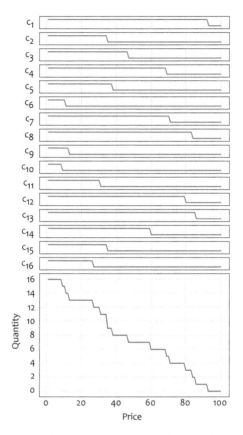

Figure R7.10: An example of a market response function for yes-no customer responses.

form distributions, and the sum of eight responses is the total market response function.

The above examples illustrate that the shape of the market response function is determined by the distribution of individual customer responses. Several standard shapes exist that are known to approximate market responses for most products reasonably well, and we discuss the two most common options in greater detail in the next sections.

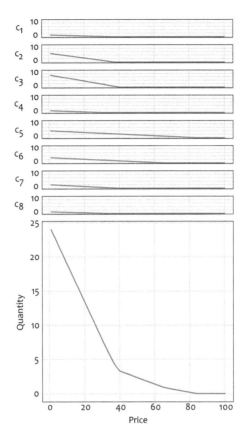

Figure R7.11: An example of a market response function for customer responses with variable quantity.

R7.3.1   *Linear Model*

One of the most basic response models can be obtained under the assumption that the distribution of maximum acceptable prices $w(p)$ in the yes-no scenario is uniform. First, let us note that the market response function for a specific price p can be obtained by integrating $w(p)$ as follows:

$$q(p) = q_{max} \int_p^\infty w(x) \, dx \qquad (R7.9)$$

where q is the total demand in units and q_{max} is the maximum achievable demand for a given number of customers. Assuming that

$w(p)$ is uniform in the range from o to p_{max}, we obtain the following demand function:

$$q(p) = q_{max} \int_p^{p_{max}} w(x)\, dx$$

$$= q_{max} \left(1 - \frac{p}{p_{max}} \right) \qquad (\text{R7.10})$$

$$= -\frac{q_{max}}{p_{max}} \cdot p + q_{max}$$

This is a linear function of price p, so we can conclude that the uniform distribution $w(p)$ implies a linear demand function. The demand curve presented earlier in Figure R7.10 indeed resembles a linear function, and we can get an arbitrarily close approximation by increasing the number of customers in the sample. Since the values q_{max} and p_{max} are not known in advance, we can specify the linear demand model simply as

$$q(p) = a - bp \qquad (\text{R7.11})$$

where a and b are the model parameters that need to be inferred from the data.

The demand function specifies the relationship between price and demand, but it is also useful to have a metric that explicitly quantifies the magnitude of the market response on a unit price change. The standard choice for such a metric is the *price elasticity of demand* defined as the ratio of the percent change in demand to the percent change in price:

$$\varepsilon(p) = -\frac{\Delta q/q}{\Delta p/p} = -\frac{\partial q}{\partial p} \times \frac{p}{q} \qquad (\text{R7.12})$$

The elasticity coefficient is the function of price, so it can take different values at different price or demand levels. High elasticity values at a certain price range generally indicate that the demand can be efficiently manipulated by price changes, while low values indicate that the demand is insensitive to price changes. For the linear model, we can insert a linear demand function into definition R7.12 to get the following expression for the elasticity:

$$\varepsilon(p) = \frac{bp}{a - bp} \qquad (\text{R7.13})$$

An example of a linear demand function and corresponding elasticities is shown in R7.12. This example illustrates how the elasticity can change at different price levels.

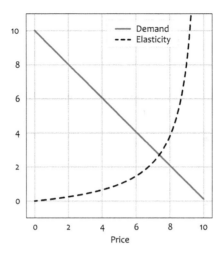

Figure R7.12: A linear demand model $q(p) = 10 - 10p$ and corresponding price elasticity.

The linear model is one of the most basic tools to use for price optimization. Conceptually, it can be fitted using just a few known price-demand points and any regression algorithm, and then various price points can be evaluated to determine the optimal price. This approach may be feasible for rough market response estimates: for example, a price management system of an online marketplace can use such a simple model to estimate the price-demand dependency based on a few data points in near real time. Many environments, however, require significantly more accurate market response modeling, and we discuss several simple extensions of the linear model that can help to achieve this in the next sections.

R7.3.2 Constant-Elasticity Model

In the linear model, price elasticity is just a secondary metric that helps to gauge the potential impact of price changes at different points of the demand curve. However, it is a known empirical fact that elasticity is relatively constant at different price points for many products, so we can build a more practical model under this constant-elasticity assumption. We can start with a hypothesis that elasticity is constant when the market response is a power function of the price:

$$q(p) = ap^{-\varepsilon} \tag{R7.14}$$

To prove this statement, let us express the derivative of the demand function as

$$\frac{\partial q}{\partial p} = -\varepsilon \cdot a p^{-\varepsilon - 1} \qquad\qquad (R7.15)$$

and then insert both R7.14 and R7.15 into the definition of the elasticity R7.12 obtaining the following:

$$-\frac{\partial q}{\partial p} \times \frac{p}{q} = \varepsilon \cdot a p^{-\varepsilon - 1} \cdot \frac{p}{a p^{-\varepsilon}} = \varepsilon \qquad\qquad (R7.16)$$

Consequently, the elasticity stays constant across the entire price range for demand function R7.14 and any given ε. This is illustrated by an example in Figure R7.13 where the demand curve clearly follows the power law and elasticity stays flat.

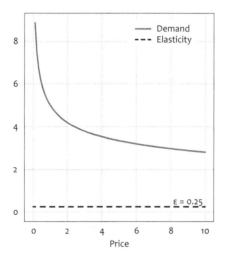

Figure R7.13: An example of a constant-elasticity demand function $q(p) = 5 \cdot p^{-0.25}$ and corresponding price elasticity.

The constant-elasticity model can be fitted on sales data using basic regression techniques, similar to the liner model. From that perspective, it is particularly convenient to rewrite expression R7.14 in the logarithmic form as follows:

$$\log q = \log a - \varepsilon \log p \qquad\qquad (R7.17)$$

This allows one to reduce the constant-elasticity model to the linear regression problem by applying a simple transformation to the input price and quantity samples. The constant-elasticity model is commonly referred to as a *log-linear model* for this reason.

R7.3.3 *Modeling the Cross-Effects*

The basic models described above are useful for estimating the correlations between product sales and individual pricing components, but most real-world response modeling problems involve multiple products, pricing components, and time intervals. One possible way to account for these factors is to build multiple constant-elasticity response models and to combine them, as summarized in Figure R7.14.

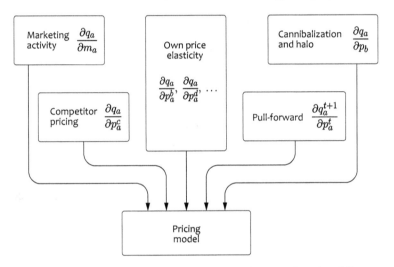

Figure R7.14: Typical composition of response models. For the sake of illustration, we assume two products, a and b. q_a stands for demand on product a, superscripts b and d stand for the baseline price and discount, respectively, superscript c denotes competitor price, superscript t denotes time interval, and m_a is the intensity of the marketing activity for product a.

First, product price often includes the base price, discounts, and surcharges, and each of these components is usually associated with a distinct elasticity value, depending on how the price is communicated to the customers. Second, we often need to account for the cannibalization and halo effects discussed earlier. These effects can be expressed in terms of cross-elasticities. For instance, the cross-elasticity of the demand on product a with regard to price changes on a related product b can be expressed as follows:

$$\varepsilon_{b \to a} = -\frac{\partial q_a}{\partial p_b} \times \frac{p_b}{q_a} \qquad \text{(R7.18)}$$

Third, the impact of competitor prices can also be expressed in terms of cross-elasticities. Fourth, the pull-forward effect can be captured by measuring the elasticities between time-shifted pairs of price and demand. Finally, it is often useful to estimate the impact of the intensity of the marketing activities on the demand as the *marketing elasticity of demand* just like we estimate the price elasticity of demand.

Let us review a numerical example that demonstrates how the above analysis can be done using only the basic tools. We consider a setup with three related products (denoted as a, b, and c), and evaluate two pricing scenarios for product a. We start by fitting four regression models to estimate their own price elasticity, cannibalization between products a and b, halo between a and c, and pull-forward effect for product a. We assume that this analysis produces the following estimates:

- The own price elasticity is about 3.00. For instance, price reduction by 50% increases sales by 150%.

- The cross-elasticity between a and b is about -0.75. For instance, price reduction for product a by 20% decreases sales of product b by 15%.

- The cross-elasticity between a and c is about 1.20. For instance, price reduction for product a by 20% increases sales of product b by 24%.

- The pull-forward effect is estimated to decrease sales by 4% for every 20% of price reduction for a period of about a quarter.

The calculations needed for scenario evaluation are presented in Figure R7.15. We evaluate and compare two possible price options: regular price of $3.00 and price reduction down to $2.50. Prices for products b and c are assumed constant.

As shown in the figure, the first option translates into the total sales of $7,150 for the current month for all three products. The second option delivers 50% volume increase for product a, 13% volume decrease for product b due to cannibalization, and 20% volume increase for product c due to halo. The total revenue for the current month increases to $7,950. At the same time, the long-term revenue for product a is expected to drop by $300 because of pull-forward, so the final total revenue number is estimated as $7,650. We can conclude that the second option (price reduction) is better than the first one in terms of revenues, although it is associated with both positive and negative effects that need to be carefully assessed and included in the ROI calculations.

	Own a			Cannibalized b			Halo c			a+b+c
	Price	Units	Sales	Price	Units	Sales	Price	Units	Sales	Total sales
Price 1	$ 3.00	1000	$ 3,000	$ 3.00	800	$ 2,400	$ 3.50	500	$ 1,750	$ 7,150
Price 2	$ 2.50	1500	$ 3,750	$ 3.00	700	$ 2,100	$ 3.50	600	$ 2,100	$ 7,950
% Change	-17%	+50%		0%	-13%		0%	20%		

Own elasticty	Cross elasticty	Cross elasticty
17% / 50% = 3.00	-13% / 17% = -0.75	20% / 17% = 1.20

Pull forward a	
	Sales for next 3 months
Baseline	$ 9,000
Forecasted	$ 8,700
Changes	- $ 300

Figure R7.15: An example of cross-effects analysis and pricing scenarios planning using basic tools.

R7.4   DEMAND FORECASTING

The econometric approach discussed in the previous section estimates the average correlations between price and demand. This can help to perform the high-level analysis and evaluation, but, in many practical applications, the demand and its relationship to price change over time. We therefore need to optimize pricing decisions for specific time intervals rather than optimizing them on average. For example, a seller might be interested to intensify promotional campaigns during the time intervals when price elasticity is at its highest. This generally requires forecasting the demand, revenue, or profit as functions of time. In this section, we briefly discuss the modeling methods that can be applied to this problem, and then develop a prototype using a realistic data sample.

R7.4.1   *Model Design*

The demand forecasting problem is a particular case of the sequence element prediction problem introduced in Section 2.4 and, in principle, we can use any sequential model to tackle it. In this section, we consider several specific design options that are commonly used in practice.

Many traditional demand forecasting methods are purely autoregressive, that is they use only the demand observations from previous time steps to predict the values at the next time step:

$$\hat{q}_{t+h} = f(q_t, q_{t-1}, \ldots) \tag{R7.19}$$

where q_t is demand at time t, h is the forecasting horizon, and values q_t, q_{t-1}, ... are the lags. The autoregressive methods typically make specific assumptions about the structure of the input time series such as smoothness, autocorrelation, or potential presence of trends and seasonal cycles. The model fitting process basically decomposes the observed series into such regularized components, and then the forecast is produced by extrapolating individual components and assembling them back into the total demand[1].

The pure autoregressive approach is often a good choice for demand forecasting, and comprehensive implementations of the standard methods are readily available in many statistical and machine learning libraries. This solution, however, has several limitations that become particularly prominent in data-rich environments. First, the quality of the forecast can often be improved by augmenting the information available in the time series itself with external signals such as competitor prices, marketing activity, and the weather. Second, making specific assumptions about the internal structure of the forecast series represents a trade-off: it helps to fit the model properly on a limited data sample, as well as producing interpretable results, but it generally limits the ability to capture complex patterns. In traditional time series analysis, these problems are usually addressed by extending the autoregressive techniques with external regressors and choosing the right model or combination of models from a large collection of methods developed based on different assumptions about the structure of the series[2].

In practice, the limitations of traditional time series models can often be overcome by using generic supervised learning models adapted to time series forecasting as described in Section 2.4.2. A typical architecture of the demand forecasting model that follows this approach is presented in Figure R7.16. This architecture assumes a high-capacity regression model such as a deep neural network that is trained to predict one value q_{t+h} based on autoregressive lags and external signals up to the step t.

---

1 The most common methods in this category include the Holt-Winters forecasting procedure, also known as triple exponential smoothing, and ARIMA models. A thorough discussion of these methods is provided in [Shumway and Stoffer, 2017], as well as in many other textbooks on time series analysis.

2 For instance, the ARIMA model has a counterpart called ARIMAX that combines the autoregression with the linear regression on external signals.

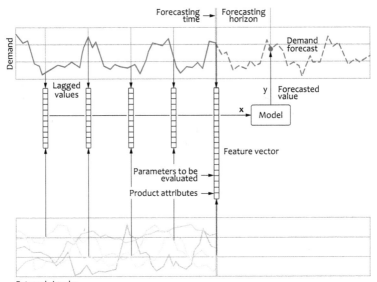

Figure R7.16: One of the typical model architectures for demand forecasting.

Each input feature vector is typically constructed as a concatenation of several lag vectors and static attributes. Each lag vector, in turn, can include the corresponding demand value and external regressors. For example, a model that produces a h-days-ahead demand forecast for an individual product can have the following design of the inputs:

$$\hat{q}_{t+h} = f(c,\ p_{t+h},\ m_{t+h},\ x_t,\ x_{t-1},\ x_{x-2},\ \dots) \tag{R7.20}$$

where c is the product category attribute, q_t, p_t, and m_t are the product demand, price, and markdown values at day t, respectively, and $x_t = (q_t, p_t, m_t)$ are the lag vectors. The model is trained to estimate q_{t+h} based on these inputs, and can then be evaluated for all valid values of p_{t+h} and m_{t+h} to determine, for example, the optimal price and markdown that maximize the profit value given by

$$\text{profit}_{t+h} = (p_{t+h} - m_{t+h}) \times \hat{q}_{t+h}$$

This basic design can be extended further with a wider range of parameters and external signals. The future values of these signals and parameters may or may not be known at the time of forecasting. For example, we can usually assume that the future price is known because we enter specific values into the feature vector for the sake of evaluation. In contrast, the future values of weather are unknown, but can often be substituted by forecasts or historical averages, or multiple scenarios can be separately evaluated.

The above approach provides significant flexibility both in terms of feature design and modeling algorithms. First, forecasting models can be trained for different scopes. For example, a brick-and-mortar retailer can train a separate model instance for each product, one model for an entire product category based on the data from all store locations combined, or one model for each combination of a category and specific store location. The models trained for broader scopes can still use granular input data and low-level entity attributes to produce granular forecasts. For example, we can train a model using a dataset that includes daily demand samples for all products in some category with each feature vector consisting of the demand value itself and also product and location attributes. This enables the demand forecasting for individual products, even new ones, based on their attributes. Building a model for a narrow scope such as a specific product-location combination is often challenging because of limited data availability for slow-moving and new products. On the other hand, building a model for a broad scope helps to enable transfer learning across products and locations, but requires the demand pattern to be somewhat consistent for all entities in the scope. It is usually preferable to start with building broad-scope models and splitting them into more specialized versions only if necessary. We continue to discuss this topic in Section R7.5.2.

Second, we might need to produce forecasts for multiple horizon values, and the above considerations also apply to this case: we can train separate models for each horizon value, use horizon as an input feature, or train only one model for some fixed horizon and use it to perform rolling forecasts for other horizon values. In the latter case, the values predicted for shorter horizons are used as inputs to make longer-term forecasts. For example, we can use a 7-days-ahead model to predict the next seven daily demand values, and then use these values as inputs (lags) for the same model to produce the forecast for up to 14 days ahead.

The design with aggregated features described above is the mainstream solution that is widely used in price optimization applications. The sequence-input models, including recurrent networks and transformers introduced in Sections 2.4.4 and 2.4.7, respectively, that directly consume individual lag vectors are alternative solutions that are also worth evaluating in many price management applications [Wu et al., 2020; Lim et al., 2021].

The selection of the core model from the various options described above, however, is only one component of the demand forecasting problem. In practice, we often need to deal with issues that are characteristic for the price management applications and which cannot be automatically addressed by the standard general-purpose time series forecasting methods. We discuss these aspects in the next section where we build a prototype of the demand forecasting solution using a realistic data sample.

R7.4.2   *Case Study*

 The complete reference implementation for this section is available at https://bit.ly/3LeFdV0

The response modeling and forecasting techniques described in the previous sections can produce meaningful results only if the input data are valid. Unfortunately, it is very common for sales and pricing data across the industries to be incomplete and contain various irregularities, resulting in the developers of price optimization solutions often having to engineer complex data preprocessing pipelines and auxiliary models to achieve useful and credible results. In this section, we review a simplified example of such a pipeline to better understand what a complete response modeling or forecasting solution can look like and what methods can be used to support the core models that were introduced earlier.

We use a dataset created based on the online orders obtained from a retailer of consumer goods. The dataset is pre-aggregated into a flat set of tuples, each of which includes the realized demand (sales quantity) and price for a certain product at a certain date:

```
Order items: 94591 rows x 4 columns
+--------------+------------+---------+----------------+
| product_id |       date |  price |  sales_units |
|--------------+------------+---------+----------------|
|            0 | 2017-06-05 |   55.9 |            1 |
|            0 | 2017-06-28 |   55.9 |            1 |
|            0 | 2017-07-27 |   55.9 |            1 |
|            0 | 2017-08-01 |   58.9 |            1 |
|            0 | 2017-08-05 |   58.9 |            1 |
|            0 | 2017-08-10 |   58.9 |            1 |
|            0 | 2017-09-13 |   58.9 |            1 |
|            0 | 2018-03-18 |   64.9 |            1 |
|            0 | 2018-05-18 |   64.9 |            1 |
|            1 | 2017-04-26 |  239.9 |            1 |
+--------------+------------+---------+----------------+
```

The dataset includes about 32,000 unique products. An example of price and sales time series for one of the products is shown in Figure R7.17. This particular example includes a relatively large number of samples and price changes, but many other products have far fewer samples and less variability in price.

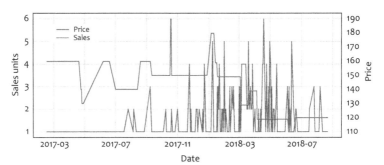

Figure R7.17: An example of price and sales series for one of the products in the dataset.

Our goal is to build a simplified demand forecasting model and use it to estimate market response functions for individual products. However, we do not aim to estimate complex economic effects such as halo and cannibalization, nor to leverage transfer learning across the products because the input dataset lacks product categorization and attribute information.

The implementation plan is presented in Figure R7.18. We start by filtering out products with insufficient sales data, so that the resulting dataset includes only active products that have had at least ten weeks with non-zero sales. The number of such products is close to 1,200 which is a sharp drop compared with the number of unique products in the original dataset. The products with insufficient data need to be handled separately using coverage expansion techniques discussed in Section R7.5.2 or dynamic price management discussed in recipe R8 (Dynamic Pricing).

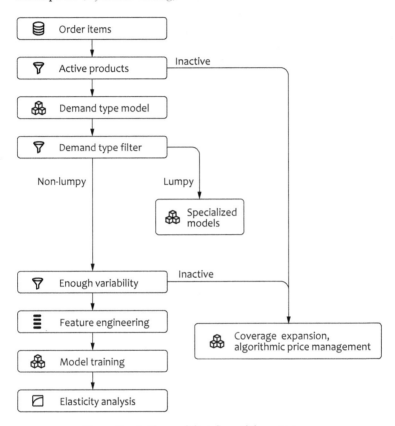

Figure R7.18: The modeling flow of the prototype.

The second step is to classify and filter the products by demand type. The rationale behind the demand type analysis is that many general-purpose forecasting methods have issues handling sparse and highly irregular time series, but irregularities are very common in the demand data. Consequently, it is common to split products into several groups based on the demand patterns and use different forecasting techniques for different groups. Most demand categorization methods use metrics that quantify various aspects of demand variability, define demand types as regions in the space spanned on these metrics, and then map products to those regions. One of the most common categorization methodologies uses the following two metrics [Syntetos et al., 2005]:

ADI   The average inter-demand interval (ADI) is a measure of demand sparsity that is defined as the average distance between two nonzero demand intervals. For a time series of length n, the ADI can be calculated simply as

$$ADI = \frac{n}{k} \tag{R7.21}$$

where k is the number of demand buckets, which are the intervals with consecutive nonzero demand values.

CV²   The squared coefficient of variation (CV²) is a measure of the demand magnitude variance. It is defined as the ratio between the variance σ_q^2 and squared empirical mean $\mathbb{E}[q]$ of the demand series:

$$CV^2 = \left(\frac{\sigma_q}{\mathbb{E}[q]}\right)^2 \tag{R7.22}$$

The above two metrics can be used to construct a two-dimensional space and define four regions that correspond to four distinct demand patterns, as shown in Figure R7.19. The threshold values for ADI and CV² can be chosen based on the theoretical analysis. The most common choice of ADI = 1.32 and CV² = 0.48 is based on the comparative theoretical analysis of two specific forecasting methods designed for smooth and intermittent patterns, and determining the optimal point for switching between the two.

Armed with the above methodology, we compute the ADI and CV² metrics for the set of active products we created in the previous step, and plot them as shown in Figure R7.20. This visualization reveals that most products have intermittent and lumpy demand patterns.

It is sometimes feasible to change the distribution of demand patterns by switching between different levels of aggregation. For example, we can aggregate the original daily series into weekly buckets and repeat the demand type analysis. The weekly series are expectedly smoother than the daily ones, so the corresponding distribution shown in Figure R7.21 has more items falling into the smooth and erratic regions compared to the daily plot in Figure R7.20.

We choose to use weekly series for further analysis, and to filter out the lumpy items so that the filtered set we work with includes about one thousand products. The lumpy items can be handled separately using more specialized modeling methods. Ideally, each of four regions

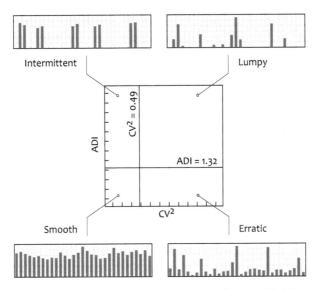

Figure R7.19: The distribution of products by demand type with daily data aggregation.

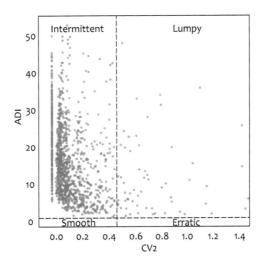

Figure R7.20: The distribution of products by demand type with daily data aggregation.

should be studied separately and the possibility of developing region-specific improvements should be explored.

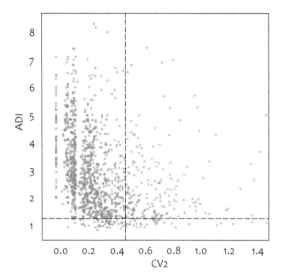

Figure R7.21: The distribution of products by demand type with weekly data aggregation.

Finally, we apply one more filter to ensure enough variability in the pricing parameters. This filter allows only for products that have changed their price at least three times, and each of these price points is required to have at least four days of sales. The final dataset we use for model training includes about 1,500 samples for approximately 50 products. This example demonstrates how a seemingly large sales dataset can shrink by several orders of magnitude after the data cleansing, resulting in a very low catalog coverage.

Once the dataset is prepared, we fit a demand forecasting model using a simplified version of the design presented earlier in Figure R7.16. We first perform some feature engineering work extending the original schema with features like month, year, and the number of days to Black Friday, and mapping the price values to the logarithmic scale. This input is then used to fit a generic supervised model with aggregated inputs. For the sake of conciseness, we skip the validation details and provide just the feature importance chart in Figure R7.22 which confirms that time, price, and product identities have significantly the most influence on the demand.

The forecasting model can be used in a number of ways, including market response analysis, price optimization, and inventory planning. The market response analysis, for instance, can be performed by fixing a specific product and date, and then evaluating the demand for a grid

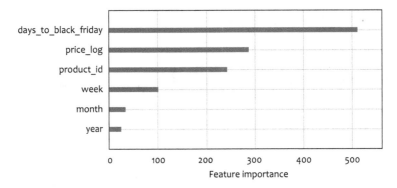

Figure R7.22: Relative feature importance for the demand forecasting model.

of price points. An example output of this procedure is shown in Figure R7.23. This output essentially represents a nonparametric market response function, and more insights such as price elasticity and its dynamics over time can be derived from it.

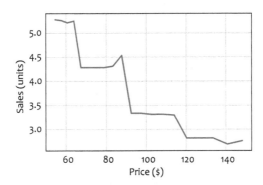

Figure R7.23: An example market response profile for one of the product-date combinations.

R7.5   IMPUTATION TECHNIQUES FOR DEMAND ANALYSIS

In the previous sections, we briefly discussed that limited data availability and variability are among the main challenges in practical demand forecasting and price optimization. We now turn to techniques that can help to overcome some of these limitations and extend the applicability of the forecasting and response modeling methods.

R7.5.1 *Demand Unconstraining*

 The complete reference implementation for this section is available at https://bit.ly/3EJdJo4

The first scenario we consider is the sales data collected in the presence of out-of-stock events, so that some samples in the demand series correspond to the true demand, but others are truncated because of capacity or inventory limitations. Such truncated samples are commonly referred to as *censored*, and the demand is said to be *constrained*. Performing forecasting or response modeling using censored data would generally result in underestimation, so we should either discard the censored samples or handle them in a special way.

Removing the censored samples from the dataset is a valid approach, and, moreover, we can backfill these elements by the corresponding predicted values once the forecasting model is built. However, the censored samples carry the information about the lower boundary of the demand (the true demand is at least as high as the capacity constraint), and we can extract it using appropriate techniques. This problem is typically framed as a stand-alone demand unconstraining problem, that is the estimation of the true demand values based on the available data. The censored samples can then be replaced by the estimates and used in the downstream analysis and modeling activities.

One of the most common demand unconstraining methods is based on the idea that the demand samples can be assumed to be drawn from some parametric probabilistic distribution, and the parameters of this distribution can be estimated using the expectation-maximization (EM) procedure [Salch, 1997]. We discuss the basic version of this method that assumes all demand samples to be independent and identically distributed, but it can be further extended to incorporate the dependencies between samples in a time series.

Let us assume that we observe a set of n demand values

$$Q = \{q_1, \ldots, q_n\} \tag{R7.23}$$

For each sample q_i, we know the corresponding maximum capacity b_i, and samples where $q_i = b_i$ are considered censored. For example, a retailer might know the stock level for a certain product at the beginning of each week and the number of units sold during that week, which cannot exceed the stock level. Let us assume that there are n_u unconstrained samples, and denote the subsets of constrained and unconstrained values as C and U, respectively.

We further make an assumption that the demand samples are drawn from the normal distribution $N(\mu, \sigma^2)$ and aim to estimate its parameters μ and σ. The procedure, however, is generic, and other parametric distributions can be inferred in the same way. We start by estimating the initial parameter values using the available unconstrained samples:

$$\mu = \frac{1}{n_u} \sum_{q_i \in U} q_i$$
$$\sigma^2 = \frac{1}{n_u} \sum_{q_i \in U} (q_i - \mu)^2$$

(R7.24)

We next replace the constrained values by the expectations conditioned on the known constraints b_i and also estimate the corresponding squared values:

$$\text{for } q_i \in C: \quad q_i \leftarrow \mathbb{E}\left[x \mid c \geqslant b_i, \, x \sim N(\mu, \sigma^2)\right]$$
$$q_i^2 \leftarrow \mathbb{E}\left[x^2 \mid c \geqslant b_i, \, x \sim N(\mu, \sigma^2)\right]$$

(R7.25)

The above values can be estimated using Monte Carlo sampling, as well as analytically. This step is commonly referred to as the expectation step.

Once the demand values are updated, we can re-estimate the distribution parameters using all available samples:

$$\mu = \frac{1}{n} \sum_{q_i \in Q} q_i$$
$$\sigma^2 = \frac{1}{n} \sum_{q_i \in Q} q_i^2 - 2q_i\mu + \mu^2$$

(R7.26)

This step is known as the maximization step. Repeating the expectation and maximization steps iteratively, we normally converge to specific distribution parameters and corrected demand values.

The above process is illustrated in figures R7.24 and R7.25. The first figure shows the input dataset; a short sales series of 18 samples and corresponding capacity constraints. It is clear from the figure that the demand values at positions 2, 5, and 7 are constrained. The second figure shows the demand values after each of the first three iterations of the EM algorithm. The constrained samples are recovered, and the process quickly converges to the stable values that are, as expected, higher than the original ones.

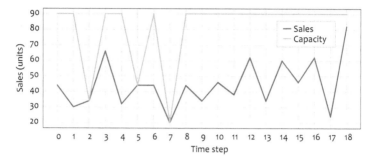

Figure R7.24: A data sample for the demand unconstraining prototype.

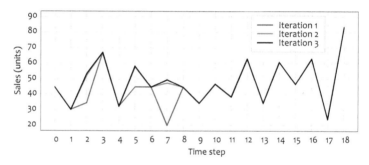

Figure R7.25: The outputs of the EM algorithm in the demand unconstraining prototype.

R7.5.2   Product Similarity Analysis

One of the most common and challenging problems in both B2C and B2B price management environments is the limited availability of sales data . The data can be limited because the product is new or slow-moving, and the percentage of such products in the assortment may be very high in certain sectors such as online marketplaces. The second reason why data can be limited is insufficient price variability. In B2B environments, for example, it is often the case that only a small fraction of items were ever on promotion. This makes it challenging to estimate the promotional price elasticity for all items and to determine which ones should really be promoted. Finally, the data can be limited because of technical and organizational issues. For example, pricing information can be scattered across multiple systems or documented in slide decks or other formats that are difficult to parse.

From the modeling perspective, the limited data availability typically leads to low catalog *coverage*, so that reasonably accurate demand forecasts can only be produced for a subset of products that have enough historical data. The coverage, however, can be improved using a number of techniques. First, one can evaluate several forecasting models that use product attributes such as category, size, and color, and various product embeddings as input features and compare the results. The use of product attributes and more sophisticated embeddings generally enables transfer learning across products, and also the forecasting for new and slow-moving products. The product embeddings can be produced based on the content and user-item interaction data using the methods discussed in recipes R2 (Customer Feature Learning) and R6 (Product Recommendations).

The second technique is to compute product similarity metrics, and make forecasts and other estimates for products that are covered insufficiently, by averaging the forecasts for the most similar products that have enough historical data. The similarity is typically estimated based on attributes and embeddings, but the specific approach and algorithms are usually selected heuristically based on the industry, available data, and other considerations. An example pipeline for coverage expansion that combines both this and previous techniques is shown in Figure R7.26. The upper part of the figure depicts several model designs that can be used to directly forecast the demand for a given product based on its identity or attributes. The lower part shows the similarity-based expansion for insufficiently covered products.

The quality of the forecast, as well as the optimization precision, is typically the highest for the products and categories with sufficient data, and the more aggressive coverage expansion techniques we use. The lower quality results from the items we expand over. In practice, it is often useful to visualize the trade-off between the quality and coverage as shown in Figure R7.27. This chart helps to trace how different expansion techniques influence the accuracy or other quality metrics, what business value is delivered by each expansion technique, and what the most useful expansion boundaries are.

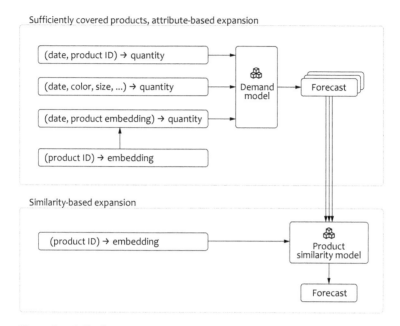

Figure R7.26: Catalog coverage expansion using content features and product similarity analysis.

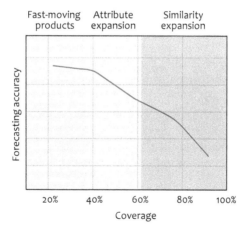

Figure R7.27: A conceptual illustration of the catalog coverage expansion analysis.

R7.6   PRICE OPTIMIZATION

The demand models developed in the previous sections allow us to forecast the demand as a function of price, and we can thus leverage them to perform price optimization. In the most basic case, the price of a single product considered in isolation can be optimized based on a profit equation such as the following:

$$\text{profit}(p) = q(p) \times (p - c_v) - c_f \tag{R7.27}$$

where p is price, q is the demand function, and c_v and c_f are variable and fixed costs, respectively. In practice, this equation needs, of course, to be customized dependent on the specific industry, business model, and pricing structure. Assuming a parametric differentiable demand model, the optimal price that maximizes the profit in expression R7.27 can be determined analytically by taking the derivative of the profit and equating it to zero. In this way, the closed-form expressions for optimal prices can be obtained, particularly for linear and constant-elasticity demand models. In practice, however, it is much more common to solve the problem numerically by evaluating the profit for all valid price points and picking the best option. This helps to account for the discreteness of price levels, to incorporate various constraints, and to perform optimization for non-parametric demand functions and arbitrary complex profit models.

The numerical price optimization for simple scenarios similar to that above, is typically straightforward, but real-world scenarios often require optimizing multiple interdependent pricing parameters. Some problems in this category can be computationally challenging, but we can tackle them using a wide range of optimization methods. In the next section, we consider several typical business scenarios that require advanced optimization and examine several options for solutions.

R7.6.1   *Multiple Products*

The complete reference implementation for this section is available at https://bit.ly/3MnX4sD

We first consider a scenario where a seller offers multiple products in some category or group, so that the products are fully or partly substitutable. As a rule, the demand function for each product depends on all individual prices of other products that can be challenging to accurately estimate and optimize. One possible simplification is to use a demand model that estimates the demand for a given product based

on both the product's own price and the average price within a group
of substitutable products [Ferreira et al., 2015]. This may be an accurate approximation in many settings because the ratio between the
product's own price and the average price in the group reflects the
competitiveness of the product and quantifies demand cannibalization.
Assuming the finite number of valid discrete price levels, the set of
possible average prices is also finite, so we can evaluate the demand
for a given product for all possible combinations of own and average
prices. This enables us to formulate the price optimization problem as
follows:

$$\max \sum_k \sum_i p_k \cdot q_{ikc} \cdot x_{ik}$$

$$\text{subject to} \quad \sum_k x_{ik} = 1, \quad \text{for all } i$$

$$\sum_k \sum_i p_k \cdot x_{ik} = c \qquad \text{(R7.28)}$$

$$x_{ik} \in \{0, 1\}$$

where q_{ikc} is the demand for product i, given that it is assigned k-th
price level and all prices in the category sum up to c, and x_{ik} is a binary
dummy variable that is equal to one if price k is assigned to product i,
and zero otherwise. Indices i and k iterate over all products and price
levels, respectively. The first constraint ensures that each product has
exactly one price, and the second constraint ensures that all prices sum
up to some value c: that is, the average price is fixed. In solving this
problem for each possible value of c and picking the best result, we
obtain the set of variables x that defines the profit-optimal assignment
of prices to products.

In expression R7.28, the values q_{ikc} need to be precomputed for all
combinations of i, k, and c which can be done using a regular demand
forecasting model. One of the main advantages of this approach is
that we make no assumptions about the demand function, so arbitrary
demand forecasting methods can be used.

The problem defined above is an integer programming problem, because the decision variables x are either ones or zeros. It can be computationally intractable to solve this problem, even for medium size
categories, especially if prices need to be updated frequently. We can
work around this problem by replacing the original integer program-

ming problem with a linear programming problem where variables x are assumed to be continuous:

$$\max \quad \sum_k \sum_i p_k \cdot q_{ikc} \cdot x_{ik}$$

$$\text{subject to} \quad \sum_k x_{ik} = 1, \quad \text{for all } i$$

$$\sum_k \sum_i p_k \cdot x_{ik} = c \tag{R7.29}$$

$$0 \leqslant x_{ik} \leqslant 1$$

This technique is known as *linear relaxation*. The resulting linear program can be solved efficiently, even if the number of products and possible average prices is high. It can be shown that the solution of the linear program gives a tight bound for the optimal solution of the integer program [Ferreira et al., 2015]. This boundary can be used to reduce the set of price sums c for which the integer problem needs to be solved. In practice, the number of integer programs that need to be solved can be reduced very sharply (e.g. from hundreds to less than ten).

The alternative approach is to set prices directly based on the solution of the linear program. In this case, each product can have more than one non-zero variables x, and the operational model needs to be adjusted to account for this. For example, a time interval for which one price is offered can be divided into multiple subintervals in proportion, specified by variables x. For instance, if there are two nonzero elements equal to 0.2 and 0.8, then the corresponding prices can be offered for 20% and 80% of the time, respectively.

Example R7.1: Price Optimization for Multiple Products

We illustrate the linear relaxation technique by a numerical example. We use a linear programming routine from the standard library that requires the input problem to be defined in the following vector form:

$$\max \quad \mathbf{r} \cdot \mathbf{x}$$

$$\text{subject to} \quad \mathbf{A} \cdot \mathbf{x} = \mathbf{b} \tag{R7.30}$$

where $\mathbf{r}$ is the cost vector, $\mathbf{x}$ is the vector of decision variables, and matrix $\mathbf{A}$ and vector $\mathbf{b}$ specify the constraints. We use the following design of the inputs to impose constraints on the sum of the prices and price weights for each product:

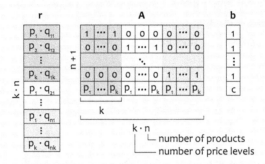

In other words, the cost vector r consists of revenues for all possible price assignments, and each row of matrix A ensures that the price weights sum to 1 for any given product, except the last row that ensures that all prices sum to the required level c. The decision vector x has $k \cdot n$ elements and it is convenient to reshape it into $n \times k$ matrix to analyze the optimal prices for each product, as we show below.

We next assume four allowed price levels

$$p = (1.00, 1.50, 2.00, 2.50) \tag{R7.31}$$

and three products with the following demands at each price level (each row corresponds to a product, and each column corresponds to a price level):

$$
q: \quad
\begin{array}{r|cccc}
\text{Price level} & 1.00 & 1.50 & 2.00 & 2.50 \\
\text{Product 1} & 28 & 23 & 20 & 13 \\
\text{Product 2} & 30 & 22 & 16 & 12 \\
\text{Product 3} & 32 & 26 & 19 & 15 \\
\end{array}
\tag{R7.32}
$$

Finally, we assume that all prices need to sum up to 5.50. We use these values to construct the inputs for the standard solver and run it to obtain the vector of decision variables that can be reshaped into the following matrix:

$$
x: \quad
\begin{array}{r|cccc}
\text{Price level} & 1.00 & 1.50 & 2.00 & 2.50 \\
\text{Product 1} & 0.0 & 0.0 & 1.0 & 0.0 \\
\text{Product 2} & 0.0 & 1.0 & 0.0 & 0.0 \\
\text{Product 3} & 0.0 & 0.5 & 0.0 & 0.5 \\
\end{array}
\tag{R7.33}
$$

This result can be interpreted as follows: assign product 1 with price 2.00, product 2 with price 1.50, and sell product 3 half of the time at price 1.50 and the other half at price 2.50.

The problem definitions R7.28 and R7.29 can be modified or extended to cover more complex scenarios with additional constraints. One of these scenarios is the price optimization for multiple products that have inventory dependencies. For example, a manufacturer can assemble different products from parts drawn from one or several shared pools of resources. In this case, we can simply add a constraint that the total number of parts needed to assemble all products must not exceed the corresponding level of in-stock inventory.

R7.6.2 *Multiple Time Intervals*

The integer programming and linear relaxation approaches can not only be used to optimize pricing parameters for multiple products, but to strategically optimize the sequence of prices over multiple time intervals. For example, a seasonal product can be purchased by a retailer at the beginning of the season and it has to be sold out by the end of the season. In this case, we might be interested not only in forecasting the demand and optimizing the price for one time interval, but in estimating the demand functions for all time intervals until the end of the season and optimizing prices under the constraint that the sum of the demands for all intervals needs to converge to the available inventory (i.e. the product needs to be sold out or the unsold units will be lost). The optimization problem for one product can then be defined as follows:

$$
\begin{aligned}
\max \quad & \sum_t \sum_k p_k \cdot q_{tk} \cdot x_{tk} \\
\text{subject to} \quad & \sum_k x_{tk} = 1, \quad \text{for all } t \\
& \sum_t \sum_k q_{tk} \cdot x_{tk} = c \\
& x_{tk} \in \{0, 1\}
\end{aligned}
$$

(R7.34)

where t iterates over time intervals within the season, and c is the available inventory. Similar to the case with multiple products, demand values q_{tk} can be precomputed using an arbitrary demand model, and linear relaxation can be used as an alternative to the integer programming formulation.

R7.6.3   *Optimization Using Reinforcement Learning*

The complete reference implementation for this section is available at https://bit.ly/3KgOHOg

The optimization model described in the previous section is quite versatile because it allows for a price-demand function of an arbitrary shape (linear, constant elasticity, etc.) and arbitrary seasonal patterns. This flexibility stems partly from the ability to precompute the demand values, and it has a major advantage in the integer programming approach. The use of the precomputed values, however, is also a major shortcoming because it limits the ability to model dependencies between products and time intervals. In the scenario with multiple products, we circumvented this problem by using the concept of average price, but it is a somewhat limited and specialized solution. In this section, we explore the ways of building a more generic solver.

R7.6.3.1   *Motivation*

Let us start with an example that illustrates how the dependencies between time intervals can impact the optimization process. In the real world, demand depends not only on the absolute price level but can also be impacted by the magnitude of recent price changes; price decrease can create a temporary demand splash, while price increase can result in a temporary demand drop. The impact of price changes can also be asymmetrical, so that price increases have a much bigger or smaller impact than the decreases [Simon and Fassnacht, 2018]. We can codify these assumptions using the following price-demand function:

$$q(p_t, p_{t-1}) = q_0 - k \cdot p_t - a \cdot \phi((p_t - p_{t-1})^+)$$
$$+ b \cdot \phi((p_t - p_{t-1})^-)$$

where

$$x^+ = x \text{ if } x > 0 \text{, and } 0 \text{ otherwise}$$
$$x^- = x \text{ if } x < 0 \text{, and } 0 \text{ otherwise}$$

(R7.35)

and p_t is the price for the current time interval and p_{t-1} is the price for the previous time interval. The first two terms correspond to a linear demand model with intercept q_0 and slope k. The second two terms model the response to a price change between two intervals. Coefficients a and b define the sensitivity to positive and negative price changes, respectively, and ϕ is a shock function that can be used to specify a nonlinear dependency between the price change and demand. For the sake of illustration, we assume that $\phi(x) = \sqrt{x}$.

We next investigate what the optimal price schedule for such a price-response function looks like. We start by implementing a simple simulator that evaluates function R7.35 for certain parameter values and computes the profit based on the evaluated demand, given unit costs, and current and new price levels. We use this simulator to visualize the price-profit curves for different magnitudes of the price increase and decrease, as shown in Figure R7.28. This plot also includes the baseline profit function computed for the no-change scenario. We can see that price increases "deflate" the baseline profit function, while price decreases "inflate" it. The simulator is then extended to compute the total profit for multiple time steps given a certain price schedule, that is a vector of price values for every time step.

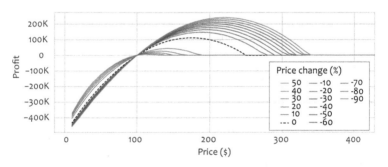

Figure R7.28: Profit functions for different magnitudes of the price change.

In this particular setup, we can construct the optimal price schedule using greedy optimization: start by finding the optimal price for the first time step, then optimize the second time step having frozen the first one, and so on. This approach produces the price schedule presented in Figure R7.29. The total profit generated by this schedule is much higher than the profit generated by any constant-price schedule.

This result is remarkable: a simple temporal dependency inside the price-demand function dictates a complex pricing strategy with price surges and discounts. It can be viewed as a formal justification of the

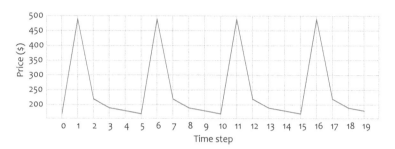

Figure R7.29: Optimal price schedule for the profit function from Figure R7.28.

Hi-Lo pricing strategy used by many retailers; we see how altering regular and promotional prices helps to maximize profit.

The above example sheds light on the relationship between price management and reinforcement learning. The price-response function we have defined is essentially a difference equation where the profit depends not only on the current price action but also on the dynamics of the price. It is expected that such equations can exhibit sophisticated behavior, especially over long time intervals, so the corresponding optimal control policies can also become sophisticated. Optimization of such policies thus requires powerful and flexible methods, such as deep reinforcement learning.

R7.6.3.2   Prototype

We prototype a reinforcement learning solution using the standard DQN algorithm described in Section 3.4.4.5. Recall that reinforcement learning considers the setup where an agent interacts with the environment in discrete time steps with the goal of learning a reward-maximizing behavior policy. At each time step t, with a given state **s**, the agent takes an action a according to its policy $\pi(\mathbf{s})$ and receives the reward r moving to the next state $\mathbf{s}'$. We redefine our pricing environment in these reinforcement learning terms as follows.

First, we encode the state of the environment at any time step t as a vector of prices for all previous time steps concatenated with one-hot encoding of the time step itself:

$$\mathbf{s}_t = (p_{t-1}, p_{t-2}, \ldots, p_0, 0, \ldots) \mid (0, \ldots, 1, \ldots, 0) \qquad (\text{R7.36})$$

Next, the action a for every time step is just an index in the array of valid price levels. Finally, the reward r is simply the profit of the seller. Our goal is to find a policy that prescribes a pricing action based on the current state in a way that the total profit for a selling season (episode) is maximized.

The agent training process starts with a random policy, but the agent quickly learns the sawtooth pricing pattern. We can get insights into this process by recording and plotting the pricing schedules realized in each training episode, as shown in figures R7.30 and R7.31. We can see that, in this particular implementation, the DQN agent learns the beginning of the right pattern in about 200 episodes, and produces a near-optimal policy in about 1000 episodes.

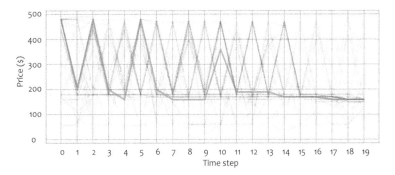

Figure R7.30: Pricing schedules produced during the first 200 episodes of DQN training. The schedule for the 200th episode is highlighted.

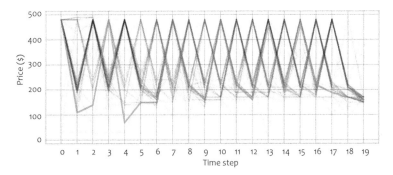

Figure R7.31: Pricing schedules produced during the last 300 out of 1000 episodes of DQN training. The schedule for the 1000th episode is highlighted.

The overall dynamics of the learning process can be visualized by plotting how the returns improve with the number of episodes, as shown in Figure R7.32. The agent finds a fairly good policy relatively quickly, but continues to improve over a large number of episodes.

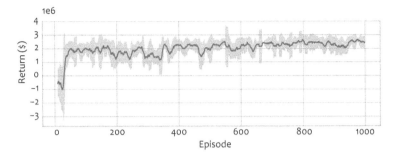

Figure R7.32: Agent training progress over 1000 episodes. The line is smoothed using a moving average filter with a window of size 10. The shaded area corresponds to two standard deviations over the window.

The quality of the policy learned by the DQN agent can be assessed more thoroughly by studying the Q-values estimated by the underlying neural network. For example, we can analyze the accuracy of the estimates by plotting the Q-values and true returns as shown in Figure R7.33. The data points for this plot are obtained by playing multiple episodes using a fully trained agent and recording the Q-value at each state, as well as the true returns.

The returns are spread over a wide range because of the ε-greedy policy randomization, but the correlation is almost ideal thanks to the simplicity of the toy price-response function we use. The correlation pattern can be much more sophisticated in more complex environments. A complicated correlation pattern might be an indication that a network fails to learn a good policy, but that is not necessarily the case as a good policy might have a complicated pattern.

We conclude this section with a remark that reinforcement learning is an extremely versatile tool for optimizing action policies in complex environments, but its practical application to enterprise problems is generally challenging. Unlike traditional optimization techniques such as integer programming, reinforcement learning algorithms tend to produce highly irregular policies that are difficult to interpret and operationalize. It is also difficult to assess how close the learned policy is to the optimal solution and to guarantee consistent behavior free of totally unreasonable actions.

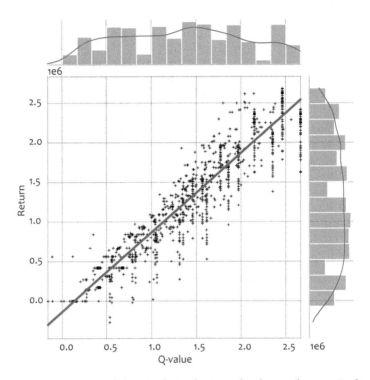

Figure R7.33: Analysis of the correlation between Q-values and true episode returns for a fully trained agent.

R7.7 VARIATIONS AND EXTENSIONS

In the previous sections, we were focused mostly on generic price management and optimization capabilities and paid little attention to industry-specific features. Price management practices, however, are very different across different industries, so we conclude this recipe with a brief discussion on the main industry profiles. We start with B2B sectors and gradually move toward B2B environments.

R7.7.1 *Retail*

Pricing is a very important competitive instrument for many retailers, and it is common to see sophisticated price management processes and models in retail industry. The main distinctive features of retail price management include the following:

- Pricing has a high impact on profitability because of relatively thin profit margins.

- Price strategy differentiation and price communication strategies are important for many retail sectors because of large assortment of items. Price management techniques also differ for seasonal and replenishable items.

- Most retailers have access to transactional and demographic consumer data which enables price and offer segmentation and personalization. This is an important capability because it allows the capture of the differences in willingness to pay across the customer base.

- Digital channels play an increasingly important role in most retail sectors. This shifts the focus from traditional planning to smart execution, dynamic and algorithmic price management.

- In both e-commerce and brick-and-mortar retail, it is relatively easy to collect competitor prices which helps to improve the price optimization models.

- Analysis and optimization of prices and discounts is complicated by strong cross-product and temporal effects including cannibalization, halo, and pull-forward.

R7.7.2 *Consumer Services*

Providers of consumer services can use very different pricing strategies depending on their ability to control the service capacity. From that perspective, we can distinguish between the following three categories:

FIXED CAPACITY Service providers such as airlines, hotels, and theaters have limited ability to change the capacity, and major capacity changes require huge investments of capital and time. Companies in this sector rely mainly on dynamic pricing and capacity-aware reservation algorithms to sell off the fixed inventory with the maximum revenue.

HIGH FIXED COSTS Software providers, video streaming companies, and media publishers typically have high fixed costs associated with content or product development, but the variable costs associated with the distribution are negligible. This makes subscription-based pricing very popular in technology and media sectors, and pricing is often set based on economic sustainability considerations.

VARIABLE CAPACITY Labor-intensive service providers such as education and legal services, can adjust their capacity by hiring or repurposing the workforce. This provides more flexibility because all terms of the profit equation (price, volume, and cost) are optimizable.

The above examples indicate that the capacity-aware price optimization and dynamic pricing methods are important for service industries. We discussed the problem of constrained optimization in Section R7.6, and continue to develop dynamic pricing methods in recipe R8 (Dynamic Pricing). However, we do not dive deeply into more specialized methods used by airlines and hotels[1].

R7.7.3   Consumer Goods

The price management processes of consumer goods manufacturers are heavily influenced by the fact that products are typically sold through retailers and other third parties. The main features of price management in this sector are as follows:

- The presence of retailers or other intermediaries generally requires them to jointly optimize both manufacturer's and retailer's actions. In theory, there are a number of econometric models that help perform such an optimization[2]. Some of these models assume the cooperation between the manufacturer and intermediary, while others assume that each agent pursues their own goals.

- In practice, manufacturers are not necessarily isolated from consumers by the intermediaries, and often have powerful means to control pricing. One common example is manufacturer-sponsored promotions. Manufacturers in many sectors routinely request retail partners to run promotion campaigns and cover the costs associated with price reductions. Another increasingly popular strategy is the development of direct-to-consumer channels that allow manufacturers to bypass the intermediaries and benefit from many of the marketing and price management techniques used by retailers.

- Manufacturers usually receive quite limited data from their retail partners. Many retailers provide only the aggregated weekly numbers, and this significantly complicates the analysis. For ex-

---

1 A more detailed treatment of such methods is provided, for instance, in [Talluri and van Ryzin, 2004]

2 See, for example, [Simon and Fassnacht, 2018] for an overview.

ample, we might have only about a hundred weekly points available for fitting a price-response model using historical data for two years.

R7.7.4   *Industrial Goods and Services*

The last sector we consider is industrial goods and services. The price setting strategies in this sector are governed by the fact that it serves organizations rather than end customers:

- Both buyers and sellers of industrial goods and services usually perform a thorough ROI analysis that helps to determine the value-based upper boundary for the price. The lower boundary is determined by costs. Advanced and innovative products and services are priced based mainly on the value considerations, while prices for commodity products and services are set mainly based on costs.

- Many industrial projects are complex and unique. This translates into complex and highly customizable pricing structures that are configured by account managers for every individual engagement or transaction. As we discussed in Section R7.1.3.2, specialized analytical tools might be needed to ensure the efficiency and consistency of these decisions across clients.

- Industrial goods and services are often sold through tenders where multiple suppliers bid for a project. Game theory offers a comprehensive framework for bid optimization, but the applicability of these methods in practice is limited for several reasons. First, making a decision exclusively based on a bid is feasible only for commodity products and services where suppliers can be deemed perfectly substitutable. For noncommodity products, the buyer usually makes a decision based on multiple considerations such as product features and supplier experience. Second, the supplier rarely has enough information about the tender setup and true value of the deal for the buyer and themselves to build a useful quantitive model. Bidders commonly use costs and estimated value as the lower and upper boundaries, respectively, and set a specific price point based on marginality, strategic growth potential, and competitive considerations.

R7.8   SUMMARY

- Price management is a complex multistage process that requires multiple decision support and decision automation models.

- The process starts with a top-level decision about price structures and price positioning. This step is usually supported by conventional business intelligence tools.

- The second step of the process is strategic analysis that focuses on price strategy differentiation, clients, and competitors. This step can benefit from market response models and other basic quantitative techniques.

- The third step is usually focused on detailed planning, scenario evaluation, and optimization. This step can significantly benefit from market response models, demand forecasting, and price optimization tools.

- The last two steps are execution and measurement. Many execution systems use automatic components that combine market response modeling with dynamic optimization, as well as personalization models. The measurement step can benefit greatly from demand decomposition and unconstraining techniques.

- Market response models aim to evaluate how price changes impact the demand. Such models generally need to account for an item's own price elasticity, cannibalization, halo, and pull-forward effects, as well as competitor pricing and marketing activities.

- Demand forecasting models are commonly built using general-purpose supervised models with aggregated or sequential inputs. This approach is more suitable for many enterprise problems compared to traditional time series models.

- Many price optimization problems can be reduced to standard formulations such as integer or linear programming. Reinforcement learning and simulations can be used for complex scenarios that cannot be easily reduced to standard formulations.

Recipe

8

DYNAMIC PRICING

Algorithmic Price Management Using Reinforcement Learning

The heavyweight pricing models, such as the models we developed in recipe R7 (Price and Promotion Optimization), aim to capture all significant factors that influence product demand and enable what-if analysis and long-term planning for complex scenarios. This approach is geared towards relatively static environments where we have access to relatively large volumes of historical sales data and focus on creating decision support tools rather than on completely automated price management agents. This is the case, for instance, for traditional brick-and-mortar retail environments where product assortments, prices, and promotions are typically planned in advance and change somewhat infrequently.

In digital and omnichannel environments, the traditional approach can be suboptimal or inapplicable. One typical example is online marketplaces with a high turnover of products or offers such as Groupon. Since many items are somewhat unique and short-lived, it is challenging to develop a good demand model based on historical data even with the similarity expansion techniques discussed in recipe R7. More broadly, the ability to re-optimize prices frequently in response to competitor moves and market changes gives a business advantage to the seller, and companies generally tend to exercise this option when it is technically possible. Digital channels, of course, provide almost unlimited flexibility in that regard, and the wide adoption of digital and omnichannel commerce has reshaped the price management practices as well. This can be illustrated by the fact that the frequency of price changes in multichannel retailers increased rapidly in the period from 2008 to 2017. The average duration for regular prices decreased from 6.7 months in 2008–2010 to 3.6 months in 2014–2017, and the duration of posted (promotional) prices followed the same pattern, decreasing from 5 months in 2008 to 3 months in 2017 [Cavallo, 2018].

In this recipe, we discuss price optimization methods that are specifically designed for dynamic environments. These methods can be used as stand-alone optimization components or they can be combined with traditional pricing models and processes.

R8.1   BUSINESS PROBLEM

Traditional price optimization requires knowing or estimating the dependency between price and demand. Assuming that this dependency is known (at least at a certain time interval), the revenue-optimal price can be found by employing the following equation:

$$p^* = \underset{p}{\mathrm{argmax}}\ p \cdot q(p) \qquad\qquad (R8.1)$$

where p is the price and $q(p)$ is the demand model. This basic model can be further extended to incorporate item costs, cross-item demand cannibalization, competitor prices, promotions, inventory constraints and many other factors. The traditional price management process assumes that the demand function is estimated from the historical sales data. That is accomplished by doing some sort of regression analysis for observed pairs of prices and corresponding demands (p_i, q_i). Since the price-demand relationship changes over time, the traditional process typically re-estimates the demand function on a regular basis. This leads to some sort of dynamic pricing algorithm that can be summarized as a sequence of the following steps:

1. Collect historical data on different price points offered in the past as well as the observed demands for these points.

2. Estimate the demand function.

3. Solve the optimization problem similar to the problem defined in equation R8.1 to find the optimal price that maximizes a metric like revenue or profit, and meets the constraints imposed by the pricing policy or inventory.

4. Apply this optimal price for a certain time period, observe the realized demand, and repeat the above steps.

The fundamental limitation of this approach is that it passively learns the demand function without actively exploring the dependency between price and demand. This may or may not be a problem depending on how dynamic the environment is. If the product life cycle is relatively long and the demand function changes relatively slowly, the passive learning approach combined with organic price changes can be efficient, as the price it sets will usually be close to the true optimal price. If the product life cycle is relatively short or the demand function changes rapidly, the difference between the price produced by the algorithm and the true optimal price can become significant, as will the lost revenue. In practice, this difference is substantial for many online retailers, and critical for retailers and sellers that rely extensively on short-term offers or flash sales such as Groupon and Rue La.

The second case represents a classical exploration-exploitation problem. In a dynamic environment, it is important to minimize the time spent on testing different price levels and collecting the corresponding demand points to accurately estimate the demand curve, and to maximize the time used to sell at the optimal price calculated based on the estimate. Consequently, we want to design a solution that optimizes this trade-off, and also supports constraints that are common in real-world environments. More specifically, we focus on the following design goals:

EXPLORATION-EXPLOITATION Optimize the exploration-exploitation trade-off given that the seller does not know the demand function in advance (for example, the product is new and there is no historical data available). This trade-off can be quantified as the difference between the actual revenue and the hypothetically possible revenue given that the demand function is known.

LIMITED EXPERIMENTATION Provide the ability to limit the number of price changes during the product life cycle. Although the frequency of price changes in digital channels is virtually unlimited, many sellers impose certain limitations to avoid inconsistent customer experiences and other issues.

DISCRETE PRICE LEVELS Provide the ability to specify valid price levels and price combinations. Most retailers restrict themselves to a certain set of price points (e.g. $25.90, $29.90, ..., $55.90), and the optimization process has to support this constraint.

CONSTRAINED OPTIMIZATION Enable the optimization of prices under inventory constraints, or given dependencies between products.

In this recipe, we develop several methods that help to achieve the above design goals, starting with the simplest ones and gradually increasing the complexity of the scenarios. Unlike some other recipes where we have just one section dedicated to prototyping, we implement prototypes for all techniques, and we thus have several sections, each of which describes both the solution design and implementation.

R8.2   SOLUTION OPTIONS

In theory, an agent that starts to sell some product online having no relevant historical data, can efficiently determine the price level that maximizes revenues or profits using multi-armed bandits that were introduced in Section 3.3. In practice, multi-armed bandits can be used as the core idea, but customizations are needed to create a complete solution that meets the requirements and constraints that we discussed in the previous section.

R8.2.1   *Limited Price Experimentation*

We first consider a scenario where the demand remains constant during the product life cycle, but the number of price changes is limited by the seller's pricing policy. This scenario is often a valid approximation of flash sales or time-limited deals. For instance, a variant of the algorithm described below was successfully used at Groupon [Cheung et al., 2017].

R8.2.1.1   *Solution Design*

Let us assume that the total duration of the product life cycle T is known to the seller in advance, and the maximum number of price changes allowed during this time range is m. Our goal is then to split time frame T into $m + 1$ intervals of arbitrary duration and assign a price level to each of them so that the expected revenue r is maximized:

$$r = \sum_{i=1}^{m+1} \tau_i \cdot p_i \cdot \mathbb{E}\left[d(p_i)\right] \tag{R8.2}$$

where τ_i is the duration of the i-th interval, p_i is the corresponding price level, and $d(p)$ is the unknown stochastic demand function. This problem statement is illustrated in Figure R8.1.

Figure R8.1: Optimization variables in the environment with limited price experimentation.

In an extreme case, only one price change can be allowed. A seller starts with an initial price guess, collects the demand data during the first period of time (exploration), computes the optimized price, and sells at this new price during the second time period that ends with the end of the product life cycle (exploitation).

It can be shown that in these settings, the optimal durations of the price intervals have to be increasing exponentially, so that a seller starts with short intervals to explore and learn, and gradually increases the intervals until the final price is set for the last and the longest interval, which is focused purely on exploitation. The proof of this fact is quite involved, and we skip the details here, referring the reader to the original paper [Cheung et al., 2017], but the final result is that the revenue-optimal interval durations can be specified as follows:

$$\tau_i = \alpha \log^{(m-i+1)} T \tag{R8.3}$$

where $\log^{(n)} x$ stands for n iterations of the logarithm, that is $\log(\log(\ldots \log x))$, and α is a coefficient that depends on the demand distribution. For practical purposes, α can be chosen empirically because the parameters of the demand may not be known. This layout is illustrated in Figure R8.2.

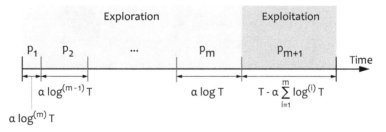

Figure R8.2: Theoretically optimal price schedule under the constraint that only m price changes are allowed.

Next, we need to specify how the prices are generated for each time interval. One simple but flexible approach is to generate a set of parametric demand functions (hypotheses) in advance, pick the hypothesis that most closely corresponds to the observed demand at the end of each time interval, and optimize the price for the next interval based on this hypothesis. In practice, the set of hypotheses can be generated based on the historical demand functions for similar products or categories. (We just need to generate a reasonably dense grid of demand curves that covers the range where the true demand function is likely to be located.)

Let us assume that we have defined k distinct demand functions $q_1(p), \ldots, q_k(p)$ that can potentially approximate the true demand function $d(p)$. For each function $q_j(p)$, we can numerically or analytically determine the optimal price p_j^* that maximizes the revenue $p_j^* \cdot q_j(p_j^*)$. We can then randomly pick one of these optimal prices, and test it in production for a relatively short time as prescribed by result R8.3, observe the actual demand that corresponds to this price, find the hypothesis that matches the observation as closely as possible, and switch to the optimal price that corresponds to this hypothesis. This process can then be repeated m times, so that the search for the best demand function approximation continues for first m time intervals and the $(m+1)$-th step is used to monetize the gained knowledge. This algorithm is summarized in listing R8.1.

Algorithm R8.1: Dynamic price optimization with limited experimentation

input:
   $q_1(p), \ldots, q_k(p)$ – set of k demand functions
   m – allowed number of price changes
   T – duration of the product life cycle

initialization:
   Compute the set of optimal prices $p_1^*, \ldots, p_k^*$

   Set the initial price p_1 to randomly picked p_j^*

for $i = 1$ **to** m **do**

   Offer price p_i for $\alpha \log^{(m-i+1)} T$ time units

   Observe the average demand per time unit d_i

   Find hypothesis j that minimizes $\left| q_j(p_i) - d_i \right|$

   Set the next price p_{i+1} to p_j^*

end

R8.2.1.2 *Prototype*

The complete reference implementation for this
section is available at `https://bit.ly/38dnAWS`

We next develop a prototype for algorithm R8.1 that can, for example, sell some product on an online marketplace. First, we need to specify the demand model that can be used to generate hypotheses. In practice, the common options are the linear and constant-elasticity models, so we choose to use a basic linear model

$$q(p) = b + a \cdot p \tag{R8.4}$$

where a and b are the parameters. For a linear model, the revenue-optimal price can be calculated by taking a derivative of the revenue with respect to price, and equating it to zero:

$$p^* : \frac{\delta}{\delta p} p \cdot q(p) = 0$$
$$p^* = -\frac{b}{2a} \tag{R8.5}$$

Second, we assume that it is possible to determine plausible price-demand ranges for the product we are going to sell using comparable historical cases and other prior knowledge. These ranges should include the true price-demand function with a high probability, but do not necessarily need to be narrow. With this assumption, we generate a set of hypotheses that covers the plausible location of the true price-demand function and compute the corresponding optimal prices using formula R8.5. These hypotheses, as well as the mean of the true stochastic demand function that we use for the simulation, are shown in Figure R8.3.

For the simulation, we assume that we run a 24-hour flash sale event and we can change the product price three times during this period. We first calculate the price schedule using expression R8.3, obtaining the following:

$$\tau_1 = 2 \text{ hours,} \quad \tau_2 = 4 \text{ hours,}$$
$$\tau_3 = 8 \text{ hours,} \quad \tau_4 = 10 \text{ hours} \tag{R8.6}$$

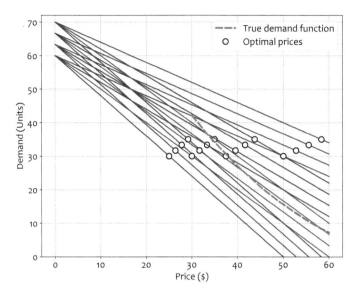

Figure R8.3: The set of price-demand function hypotheses used in the prototype. The revenue-optimal prices for the corresponding functions
are shown as the circle markers.

As we discussed earlier, the schedule depends on the properties of
the demand distribution, which is unknown to the seller, so we choose
the scaling coefficient $\alpha = 2$ heuristically.

The results of the simulation are shown in Figure R8.4. Each row
represents the state of the system at the end of the corresponding pricing interval τ_i. The plots in the left-hand column show the current and
past price-demand function hypotheses, as well as the realized price-
demand pairs. The charts in the right-hand column show how the price
and demand change over time. The agent initially chooses the hypothesis far below the true curve, sets a relatively low price, and observes
that the actual demand is higher than that predicted by the hypothesis. This situation is shown in the first row. Consequently, the agent
switches to another hypothesis that happened to be above the actual
curve, sharply increases the price, and observes that now the average
demand is a bit lower than predicted, as shown in the second row. In
the next two intervals, the agent makes smaller adjustments converging
to the near-optimal demand curve estimation and near-optimal price.

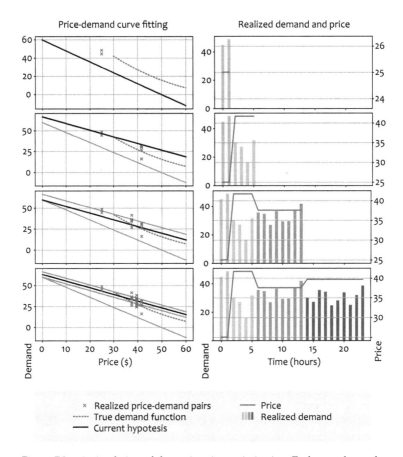

Figure R8.4: A simulation of dynamic price optimization. Each row shows the state of the system at the end of the corresponding pricing interval.

R8.2.2   Continuous Experimentation

The algorithm described in the previous section is a simple yet efficient solution for settings where the demand function can be assumed to be stationary. In more dynamic settings, we might need to use more generic tools that can continuously explore the environment, while also balancing the exploration-exploitation trade-off. Fortunately, reinforcement learning offers a wide range of methods designed specifically for this problem. In this section, we aim to develop an algorithm that supports continuous experimentation and also allows us to constrain the set of valid prices.

R8.2.2.1 *Solution Design*

We can start with an observation that the approach used in the previous section can be improved in the following two areas:

- First, we can expect to build a more flexible and efficient framework by utilizing Bayesian methods for demand estimation. Using a Bayesian approach will enable us to accurately update the demand distribution model with every observed sample, as well as to quantify the uncertainty in the model parameter estimates.

- Second, we should replace the fixed price change schedule with continuous exploration. Again, a Bayesian approach can help to better control the exploration process, as the time allocated for exploration and the breadth of exploration can be derived from the uncertainty of the demand estimates.

These two ideas are combined in Thompson sampling that we discussed in Section 3.3.3, and we use it as the foundation for developing a flexible dynamic pricing framework that can be customized to support a number of use cases and constraints [Ferreira et al., 2018]. A variant of this framework was tested by Walmart with positive results [Ganti et al., 2018].

Let us reformulate the price optimization problem in Thomson sampling terms. Recall that the Thompson sampling algorithm decides which action to take based on parameters that it samples from some probabilistic model, executes the action, and updates the model based on the observed result. In the price optimization context, the action corresponds to price that can be chosen from a discrete or continuous set of allowed prices, and the model can be a demand distribution $q(d \mid \theta)$ conditioned on the vector of parameters θ. Using this notation, we can rewrite the Thompson sampling algorithm as shown in listing R8.2. Thompson sampling controls the amount of exploration by sampling the model parameters for a probabilistic distribution that is refined over time. If the variance of the distribution is high, we will tend to explore a wider range of possible demand functions. If the variance is low, we will mostly use functions that are close to what we think is the most likely demand curve (that is, the curve defined by the mean of the distribution), and explore more distant options just occasionally.

Algorithm R8.2 is a generic template, and we need to specify a probabilistic demand model q to make it concrete. One possible way to accomplish this task is to use a continuous model such as linear or constant-elasticity. In this case, we have only one model $q(\theta, p)$ that is parametrized by vector θ which can be the slope coefficients or elas-

---

Algorithm R8.2: A general form of the dynamic pricing algorithm using Thompson sampling

initialization:

Specify the prior distribution of the demand model parameters $q(\theta)$

Specify the demand distribution $q(d \mid \theta, p)$ conditioned on a vector of parameters θ and price p

execution:

for each time step t **do**

Sample the demand parameters $\theta_t \sim q(\theta)$

Find the optimal price for the sampled demand parameters:
$$p^* = \underset{p}{\operatorname{argmax}} \; p \times \mathbb{E}\left[q(\theta_t, p)\right]$$

Offer the optimal price and observe the demand sample d

Update the parameter distribution using the likelihood of the observed demand:
$$q(\theta) \leftarrow q(\theta) \times q(d \mid \theta, p)$$

end

---

ticity coefficients, and this model can be evaluated for any price p to obtain the corresponding demand value. Another way is to assume a discrete set of price levels p_i, and maintain a parameter vector θ_i for each level. In this case, we can have a separate demand distribution model $q(\theta_i)$ for each price level, assuming that the levels are independent. The models do not take price p as an argument; we just pick the right model based on the price. This approach is preferable in many environments because many companies, especially retailers, have a pricing policy that prescribes a certain set of price levels (e.g. \$5.90, \$6.90, etc.), and we further focus on this setup.

The overall demand model represents a table with k price levels. Since each price level is associated with its own demand probability density function (PDF) specified by some parameters, we can visualize the overall demand curve by plotting the price levels and their mean demands, as shown in Figure R8.5. This is convenient because the curve can have an arbitrary shape and can approximate a wide range of price-demand dependencies, including linear and constant-elasticity models.

Continuous price-demand model

Linear $q(p) = \theta_1 + \theta_2 p$

Constant-elasticity $q(p) = \theta_1 p^{\theta_2}$

Discrete price-demand model

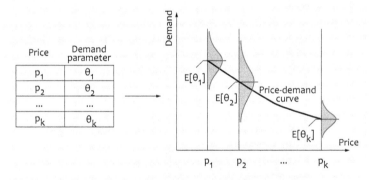

Figure R8.5: Examples of price-demand models that can be used in the Thompson sampling-based dynamic pricing algorithm.

We next need to specify the demand distributions for individual price levels. We previously assumed that the levels are independent, meaning that the demand distribution for level i depends only on its own parameter θ_i but not on parameters of the other levels. We also captured the shape of the demand curve point by point using a table, so we can use some simple parametric distribution to specify each level. For instance, we can assume that the demand samples observed at a given price have a Poisson distribution (a natural choice because each sample represents the number of purchases per unit of time):

$$d_1, \ldots, d_n \sim \text{poisson}(\theta) \tag{R8.7}$$

In this case, each level can be specified by a scalar parameter θ that is simply the mean demand at the corresponding price level. The prior distribution of θ can be chosen to be gamma because it is conjugate to the Poisson distribution:

$$q(\theta) = \text{gamma}(\alpha, \beta) = \frac{\beta^\alpha}{\Gamma(\alpha)}\theta^{\alpha-1}e^{-\beta\theta} \tag{R8.8}$$

where α and β are the parameters. Consequently, the full model for k price levels is specified by k pairs (α_i, β_i).

Assuming that price p_i was offered n times and thus n demand samples d_i were observed for it, the likelihood of this observation given the demand hypotheses θ can be evaluated as

$$q(d \mid \theta) = \prod_{i=1}^{n} \frac{e^{-\theta}\,\theta^{d_i}}{d_i!} = \frac{e^{-n\theta}\,\theta^{\sum_i d_i}}{\prod_i d_i!} \tag{R8.9}$$

Finally, the update rule for the posterior distribution of the parameter θ is obtained as a product of the prior and likelihood:

$$q(\theta) \leftarrow q(\theta) \cdot q(d \mid \theta) = \text{gamma}(\alpha + \sum d_i,\ \beta + n) \tag{R8.10}$$

In other words, we update the prior distribution at a certain price point by adding the number of times this price was offered to hyperparameter β, and the total demand observed during these times to the hyperparameter α.

Collecting the above assumptions together, we can rewrite the generic template R8.2 into a specific algorithm R8.3 that includes all the details needed for implementation. At each step, the agent samples an expected demand value for each price level, computes the corresponding revenues, and picks the revenue-maximizing price. The price is offered to customers for one time step, and the model's parameters are updated based on the observed demand. In the next section, we develop a prototype of this solution, and then discuss how more complex demand models can be plugged into the agent.

R8.2.2.2 *Prototype*

The complete reference implementation for this section is available at https://bit.ly/3MrudDE

> **Algorithm R8.3: A pricing agent that assumes discrete price levels and the Poisson-Gamma demand model**
>
> **initialization:**
> Specify prior distributions for all price levels:
>
> $$q_i(\theta) = \text{gamma}(\alpha_i, \beta_i), \qquad i = 1, \dots, k$$
>
> **execution:**
> **for** each time step t **do**
>
>   Sample the mean demand $d_i \sim q_i(\theta)$ for each price level i
>
>   Find the optimal price index:
>
> $$j = \underset{i}{\text{argmax}} \; p_i \times d_i$$
>
>   Offer the optimal price p_j and observe the demand d_t
>
>   Update the model parameters for price level j:
>
> $$\alpha_j \leftarrow \alpha_j + d_t$$
> $$\beta_j \leftarrow \beta_j + 1$$
>
> **end**

We evaluate algorithm R8.3 in a simple environment where the market responses to price p with demand

$$d(p) = 50 - 7p + \eta \tag{R8.11}$$

and η is a Poisson-distributed noise. We assume that the set of prices is limited to the following six values due to the seller's business constraints:

$$\$1.99, \quad \$2.49, \quad \$2.99, \quad \$3.49, \quad \$3.99, \quad \text{and} \quad \$4.49$$

We can verify that the revenue-maximizing price in this setup is $3.49, and we can use this fact to validate the results of the simulation. For the simulation, we set the same noninformative prior for all

price levels, as shown in the first row of Figure R8.6, and run the algorithm for 50 time steps drawing the "observed" demand samples from
function R8.11. The posterior demand and revenue distributions for all
price levels at the 50-th time step are shown in the second row of Figure R8.6. We can see that the agent correctly determines that the mean
revenue is maximized under the price level of $3.49.

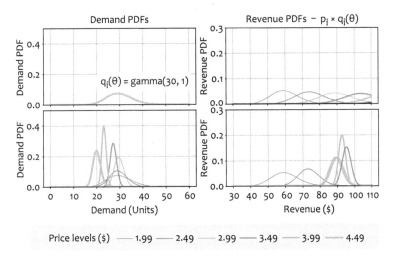

Figure R8.6: Simulation results for the Thompson sampling-based price optimization algorithm R8.3. The first row corresponds to the initial
state of the model, the second row corresponds to the state after 50
time steps.

R8.3   VARIATIONS AND EXTENSIONS

The two solutions described in the previous section can be used in
real digital environments to optimize pricing for products and offerings that are relatively short-lived and independent from each other. In
many settings, however, we need to account for dependencies between
related products and other constraints. This can be accomplished using more sophisticated demand models or more complex optimization
algorithms. In this section, we discuss several techniques that can be
handy in such cases.

R8.3.1   *Bayesian Demand Models*

 The complete reference implementation for this section is available at https://bit.ly/3k3TB6z

In stationary environments and long-term price planning, it is common to use complex demand models that account for demand evolution over time similar to what we discussed in recipe R7 (Price and Promotion Optimization). In dynamic environments, this approach might not be feasible, and lightweight demand models such as linear or constant-elasticity is often a more appropriate choice. Since we dynamically collect the feedback from the environment, the model fitting procedure should work well on limited amounts of data, and the Bayesian approach is often preferable from that perspective. In particular, we might need to generate the set of demand function hypotheses for limited-experimentation algorithm R8.1 using limited data, and the Thompson sampling algorithm R8.2 explicitly requires a Bayesian model.

The implementation of such models using just basic tools can be quite involved. Even in our simple example with the Poisson-Gamma model (algorithm R8.3), we had to do some math and manually implement the update rules for the distribution parameters. This process can be even more complicated if we need to use multivariate distributions for interdependent products, or to customize the model based on business requirements and constraints. Fortunately, we can work around this issue by using probabilistic programming frameworks that allow us to specify models in a declarative manner and abstract the inference procedure. Internally, these frameworks use generic methods such as Markov chain Monte Carlo (MCMC) and variational inference (VI) to infer the model parameters. In this section, we develop three basic examples that demonstrate the probabilistic programming approach and some of its capabilities.

R8.3.1.1   *Poisson-Gamma Model*

As in the first example, we reimplement the basic Poisson-Gamma model to illustrate the difference between the analytical solution in algorithm R8.3 and probabilistic programming solution.

In probabilistic programming, we specify the structure of some distribution using a directed graph of random variables, lock the prior distributions for the root variables in this graph, and provide samples of the observed leaf variables as reference data points. The framework then generates a sequence of samples for each variable that approximates its posterior distribution given the structure we have specified, prior distributions, and data points.

In the case of the Poisson-Gamma model, we specify a separate model instance for each price level as a graph with two variables: the gamma-distributed mean demand θ and the Poisson-distributed observed demand d conditioned on the mean, as shown in Figure R8.7. We also have to specify the prior distribution for the mean demand and provide the actual data samples d_i for the observed demand variable.

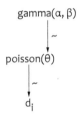

Figure R8.7: The graphical structure of the Poisson-Gamma demand model.

We can illustrate the implementation of this model using the probabilistic programing approach using the following example. We start with the prior distribution gamma(α = 15, β = 1) which means that our initial guess is, assuming some fixed price, that the mean demand is 15 units. We then observe five actual demand samples of 20, 28, 24, 20, and 23 units. In most probabilistic programming frameworks, the specification of this model and sampling from the posterior distribution, the mean demand will look similar to the following pseudocode:

```
observed_demand = [20, 28, 24, 20, 23]
θ_prior = gamma(15, 1)
likelihood = poisson(θ_prior, observed_demand)
θ_samples = sample(likelihood, 5000)
```
(R8.12)

The last line of the above implementation instructs the framework to draw 5000 samples from the posterior. The histogram of these samples, as well as the prior distribution, are shown in Figure R8.8. This figure indicates that the mean demand was underestimated in the prior, and the posterior was shifted significantly towards the higher value based on the observations.

The implementation R8.12 can be plugged directly into the algorithm R8.3 as a replacement for the analytically derived model update rules. Although the Poisson-Gamma model is fairly basic, it is apparent that the probabilistic programming approach can sharply reduce the effort associated with the implementation of the model inference logic.

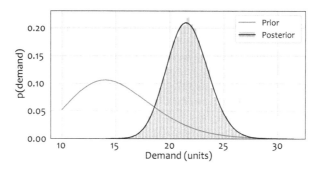

Figure R8.8: An example of estimating the posterior distribution for the Poisson-gamma demand model using probabilistic programming.

R8.3.1.2   Constant-Elasticity Model

The second example we consider is the constant-elasticity model described in Section R7.3.2, which is arguably the most common choice in enterprise practice. Unlike the model with discrete price levels, the constant-elasticity model assumes the following continuous relationship between price and demand:

$$d(p) = b \cdot p^c \tag{R8.13}$$

where d is demand, p is price, b is the scale coefficient, and c is the price elasticity of demand. Assuming that we have collected a number of price-demand pairs, the model can be specified and inferred using the probabilistic programming approach as shown in the following example:

```
observed_price = [15, 14, 13, 12, 11]
observed_demand = [20, 28, 35, 50, 65]
b = normal()
c = normal()                                        (R8.14)
d = b * power(observed_price, c)
likelihood = poisson(d, observed_demand)
samples = sample(likelihood, 5000)
```

where parameters b and c are assumed to have standard normal priors. The samples drawn from this model are tuples that include values of variables b, c and d. Consequently, we can create a demand curve for each sample by inserting the values of b and c into expression R8.13. The set of curves generated using this approach is visualized in Figure R8.9. This illustration makes it clear that we can estimate the demand distribution at any price point. We can also plug this model into the Thompson sampling algorithm, so that at each time step we draw a sample demand curve, find an optimal price for it, offer this price to the market, add the observed price-demand pair to the data, and re-infer the model.

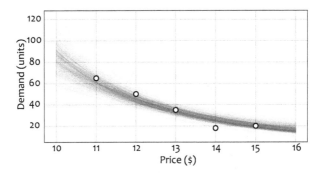

Figure R8.9: An example of estimating the posterior distribution for the constant-elasticity demand model using probabilistic programming. The circle markers represent the observed price-demand pairs.

Implementation R8.14 can be further detailed and improved using additional data and domain knowledge. For example, we can use the fact that the price elasticity c is negative in most practical settings, and specify its prior distribution to be a semi-infinite (e.g. half-normal).

R8.3.1.3   Cross-Product Dependencies

The third example demonstrates how the constant-elasticity model can be extended to account for cross-product dependencies. We consider the case of two products, each of which obeys the constant-elasticity model, but we believe that the elasticity coefficients in the two models are strongly correlated. This can be the case, for instance, for two substitutable products such as fat-free and low-fat milk. We can put together a model that implements this assumption as follows:

$$b = \text{normal}(\mu = [0\ 0], \Sigma = \begin{bmatrix} 1 & 0 \\ 0 & 1 \end{bmatrix})$$

$$c = \text{normal}(\mu = [0\ 0], \Sigma = \begin{bmatrix} 1 & \rho \\ \rho & 1 \end{bmatrix})$$

```
d = b * power(observed_price, c)                           (R8.15)
likelihood = poisson(d, observed_demand)
samples = sample(likelihood, 5000)
```

This implementation is a generalization of one-dimensional model R8.14 to the vector case. Random variables b and c are now two-dimensional vectors drawn from the multivariate normal distribution specified using mean vector μ and covariance matrix Σ, and the observed prices and demands are now matrices that include samples for each of the two products. The correlation between the products is specified using parameter ρ, that varies between 0 (independent demand function) and 1 (perfectly correlated elasticities).

We infer model R8.15 using a small dataset with 5 price-demand pairs for each product plotted in Figure R8.10, and then sample the demand function parameters from it. The results for two different values of ρ are shown in Figure R8.11. These plots illustrate how the affinity between the two demand functions can be controlled. This model can be plugged into the Thompson sampling agent in a similar manner to the single-product model.

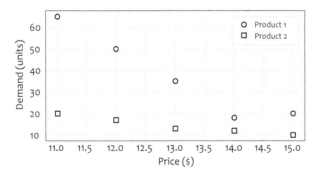

Figure R8.10: The observed price-demand points for the example with two related products.

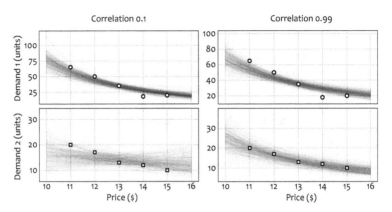

Figure R8.11: The estimated posterior distributions for the example with two related products. The left- and right-hand graphs correspond to the
low level of elasticity correlation (ρ=0.1) and high level (ρ=0.99z),
respectively.

R8.3.2 *Multiple Products and Inventory Constraints*

The correlation between elasticity coefficients is just one, mainly illustrative, example of interdependent demand functions. In Section R7.6,
we discussed two other important examples: cross-product demand
cannibalization and inventory-constrained sales planning. For the cannibalization case, we found that it is possible to use discrete prices,
precompute demand values for possible ratios of product own price
and category-average prices, and use linear or integer programming to
jointly optimize prices for interdependent products. For the inventory-
constrained sales planning, we determined that a similar approach can
be used to jointly optimize prices for multiple time steps ahead, under
non-stationary demand.

These two solutions are feasible for dynamic pricing as well. Assuming that we develop a proper Bayesian model that allows us to sample
demands at different product-category price ratios or time intervals,
we can solve a linear or integer programming problem to find the optimal prices for several products or time intervals. We can then plug
this process into Thompson sampling just as we did for several other
models we developed earlier in this recipe.

- The ability to actively explore the price-demand relationship and respond to market changes using dynamic pricing is a major advantage for a seller. Sellers from many industries exercise this advantage, developing algorithmic price management components that can be connected to digital channels and marketplaces.

- Dynamic pricing is particularly important in environments with a high inflows of new products, offers, or users, because we either need to learn a price-demand function from scratch or to efficiently validate hypotheses created based on prior knowledge or historical data.

- Dynamic price management requires addressing several challenges such as unavailability of historical data, necessity for active environment exploration, and limited frequency of price changes. Traditional price optimization methods and models do not properly address these requirements.

- In many settings, the frequency of price changes is limited based on the business and customer experience considerations. In case of flash sales, it can sometimes be permissible to change the price just once or twice during the product or offer life cycle. We can attempt to optimize pricing in such environments by generating a set of price-demand function hypotheses, and iteratively determine the best hypothesis.

- We can use multi-armed bandits for dynamic price optimization when the environment allows for continuous experimentation. Thompson sampling is a common choice for this category of problems, and it can be combined with a wide range of demand and pricing models.

- Simple Bayesian models for Thompson sampling can be designed analytically and then manually coded. For more complex models, such as models with cross-product dependencies, probabilistic programming provides a flexible framework that separates model specification from the mechanics of model inference.

- In environments with strong cross-product effects or inventory constraints, we can employ the same optimization methods as in the traditional price management problems.

Recipe
9

INVENTORY OPTIMIZATION

Planning and Managing Inventories Using Simulations and Reinforcement Learning

---

Manufacturing and distribution processes represent complex multistage pipelines through which raw materials, parts, and finished products move. The connections between the stages of such pipelines are often imperfect in the sense that different stages consume and produce batches of different sizes, have different operational schedules, change their capacities over time, and are prone to various disruptions related to transportation delays, equipment failures, natural disasters, and economic crises. This generally requires designing the supply, manufacturing, and distribution processes in a way that makes them resilient to external and internal shocks. The solution to this problem may involve the use of multiple procedures ranging from organizational to mathematical methods. Among these methods, inventory bufferization is one of the most fundamental concepts. Various inventory buffers such as warehouses and backrooms are critically important for integrating otherwise incompatible processes into a solid value chain and protecting them from disruptions.

Inventory buffers are associated with additional inventory costs, storage charges, and labor expenses. In practice, these costs usually amount to levels that significantly impact the overall financial performance of the company, so that inventory mismanagement can directly result in major business issues. For example, it is possible for an apparel retailer to be thrown into bankruptcy because of major miscalculations related to seasonal merchandise. This makes inventory management and optimization one of the most important problems in enterprise data science. In fact, the impact of supply chain efficiency on business performance is so high that it is possible to link the average efficiency metrics with the macroeconomic performance indicators. For example, there is strong theoretical and empirical evidence that the magnitude and duration of economic crises have a certain dependency on the ability of corporate supply chains to adapt to the initial shocks and costs associated with such accommodation [Bloom et al., 2018].

In this recipe, we focus on simulation and reinforcement learning-based techniques for inventory optimization, evaluate them for several basic supply chain scenarios, and compare this approach to traditional analytical methods.

R9.1   BUSINESS PROBLEM

Inventory optimization is a broad problem because supply, production, and distribution processes vary significantly across industries, so many different problem formulations exist that rely on different sets of assumptions about the environment. We start this section by discussing some aspects of production and inventory management processes to set the context for designing inventory optimization solutions, and then define the formal environment models that can be used for solution development.

R9.1.1   *Inventory in the Context of Production Processes*

Inventory bufferization is a way of adapting different stages of the value chain to each other and providing shock-absorbing isolations. However, the specific roles of inventory buffers can vary significantly depending on the industry and location of the buffer in the value chain. From that perspective, we can distinguish between several categories of inventories that might require different management and optimization approaches [Silver et al., 2016]:

CYCLE INVENTORY Most manufacturing and distribution processes operate in batches, and batch sizes can vary across the value chain. Inventory pockets needed to adapt processes with different batch sizes to each other are called cycle inventory.

CONGESTION STOCK Production and distribution processes can share the same infrastructure or capacity, and inventory can be temporarily accumulated waiting for machines, vehicles, or other resources to become available. We categorize this inventory as congestion stock.

DECOUPLING INVENTORY Inventory buffers can sometimes be created to decouple business entities and organizations. For example, regional operations can be decoupled from central operations by introducing a local warehouse.

SAFETY STOCK In most environments, inventory production and consumption are affected by disruptions such as transportation delays, weather conditions, strikes, and consumer demand surges. Creating safety stock buffers is one of the main ways to protect against such uncertainties.

ANTICIPATION INVENTORY Inventory can be accumulated in anticipation of seasonal demand surges, supply shortages, or price changes.

PIPELINE INVENTORY Finally, the inventory that currently moves through production or transportation processes rather than sitting in the buffers is called pipeline inventory. This includes work-in-progress and in-transit units.

The above categorization suggests that inventory bufferization aims to address two major groups of concerns. The first of these can be related to the *economy of scale*. Inventory buffers are needed to deal with storage and transport capacity constraints, large batch sizes, long lead times, volume discounts, and other restrictions. The creation and management of such buffers would be unnecessary in an ideal world where arbitrary amounts of inventory are instantaneously available to the buyer. The second group of concerns is related to *uncertainty*. Bufferization is needed to deal with imperfect demand forecasts, demand spikes, supply delays, and various types of disruptions. One would not need to deal with such issues in an ideal, perfectly predictable world. The formal environment models that we define in the next sections incorporate both the scale and uncertainty features.

R9.1.2 *Inventory Optimization Strategies*

The most fundamental approach to inventory optimization is the redesign of production processes in a way that reduces the need for inventory bufferization. A canonical example of such optimization is the just-in-time (JIT) manufacturing methodology that uses techniques such as setup time reduction, pull-based replenishment, and lot size minimization to reduce inventory requirements. This approach does not necessarily require the use of modeling and mathematical optimization.

The second layer of improvements is related to better production planning, scheduling, and inventory control using material requirements planning (MRP) systems. MRP aims to efficiently coordinate all resources and activities associated with the manufacturing process, which can thus help to eliminate inefficiencies in inventory usage, lower inventory requirements, and provide guidance for the inventory management system. However, low-level inventory management is not necessarily a part of the scope of MRP.

Finally, inventory optimization models and control policies can be developed to automatically or semi-automatically manage the inventory according to the targets and service level agreements produced by the MRP or other upstream processes. This layer is our main focus in the rest of this recipe.

R9.1.3   Inventory Management Process

In the previous sections, we outlined how the inventory flows through the various stages of manufacturing and transportation processes, where it can accumulate, and what the fundamental approaches are to reducing the costs and risks associated with inventory bufferization. We assume that the topology of the supply chain, including the locations and capacities of the inventory buffers (nodes) and transportation options between the nodes, suppliers, and consumers, is established based on these considerations, and we consider it as a fixed input to the inventory management process.

The inventory management process is typically designed and decomposed into specific tasks based on the inventory life cycle. This life cycle is different for different industries and types of goods, but some tasks are common to several environments. Let us consider an example of an apparel retailer who needs to manage seasonal inventory according to the life cycle presented in Figure R9.1. At the beginning of each seasonal cycle, the retailer plans the procurement according to the long-term demand estimates and places the orders with the suppliers. Once the merchandise is produced, the retailer refines the estimates and allocates the inventory to specific facilities such as warehouses and stores. The inventory is then transported to the facilities and becomes available to the customers. Throughout the season, the retailer can manage the demand using price changes and promotions, rebalance the inventory across the facilities, and place additional replenishment orders with the suppliers. These activities should be coordinated to minimize the costs, lost sales, and unsold inventory.

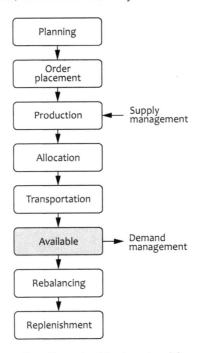

Figure R9.1: Example of the inventory life cycle.

There are two different ways of approaching the individual tasks in the above process. The first option is to specify and solve an optimization problem that captures all important objectives and constraints. For example, we attempt to determine optimal inventory allocations based on the expected demands at different locations, shipping costs, and other factors. This optimization procedure can be invoked for the initial planning, but it can also be used in order to repeatedly guide the rebalancing and replenishment decisions. We refer to this approach as *aggregate planning*. The second option is to design or learn an *inventory control policy* that dynamically makes rebalancing and replenishment decisions to manage cycle and safety inventory. In general, these two control styles are often combined to optimize the inventory in strategic and tactical contexts, respectively.

R9.1.4   *Environments*

The previous sections outlined how inventory optimization tasks fit the bigger picture of supply chain management. In this section, we turn to more formal environment specifications that can be used to develop inventory optimization algorithms.

R9.1.4.1   *Single-Echelon Environment*

The first environment model we consider is a basic setup that includes a supplier, warehouse (buffer), and client. This model, depicted in Figure R9.2, can be viewed as an elementary inventory bufferization unit, and more complex pipelines can be assembled by chaining multiple units together. In supply chains with multiple layers such as factories, central warehouses, and regional distribution centers, each layer is referred to as an *echelon*, and thus the basic environment depicted in Figure R9.2 is known as a *single-echelon* supply chain.

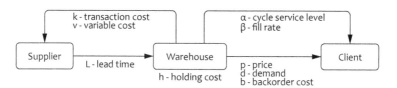

Figure R9.2: Single-echelon supply chain model.

We assume that the environment operates in discrete time. We also assume that the chain serves only one stock-keeping unit (SKU) which we also refer to as an *item*. Alternatively, we can assume that each item is managed completely independently. At each time step, the client indicates their intent to purchase d units from the warehouse, and we call this value a *demand*. The demand samples d are assumed to be independently drawn from the demand distribution p(d). The warehouse can fully or partially serve the demand, charging a constant price p for each unit. If the demand cannot be fully fulfilled, that is the current stock is less than d, there are two options for handling the difference between the demand and the available quantity. This difference can be discarded, resulting in *lost sales*, or it can be *backordered*, which means that it is carried over to a future time step. In the latter case, the warehouse is charged a penalty b which can be either a zero or a nonzero constant. In either case, the actual number of units sold over a particular time interval is less than or equal to the sum of demands over that interval.

On the supply side, the warehouse orders the item in batches of arbitrary size from the supplier. Each order has a fixed transaction fee k, and the per-unit cost is v. The transaction fee is supposed to include production setup costs, volume-independent transportation costs, and other operational expenses. Each order placed by the warehouse is delivered by the supplier in L time steps after the order is placed. The latencies L, called *lead times*, are assumed to be independently drawn from distribution p(L) for each order. Finally, the *holding cost* per unit per time step at the warehouse is assumed to be h. The holding cost generally includes operational expenses, property-related expenses, as well as risk factors associated with potential inventory and capital losses.

We refer to the inventory that was ordered from the supplier but which is not yet available in the warehouse as *in-transit inventory*, inventory that is physically available for a client to purchase as *on-hand inventory*, and the sum of on-hand and in-transit inventories minus backorders as *net inventory*.

The monetary aspects of the environment defined above can be summarized in the following profit equation for a certain time period τ:

$$\text{profit}(\tau) = p \cdot d_\tau - h \cdot I_\tau^h - k \cdot n_\tau^t - b \cdot n_\tau^b - v \cdot n_\tau^u \qquad (R9.1)$$

where d_τ is the total filled demand over the period, I_τ^h is the average on-hand inventory, n_τ^t is the number of orders on the supply side, n_τ^b is the number of backorders, n_τ^u is the total number of units purchased from the supplier. If backorders are not allowed, n_τ^b will be zero, but lost sales will be subtracted from filled demand d_τ.

The environment model does not assume or prescribe any specific dependency between the demand and supply sides. It is the function of the inventory control algorithm deployed at the warehouse to determine the optimal ordering cadence and parameters based on the observed demand, price, costs, and required service levels. We discuss service levels, performance metrics, and optimization objectives for the single-echelon environment in the sections that follow.

R9.1.4.2   *Multi-Echelon Environment*

The single-echelon model described above can normally be used to represent some basic real-world supply chains, such as the supply chain of a small retailer. Supply chains in large companies, however, usually include multiple echelons such as production facilities, central warehouses, and distribution centers. A basic example of a supply chain that includes three serially connected echelons is presented in Figure R9.3.

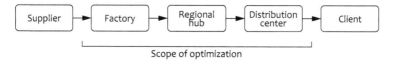

Figure R9.3: Example of a serial multi-echelon supply chain.

The real-world supply chain topologies are usually more complex than just a serial connection. Other typical examples include assembly chains where multiple inventory streams merge together (e.g. parts are assembled into the final product) and distribution chains where one source node serves multiple destinations (e.g. consumer goods distribution). In some cases, inventory can move between the facilities within the same layer, creating even more complex mixed topologies. These cases are illustrated in Figure R9.4.

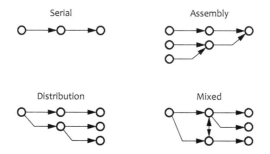

Figure R9.4: Typical topologies of multi-echelon supply chains.

The problem of multi-echelon supply chain management can be approached in several different ways. One possible approach is to manage each node separately using single-echelon methods. Despite this solution having certain advantages and being in common use, additional gains can be unlocked through simultaneous optimization of multiple echelons. Later in this recipe we examine how this can be accomplished using both traditional optimization methods and reinforcement learning.

R9.1.5   *Performance Metrics*

The inventory optimization algorithm for the supply chain model depicted in Figure R9.2 should account for several objectives. First, we generally have the goal to minimize the operational costs or maximize operational profit based on expression R9.1. Second, the average on-hand inventory term I_τ^h in the profit expression is special. On the one hand, it is associated with the holding costs, and it should thus be minimized in order to maximize profits. On the other hand, inventory is one of the major corporate assets that can be examined from the accounting and financial health standpoint. From that perspective, the primary metric that describes the overall inventory-efficiency of the company is the inventory turnover:

$$\text{inventory turnover} = \frac{\text{annual sales (\$)}}{\text{average inventory (\$)}} \qquad (\text{R9.2})$$

The turnover metric is closely monitored by management and investors as a measure of operational efficiency and capital allocation risks, so minimization of the average inventory is a major goal even outside of the cost minimization context.

Finally, the above objectives cannot be considered separately from the service levels guaranteed to the client. In practice, supply chains almost always need to guarantee certain levels of inventory availability or lead times. These may or may not coincide with the levels attained when the control parameters are set purely based on the profit-optimality considerations. The service level measures are generally dictated by the business model of a company, and companies sometimes design custom measures that reflect their value proposition to the customers, but the following metrics are considered to be standard:

CYCLE SERVICE LEVEL (α) Although the inventory control environment does not require inventory to be replenished in batches, irregular policies that reorder arbitrary quantities at arbitrary times are impractical, and most algorithms operate in some sort of cycle. Consequently, it is common to track and optimize the probability of not hitting a stock-out during a replenishment cycle, which is usually defined as the time between the receipt of subsequent orders from the supplier. This metric is known as the cycle service level and is usually denoted as α. It can be estimated based on the observed cycles as

$$\alpha = \frac{\text{number of cycles without a stock-out}}{\text{total number of cycles}} \qquad (\text{R9.3})$$

PERIOD SERVICE LEVEL (α_τ) Similar to the cycle service level, we can track the probability of not experiencing a stock-out during some fixed period τ such as a day, week, or month. This metric can be more meaningful from a business standpoint than the cycle service level as it is not attached to cycles which are basically the internals of the inventory management process.

FILL RATE (β) The fill rate is defined as the fraction of the demand that is supplied from the on-hand inventory. Assuming that the system operates over τ time steps, and denoting the demand at each step as d_t and on-hand inventory as I_t^h, the fill rate can be estimated as

$$\beta = \frac{\text{fulfilled demand}}{\text{demand}} = \sum_{t \in \tau} \frac{\min(I_t^h, d_t)}{d_t} \qquad (R9.4)$$

We use the cycle service level and fill rate as the main optimization objectives to develop inventory control policies later in this recipe. Assuming relatively long inventory management cycles, the cycle service level can be viewed as a strict coarse-grained metric that equally penalizes short and long stock-outs. The period service level is less restrictive, assuming that the period duration τ is less than a cycle, and the fill rate is the finest-grained measure because it is computed based on individual time steps. It is easy to see that the following relationship holds when the period duration τ is less than a cycle:

$$\alpha < \alpha_\tau < \beta \qquad (R9.5)$$

In practice, supply chain operations and analytics teams often track many more business-oriented metrics and events such as the percentage of backorders, lost sales, and risky anomalies.

R9.2 SOLUTION OPTIONS

The problem with inventory optimization in single-echelon and multi-echelon environments as introduced earlier can be approached from several different angles. We can attempt to determine the optimal inventory levels analytically, to develop deterministic inventory control algorithms, or to learn inventory control policies using machine learning methods in the spirit of Chapter 3. In the next sections, we explore all of these approaches. We start with a discussion of how aggregate planning can be performed using the standard optimization algorithms. Next, we review the basic inventory control policies for a single-echelon environment and demonstrate how such policies can be evaluated and optimized using both analytical and simulation approaches.

We develop inventory management policies for several environment types starting with the most basic settings and moving towards more complex problem definitions. Finally, we discuss the inventory control problem in multi-echelon environments and develop a prototype using the reinforcement learning approach.

R9.3   AGGREGATE PLANNING

The aggregate planning problems introduced in Section R9.1.3 can often be solved using standard mathematical programming methods. In particular, tasks that require the optimal inventory levels to be determined can usually be represented as linear programming models, and tasks that require the determining of optimal locations among available options can be formulated as integer programming models.

We can illustrate this approach using the inventory allocation task discussed in Section R9.1.3. Let us assume an online retailer has n warehouses that collectively serve customer orders from m regions (markets). At the beginning of each season, the retailer estimates the total expected demand for each market and then determines the optimal inventory level for each warehouse with a goal to maximize profits, minimize shipping costs, and avoid stock-outs. We further assume that each product is optimized independently, product prices can be different across the markets, and shipping costs can be different for each pair of a warehouse and market. These assumptions lead us to the following linear program for each product:

$$
\max_{q_{ij}} \quad \sum_{j=1}^{m} p_j \sum_{i=1}^{n} q_{ij} - \sum_{i=1}^{n} \sum_{j=1}^{m} c_{ij} q_{ij}
$$
$$
\text{subject to} \ \sum_{i=1}^{n} q_{ij} \leqslant d_i \quad \text{for } j = 1, \ldots, m
$$

(R9.6)

where p_j is the unit product price for market j, c_{ij} is the cost of shipping one unit from warehouse i to market j, d_i is the demand in market i, and q_{ij} is the number of units that should be allocated at warehouse i for market j. In other words, we are seeking to maximize the profits under the constraint that the merchandise must be completely sold out by the end of the season. Once the optimal allocation values q_{ij} are determined, they can be summed over markets to obtain the final stock levels for each warehouse. In the linear programming formulation, the allocation values are the real numbers, but we assume that they can be rounded to the integer unit quantities without significant degradation of the decision quality. The integer programming formulation can be used in applications that require higher precision.

This approach provides significant flexibility and can be used to construct more complex models that incorporate a broad range of considerations. First, the basic model specified above can be extended with additional costs and constraints such as the storage cost and capacity constraints. Second, the optimization can be done for frequent itemsets rather than for individual products to avoid order splitting. The third common extension is to optimize the inventory levels for multiple time intervals rather than for one interval such as a season. Finally, aggregate planning can be integrated with the price management processes discussed in recipe R7 (Price and Promotion Optimization) to coordinate supply and demand management. We do not aim to provide a comprehensive catalog of such model variants in this recipe, but a large number of off-the-shelf models are readily available in the literature.

 The prototypes of the inventory allocation optimizers for individual items and itemsets are available at https://bit.ly/39QUgpQ

R9.4   SINGLE-ECHELON CONTROL POLICIES

The optimization techniques presented in the previous section can be applied iteratively to manage not only the long-term allocation but the replenishment decisions as well. The replenishment process, however, requires making repeated decisions based on the current inventory state, so we can consider using a control policy instead of solving a complete optimization problem at each iteration.

In this section, we discuss several standard rule-based policies for managing the inventory in single-echelon environments. The properties of these policies are well-researched for different environment models, and optimal policy parameters for the environments that comply with such models can be determined using the formulas or numerical procedures derived analytically. The disadvantage of the analytical approach is that any change in the environment model results in a new optimization problem for which an analytical solution might not be readily available. The alternative approach is to develop a simulator of the environment that allows us to evaluate given policies and search for optimal policy parameters. This approach helps with handling complex scenarios such as cross-product dependencies to achieve greater fidelity of the model. In this section, we develop analytical solutions and simulators in parallel for the standard environments.

R9.4.1 *Inventory Policies*

In general, one can use an arbitrary sophisticated or irregular algorithm to place replenishment orders. In practice, however, it is usually preferable to use regular and relatively simple control policies because of logistics and production limitations, contractual terms on both the supply and demand side, and other factors.

The first standard control policy we consider is known as a *continuous review policy* that is defined as follows:

> *As soon as the net inventory reaches the threshold s or goes below it, order a fixed number of units Q.*

This policy is specified by two parameters, reorder point s and order quantity Q, commonly abbreviated as (s, Q) policy. A conceptual example that illustrates its execution is presented in Figure R9.5. The first time the net inventory reaches the reorder point, the order for Q units is placed, and these units are received with a delay that corresponds to the lead time L. The net inventory, however, is sufficient to cover the demand until the order is received. The second time the reorder point is reached, a replenishment order is placed again, but the realized demand exceeds the net inventory before the order is received, and stock-out occurs.

One of the main advantages of the continuous review policy is that the order quantity is fixed, which usually allows overheads to be minimized and discounts maximized. The policy also provides strict service level guarantees in the sense that the stock-out time cannot exceed the lead time. The main disadvantage of the continuous review policy is the variable cycle duration. A replenishment order can be placed at any time but this is not always possible in practice because of supply and transportation constraints. The irregular order timing also makes it difficult to group orders together for multiple SKUs.

The second standard policy we examine is a *periodic review policy* that operates according to the following logic:

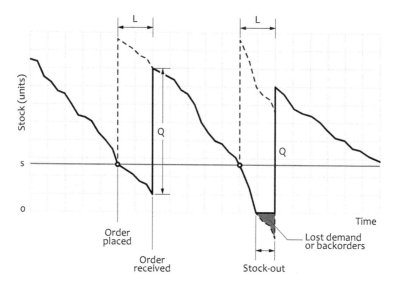

Figure R9.5: The main concepts of the (s,Q) policy.

Every R time steps, order the difference between the up-to level S and net inventory.

Like the continuous review policy, the periodic review policy has two parameters: review period R and up-to level S. This policy is commonly abbreviated as (R, S) policy. Its execution is illustrated in Figure R9.6 where the order placement cadence is fixed and is independent of the inventory level, but the ordered amount can vary.

The periodic review policy is the reverse of the continuous review policy in terms of advantages and trade-offs. On the one hand, fixed replenishment cycles enable order grouping, which helps to integrate production and transportation schedules. On the other hand, the periodic review policy requires dealing with variable order quantities and imposes a risk of stock-outs that can be as long as the review period. However, the periodic review policy is arguably the most commonly used inventory control algorithm.

The above concepts can be used to define more sophisticated control policies. For example, one can define a (R, s, Q) policy that reviews the inventory every R units of time and places an order of fixed quantity Q only if the net inventory is below the threshold s. It is not uncommon for large companies to develop and use non-standard control policies to meet their specific needs [Agarwal, 2014].

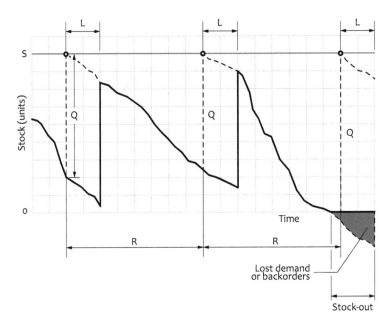

Figure R9.6: The main concepts of the (R,S) policy.

R9.4.2 *Environment Simulator*

 The complete reference implementation for this section is available at https://bit.ly/3Ms6ovu

The parameters of the inventory control policies described in the previous section can be optimized analytically under certain assumptions about the demand and lead time distributions. The analytical approach helps to explain the fundamental dependencies between various environment and policy parameters, but the practical use of analytical solutions faces a number of challenges including the following:

- Analytical methods typically assume that the demand and lead times have certain parametric distributions $p(d)$ and $p(L)$, respectively, with the normal and gamma distributions being the most common choices. This approach can be restrictive in several ways. First, available theoretical solutions might not fit well in the real-world environment, and adjusting or reworking these solutions analytically can be prohibitively slow and expensive. Second, relatively limited changes in the environment layout might require a complete solution redesign. For example, there is a major difference between how continuous and discrete demand distributions need to be handled.

- Traditional models assume demand and lead time samples to be independent and identically distributed values. In real environments, the demand and lead time samples are not independent and follow complex patterns due to seasonality, price changes, market-level trends and disruptions, and other factors. In particular, the volatility of demand can change over time according to a complex pattern requiring the inventory bufferization policy to change accordingly. Consequently, the optimization model should generally incorporate forecasting models similar to those we discussed in Section R7.4 which are challenging to handle analytically.

The alternative to the analytical approach is to use simulations. Simulation-based optimization is extremely versatile because the environment is specified in a procedural way allowing arbitrary complex assumptions and constraints to be incorporated in a relatively straightforward way. The simulation-based approach is also consistent with advanced control optimization methods such as reinforcement learning, so we use simulations extensively in this recipe.

Our first step toward simulation-based optimization is to develop a single-echelon supply chain simulator that can evaluate specific inventory control policies. This simulator closely follows the environment description provided earlier in Section R9.1.4.1. It tracks costs and service level metrics, supports arbitrary demand and lead time distributions, and allows arbitrary inventory control policies to be plugged in. These make ordering decisions at every time step based on the environment's state.

The best way to understand how the simulator works is to review an example output presented in Figure R9.7. The simulation parameters are summarized in the lower section of the figure. We specified three cost parameters (transaction cost k, variable cost v, and holding cost h), chose to use an (s, Q) policy, and configured demand and lead time samples to be drawn from the folded normal distribution defined as follows:

$$x \sim N^+(\mu, \sigma^2) \quad \Longleftrightarrow \quad x = |y|, \quad y \sim N(\mu, \sigma^2) \tag{R9.7}$$

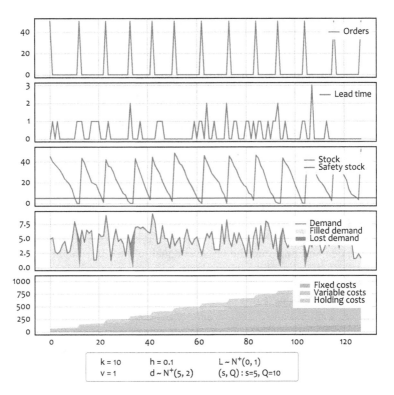

Figure R9.7: Example run of the supply chain simulator.

The simulator then executes the logic on the supplier, warehouse, and client sides for 128 time steps, recording the order times and quantities, corresponding lead times, current stock levels, actual and filled demands, and cumulative costs. These recorded values are grouped into four time series charts presented in Figure R9.7. We can clearly see the irregular sawtooth-like pattern which is expected for the continuous review policy.

The simulator enables us to evaluate supply chain performance for various environment and policy parameters, to study the relationships and trade-offs between these parameters, and to determine the optimal parameter combinations. We examine several basic scenarios using this approach in the next sections, and the simulator can be further extended to handle significantly more complex real-world problems.

R9.4.3   *Scenario 1: Constant Demand, Zero Lead Time*

We start with a basic scenario where the demand rate, that is the number of inventory units sold during one time step, is assumed to be constant and lead time is assumed to be zero. This is a strictly deterministic environment, so we do not need to create any inventory buffers to protect against uncertainties of any kind, and the problem reduces to the cost optimization.

Under the above assumptions, the continuous and periodic review policies are equivalent, as illustrated in Figure R9.8. On the one hand, we can use a continuous review policy with safety stock set to zero and order quantity Q which should be chosen based on the cost considerations. On the other hand, we obtain exactly the same behavior using a periodic review policy with a review period set to $R = Q/d$ where d is the demand rate, and the up-level equal to the order quantity, that is $S = Q$. Consequently, the problem boils down to determining the cost-optimal order quantity Q which is commonly referred to as the *economic order quantity* or EOQ.

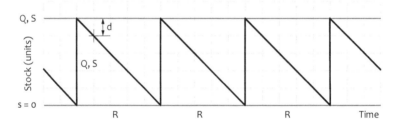

Figure R9.8: Replenishment process with a constant demand rate and zero lead times.

To determine the optimal order quantity Q, we can first express the total costs for some long time period of τ time steps as

$$c_\tau(Q) = h\frac{Q}{2} + k\frac{\tau d}{Q} + v\tau d \tag{R9.8}$$

where the first term corresponds to the holding costs (the average stock level, as shown in Figure R9.8, is $Q/2$), the second term is transaction costs, and the last term is variable costs. We next take the derivative with respect to Q

$$\frac{dc_\tau(Q)}{dQ} = \frac{h}{2} - k\frac{\tau d}{Q^2} \tag{R9.9}$$

and, equating it to zero, we obtain the following expression for the economic order quantity, assuming a planning horizon τ:

$$Q^* = \sqrt{\frac{2k\tau d}{h}} \qquad (R9.10)$$

This result agrees with the intuition that it makes sense to order larger batches when the transaction costs are relatively high, and smaller batches when the holding costs are relatively high. The relationship given by R9.10 is one of the oldest classical inventory optimization models [Harris, 1913; Wilson, 1934].

The result R9.10 can be reformulated in terms of the periodic review policy by setting the up-to level to $S^* = Q^*$ and computing the review period as the ratio between the economic order quantity and the total demand for the planning horizon:

$$R^* = \frac{Q^*}{\tau d} = \frac{1}{\tau d}\sqrt{\frac{2k\tau d}{h}} = \sqrt{\frac{2k}{\tau dh}} \qquad (R9.11)$$

We can perform more elaborate analyses using simulations. In the first experiment, we draw the demand and lead time from a low-variance folded normal distribution, so that the samples are near-constant but the sensitivity to random deviations is also measurable. We also set the safety stock threshold to be a small positive value instead of zero to maintain a near-perfect fill rate in the presence of these deviations. We then evaluate a number of (s, Q) policies with different order quantity values separately , and plot the holding, fixed, and total costs, as well as the fill rate in Figure R9.9. For each value of Q, we perform multiple simulations, so we can measure the variance of the estimated costs as well. The result agrees with the analytical solution. There is a global minimum for the total costs at the point where the fixed costs match the holding costs.

This visualization also enables several versions of the sensitivity analysis. First, we can see that the total costs stay relatively flat around the minimum, so the order quantity can be adjusted in a relatively wide range without a significant impact on performance. In this particular example, the optimal order quantity of around 30 units can be changed to 20 or 40 (because of batching considerations, for instance), with a very small impact on the total costs. Second, we can see that the variance of the cost estimates increases slightly but consistently as the order quantity increases because of the finite simulation duration. Finally, it is important to monitor that the fill rate and its variance stay

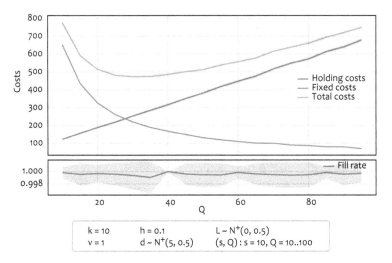

Figure R9.9: Economic order quantity optimization using simulations. The width of the shaded areas is two standard deviations around the mean.

relatively flat over the entire range of evaluated parameters to ensure that the apple-to-apple comparison of the estimated costs can be made.

The second experiment we do is more comprehensive, and it aims to analyze the interplay of the safety stock and order quantity parameters in the (s, Q) policy. The result is presented in Figure R9.10 where each point on a two-dimensional grid is obtained by averaging the results of multiple simulation sessions. The total cost profile in Figure R9.9 basically corresponds to a horizontal slice of the total cost surface shown on the right-hand image in Figure R9.10 at a fixed value of the safety stock.

Since we use near-constant but not perfectly constant demand distribution, the fill rate can degrade at low levels of the safety stock as apparent from the left-hand image in Figure R9.10. Consequently, there is a complex interplay between the service level and cost considerations. For example, the cost can be minimized only down to a certain level if we require the fill rate to be near-perfect (e.g. above 0.99), but lower costs can be achieved if the fill rate requirements are relaxed. We can precisely visualize the Pareto frontiers that describe the best achievable result according to one performance metric under the constraints in another metric by overlaying the left and right images presented in Figure R9.10.

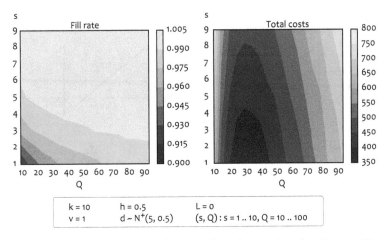

Figure R9.10: Pareto frontier analysis for the safety stock and order quantity parameters.

In this section, we used the stochastic demand and safety stock only to illustrate the sensitivity and trade-off analysis. The optimization of the safety stock parameters in the face of uncertainty, however, is the central problem in inventory management, and we study it in the next sections in greater detail, both analytically and through simulations.

R9.4.4   *Scenario 2: Constant Demand and Lead Time*

The second scenario we consider also assumes that the demand and lead time are constant, but the lead time can be greater than zero. Nonzero lead time basically means that a replenishment order should be placed at a point when the on-hand inventory becomes insufficient to cover the demand that is expected to realize during the lead time. This scenario is depicted in Figure R9.11.

The assumption about the nonzero lead time impacts the continuous and periodic review policies as follows:

CONTINUOUS REVIEW In the case of a continuous review policy, we need to only change the reorder threshold s to place orders proactively to ensure that the lead time interval is covered. Assuming the constant demand rate d, lead time L, and denoting the demand realized during the lead time as d_L, we get the following threshold:

$$s = d_L = d \times L \tag{R9.12}$$

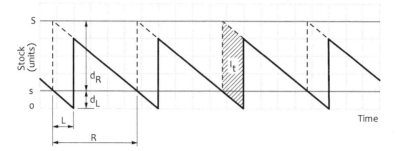

Figure R9.11: Replenishment process with constant demand and lead times.

The optimal order quantity Q can still be computed using expression R9.10

PERIODIC REVIEW   In the case of the continuous review policy, we need to change the up-to level S to cover both the review period demand d_R and lead time demand d_L which results in the following rule:

$$S = d_L + d_R = d \times L + d \times R \qquad (R9.13)$$

The corresponding optimal review period R can be calculated using expression R9.11.

For both (s, Q) and (R, S) policies, the amount of in-transit inventory I_t is determined only by the lead time and demand rate:

$$I_t = d \times L \qquad (R9.14)$$

We can summarize that, in the deterministic environment, we can incorporate a non-zero lead time into the analytical solution in a relatively straightforward way, and the same can be done for simulations. The case of a stochastic lead time, however, can be somewhat more sophisticated and we explore this case in great detail in one of the next sections.

R9.4.5   *Scenario 3: Stochastic Demand, Constant Lead Time*

We turn next to building an inventory control policy that is resilient to uncertainties, and the first step is to replace the constant demand with stochastic demand. Let us assume that the demand samples are drawn from the normal distribution:

$$d \sim N(\mu_d, \sigma_d^2) \qquad (R9.15)$$

This commonly used assumption is not perfect because it allows for negative demand, which is invalid. However, it is feasible practically when the demand variance is small compared to the mean which is usually the case.

We next want to quantify the amount of inventory needed to maintain a certain cycle service level α. Recall that the probability that a value drawn from the standard normal distribution does not exceed threshold z is given by the cumulative distribution function $\Phi(z)$:

$$\Phi(z) = p(x \leqslant z) = \int_{-\infty}^{z} p(x)dx, \qquad x \sim N(0,1) \tag{R9.16}$$

Consequently, the level of inventory needed to guarantee that the probability of a stock-out even during one time step will not exceed α can be expressed using the inverse cumulative distribution function $\Phi^{-1}(\alpha)$:

$$I_\alpha = \mu_d + \sigma_d \Phi^{-1}(\alpha) \tag{R9.17}$$

The first term in this expression can be interpreted as the expected demand that needs to be covered, and the second term is the *safety stock* that is proportional to both the demand variance and the required service level.

The total demand over τ independent and identically distributed time steps has the mean of $\tau\mu_d$ and variance equal to $\sigma_d\sqrt{\tau}$, and thus the level of inventory needed to cover τ time steps is as follows:

$$I_\alpha(\tau) = \tau\mu_d + \Phi^{-1}(\alpha) \cdot \sigma_d\sqrt{\tau} \tag{R9.18}$$

The above result has the following implications on the inventory control policies:

CONTINUOUS REVIEW Under a continuous review policy, the maximum time one has to wait to receive the order is equal to the lead time L. Therefore, the reorder point can be calculated by evaluating expression R9.18 for L time steps:

$$s = d_L + \Phi^{-1}(\alpha) \cdot \sigma_d\sqrt{L} \tag{R9.19}$$

The first term is the mean demand that is expected to realize during the lead time, and the second term is the safety stock. The optimal order quantity Q is still calculated using the EOQ model.

PERIODIC REVIEW For a periodic review policy, the maximum time one needs to wait for a replenishment is the sum of a review time and a lead time, so the up-to level should be computed by evaluating the expression R9.18 for $L + R$ time steps:

$$S = d_R + d_L + \Phi^{-1}(\alpha) \cdot \sigma_d \sqrt{R + L} \qquad \text{(R9.20)}$$

where d_R and d_L are the expected demands for the review period and lead time, respectively. In a similar manner to the continuous review policy, the review period R is set based on the cost considerations.

The above analysis provides the basic framework for inventory optimization under the stochastic demand. We start with linking the demand variance to the probability of a stock-out at a certain time step, then provide a rule for demand aggregation over multiple time steps, and finally update the policy parameters to achieve the required service level. This framework can be extended further to account for non-stationary demand, correlated demand samples, and other complexities of real-world environments, but the analytical solution gets quickly convoluted as additional requirements and details mount up.

The alternative approach is to use simulations, and the simulator we have previously developed provides all the necessary capabilities to perform the safety stock analysis. The most basic experiment we can do is to examine how the cycle service level α depends on the reorder level parameter s. The simulation results for a setup with the folded-normally distributed demand are presented in Figure R9.12. It is apparent that the dependency curve closely follows the cumulative distribution function (CDF) of the folded normal distribution which agrees with the theoretical analysis presented above. It is also apparent that the improvement delivered by the safety stock increase follows the law of diminishing returns, and achieving high service levels such as $\alpha = 0.999$ can be prohibitively expensive due to high inventory storage costs.

A more comprehensive view can be obtained by changing both the demand variance and reorder level, as shown in Figure R9.13. This analysis indicates that the cycle service level is sensitive to the demand variance, and relatively small changes in the demand distribution are required to significantly increase the safety stock level in order to maintain the given service level. We can also see that the fill rate, which is defined as a continuously changing ratio, is less sensitive to demand

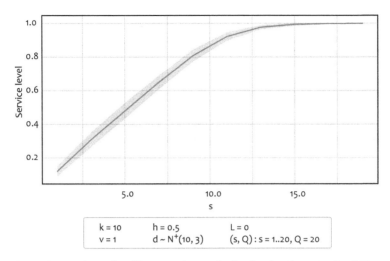

Figure R9.12: The trade-off between the reorder level and cycle service level. The width of the shaded area corresponds to two standard deviations.

variance than the service level which is defined using the all-or-nothing rule (stock-out or no stock-outs).

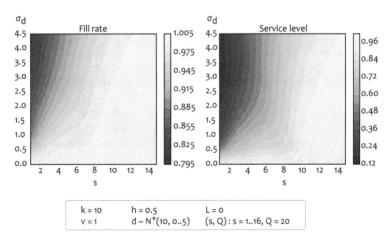

Figure R9.13: Dependency between the reorder level, demand variance, and service levels.

The simulation model can also be used to analyze the dependency between the service levels and inventory costs. We have previously stated that order quantity Q and review period R can be computed using the EOQ model that was originally developed for the case of deterministic demand. This statement is not perfectly accurate for the stochastic setup because stock-outs can occur, and this invalidates the basic assumption about the holding costs we made to derive the EOD formulas. This limitation can be addressed by incorporating stock-outs into the cost equation and performing simultaneous optimization of s and Q (or R and S) parameters.

R9.4.6   *Scenario 4: Stochastic Demand and Lead Time*

In real-world supply chains, the lead time is usually a complex variable that includes multiple components such as the time needed by a supplier to review the order, incorporate it into the production schedule, and prepare the freight for shipment; transportation time; and delays associated with various disruptions such as storms and labor strikes. Many of these components are associated with at least some level of uncertainty, and thus the lead time should generally be modeled as a stochastic variable. In this section, we consider a scenario that assumes both the demand and lead times to be random variables.

We have previously established that the safety stock I^s required to absorb the demand variance depends on the cycle service level α, magnitude of the variance σ_d, and duration τ of the interval that needs to be covered (see expression R9.18):

$$I_\alpha^s(\tau) = \Phi^{-1}(\alpha) \cdot \sigma_d \sqrt{\tau} \tag{R9.21}$$

We have also shown that the continuous and periodic review policies have different intervals to be protected (expressions R9.19 and R9.20), but this interval depends on the lead time L in both cases. Assuming that the lead time is a random variable, we need to develop a new version of expression R9.21 under the assumption that the interval duration τ is stochastic.

We can start with the general fact for a sum of random variables. Let us assume n independent and identically distributed variables x with n being a random variable itself. It then can be shown that the sum of these variables

$$y = \underbrace{x + x + \ldots + x}_{n \text{ times}} \tag{R9.22}$$

has the following mean and variance:

$$\mathbb{E}[y] = \mathbb{E}[n]\,\mathbb{E}[x]$$
$$\mathrm{Var}[y] = \mathbb{E}[n]\,\mathrm{Var}[x] + \mathrm{Var}[n]\,\mathbb{E}[x]^2 \tag{R9.23}$$

Going back to the inventory management problem, we can assume that the lead time is normally distributed

$$L \sim N(\mu_L, \sigma_L^2) \tag{R9.24}$$

and the demand that needs to be protected using the safety stock is a sum of either L or L + R demand values d, depending on which policy we use. Consequently, we can rewrite the rules developed in the previous section as follows:

CONTINUOUS REVIEW The continuous review policy has a risk period of L time steps, and thus we can derive the following expression for the safety stock by replacing the variance in expression R9.21 with the variance computed using rule R9.23:

$$I_\alpha^s(\tau) = \Phi^{-1}(\alpha) \cdot \sqrt{\mu_L \sigma_d^2 + \sigma_L^2 \mu_d^2} \tag{R9.25}$$

PERIODIC REVIEW Under the periodic review policy, the risk period is L + R where R is a constant review period, so we get the following expression for the safety stock:

$$I_\alpha^s(\tau) = \Phi^{-1}(\alpha) \cdot \sqrt{(\mu_L + R)\sigma_d^2 + \sigma_L^2 \mu_d^2} \tag{R9.26}$$

The above expressions suggest that small changes in the lead time variance σ_L^2 can have a major impact on the service level when the expected demand μ_d is large. This can also be illustrated using simulations. The example presented in Figure R9.14 shows how the increase in the lead time variance causes a far more severe degradation of the fill rate and cycle service level compared to the increase in the demand variance.

R9.4.7 *Lost Sales and Demand Unconstraining*

All analytical models and simulation techniques discussed in the previous sections assume that the demand distribution is known. Most of these methods, particularly those that are simulation-based, can readily be extended to use time-dependent demand forecasts rather than assuming that demand samples are independent and identically distributed. We have discussed the demand estimation and forecasting methods in recipe R7 (Price and Promotion Optimization) and emphasized that the forecasting based on the sales data with stock-outs can result in underestimates, and specialized demand unconstraining procedures should be used to work around this problem. In this section,

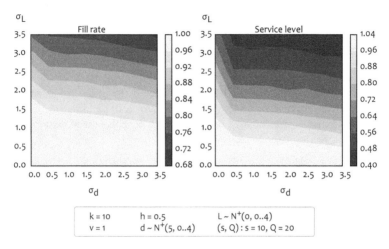

Figure R9.14: Dependency between the demand variance, lead time variance, and service levels.

we review the stock-out problem once again but this time through the lens of the inventory management problem.

In an ideal supply chain, all the demand generated by clients is converted into sales. Historical sales data are used to build a demand forecast, inventory is replenished in time according to this forecasts, and then the cycle repeats. If the realized demand exceeds the on-hand inventory, the excess demand translates into backorders or lost sales, as depicted in Figure R9.15. Backorders are eventually converted into sales and accounted for in the forecast, but lost sales are generally challenging to measure even with the aid of demand unconstraining models. Underestimated lost sales result in underestimated demand forecasts, then lower-than-needed inventory levels, stock-outs, and finally additional lost sales. This process can repeat itself, turning into a downward spiral if not controlled properly.

The flow depicted in Figure R9.15 suggests that the problem of unaccounted lost sales can be mitigated using backorders and demand unconstraining techniques. Backorders are commonly used in B2B environments, and B2B clients are generally accustomed to it, but lost sales can still occur due to switching to alternative providers with better SLAs, reputation damages, and other hard-to-measure factors. In B2C verticals, such as retail, stock-outs are much more likely to result in lost sales due to the higher availability of alternatives and less common use of backorders. Demand unconstraining can help to correct the forecasts under such circumstances, but the problem is known to

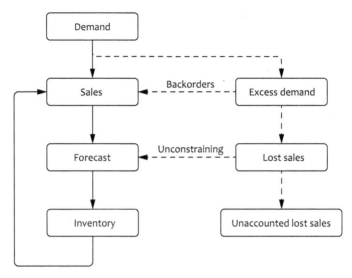

Figure R9.15: The impact of lost sales on the inventory management process.

be challenging because of complex long-term effects related to brand perception and shifts in purchasing behavior.

R9.5 MULTI-ECHELON CONTROL POLICIES

The models discussed in the previous sections help to optimize inventory decisions at one node, but multi-echelon supply chains introduced in Section R9.1.4.2 generally require the coordination of inventory decisions across the nodes. For example, consider a supply chain that includes three serially connected nodes: factory warehouse, distribution center, and retail location. These three nodes have different holding costs, transaction costs, and lead time distributions. Depending on the ratios between these parameters, it might be optimal to maintain safety stock only at the retail location and keep no inventory at the factory and distribution center, or to maintain safety stock only at the distribution center, or evenly distribute safety stock across all three echelons. We can optimize inventory control policies at each of these nodes in isolation using single-echelon methods, but this requires freezing the service levels of the upstream nodes (suppliers) and demand levels of the downstream nodes (consumers). These levels, however, are determined by the policies used at the corresponding nodes, and these policies are also the subjects of optimization. Consequently, all policies need to be optimized simultaneously.

In this section, we discuss two approaches to the control policy optimization in complex environments with multiple echelons. The first one is a traditional solution that reduces the problem to the mathematical programming formulation. The second one is dynamic policy learning based on the interactions with the environment simulator.

R9.5.1 *Guaranteed-Service Model*

The problem of inventory policy optimization in a multi-echelon environment can be approached using the idea that, in order to meet the final customer service requirements, each echelon needs to guarantee certain service times, and safety stock at each node can then be computed to ensure these guarantees. In this section, we discuss the basic implementation of this idea known as the *guaranteed-service model* (GSM) [Simpson, 1958].

Let us consider a generic supply chain topology with a set of supply nodes, a set of demand nodes, and an arbitrary network of intermediate nodes, as shown in Figure R9.16. We assume that each demand node k observes demand samples d_k from external clients and this demand is propagated back through the chain. The demand samples are assumed to be random variables with known means μ_k, and we also assume that the demand is distributed across the source nodes in a fixed proportion that can be expressed as

$$d_j(t) = \sum_{i \in B_j} \theta_{ij} d_i(t) \tag{R9.27}$$

where j is an intermediate or supply node, B_j is a set of its downstream (destination) nodes, and θ are the known fixed coefficients. This assumption implies that we can recursively compute the demand at any node knowing the initial demand values for the demand nodes.

The inventory flows in the opposite direction, from the supply to demand nodes. We denote the holding costs at node j as h_j, and the lead time, that is the time between receiving the input and producing the output, as L_j. We also denote the set of upstream (source) nodes for node j as A_j.

Finally, the central assumptions made by the GSM model are that all nodes provide strict service time guarantees to their consumers (client or downstream nodes) and the demand has a strict upper boundary. The service time guarantee means that node j must fill the demand

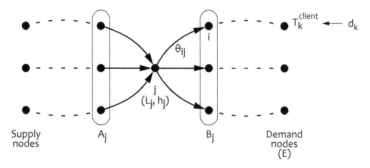

Figure R9.16: Supply chain representation in the GSM model.

requested by any of its consumers B_j in T_j^{out} time steps or less, and, in particular, each demand node k guarantees the service time of T_k^{client} to its external clients. This assumption implies that the time needed for node j to receive the inventory ordered from the upstream nodes A_j is also limited by time T_j^{in}. The strict upper boundary for demand means that the total demand at any node j for any specific time period τ is limited by a known demand boundary function $D_j(\tau)$:

$$\sum_{t \in \tau} d_j(t) \leq D_j(\tau)$$

(R9.28)

The GSM model does not specify how exactly the assumption about the bounded demand is implemented in a real supply chain. In practice, one does not necessarily need to guarantee that the realized demand is strictly limited, and, instead, one can use methods such as backorders and negotiations to handle the excess demand.

The set of assumptions described above allows us to concisely express the safety stock level needed to maintain the guaranteed service times at each node. Let us consider node j that receives the demand of $d_j(t)$ units at time t. The node can replenish this quantity by pulling the inventory from the upstream nodes by time $t + T_j^{in} + L_j$ and it also guarantees that the demand will be delivered to the downstream nodes by time $t + T_j^{out}$. Assuming the pulling time is longer than the fulfillment time, that is $T_j^{in} + L_j > T_j^{out}$, the safety stock needs to be sufficient to cover the following critical interval:

$$\tau_j = T_j^{in} + L_j - T_j^{out}$$

(R9.29)

The relationship between these variables is depicted in Figure R9.17. At the same time, the safety stock level can then be expressed as the difference between the upper boundary and the expected demand for the critical interval:

$$\text{safety stock at } j = D_j(\tau_j) - \mu_j \cdot \tau_j \qquad (R9.30)$$

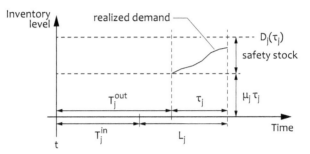

Figure R9.17: Safety stock in the GSM model.

The inventory optimization problem can then be formulated in mathematical programming terms as follows:

$$\min_{T_j^{in}, T_j^{out}} \quad \sum_j h_j \cdot \left(D_j(\tau_j) - \mu_j \cdot \tau_j\right)$$

$$\text{subject to} \quad \tau_j = T_j^{in} + L_j - T_j^{out}$$

$$T_i^{out} \leqslant T_j^{in}, \quad i \in A_j \qquad (a)$$

$$T_j^{out} \leqslant T_j^{client}, \quad j \in E \qquad (b)$$

$$\tau_j, T_j^{out}, T_j^{in} \geqslant 0 \text{ and integer} \qquad (c)$$

(R9.31)

In this problem specification, the objective function corresponds to the total holding costs for the safety stock. Constraint (a) requires that for any intermediate or demand node j, all of its source nodes have to have service times less than their input time. Constraint (b) requires service times at the demand nodes to meet the guarantees to the external clients. Finally, constraint (c) requires service levels to be non-negative integers.

In a general case, optimization problem R9.31 can be solved using mathematical programming methods. The solution is a set of guaranteed service times that can be used to determine the safety stocks at all nodes and then manage the replenishment accordingly.

The generic GSM model can be used to derive relatively simple rules for some special cases such as serial supply chains, so that only a few policy combinations might need to be evaluated instead of solving a generic optimization problem. The GSM approach, however, assumes a relatively simple environment model that does not support several important features such as stochastic lead times. However, there are a number of specialized extensions in existence that close these gaps [Humair et al., 2013; Eruguz et al., 2016]. One notable alternative to dealing with these complexities analytically is to use generic methods from control theory and reinforcement learning. We spend the next section building a prototype that demonstrates both the advantages and shortcomings of this approach.

R9.5.2 *Control Using Reinforcement Learning*

 The complete reference implementation for this section is available at https://bit.ly/38jFCa4

Thus far, we have discussed two principal approaches to inventory optimization; analytical models and simulations. We have seen that the simulators can be used to evaluate supply chain performance for specific combinations of parameters, and it is also possible to build various value maps to graphically identify the optimal configurations. We can further combine the simulators with parameter optimization algorithms such as grid search or Bayesian optimization to automatically find optimal configurations. This approach is feasible in practice, but searching through a multidimensional space of parameters is computationally heavy, and this imposes certain limitations on the problem size and level of sophistication of the control policies. The brute force approach becomes particularly challenging for multi-echelon problems where the number of possible control configurations grows exponentially with the number of nodes.

We can attempt to improve the efficiency of the optimization process using reinforcement learning methods that are specifically designed to learn control policies in a sample-efficient way by interacting with the simulation environment. We demonstrate this approach using a custom environment that is substantially more complex than the academic models we used previously. This environment includes multiple locations of different types, production and transportation controls, seasonal demand changes, and storage capacity constraints.

R9.5.2.1   *Environment Specification*

We start by defining the environment model that includes a factory, central factory warehouse, and w distribution centers [Kemmer et al., 2018; Oroojlooyjadid et al., 2017]. An instance of such an environment with three warehouses is shown in Figure R9.18.

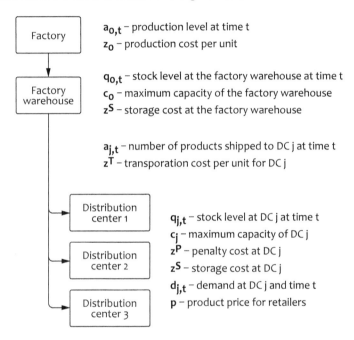

Figure R9.18: Environment specification for multi-echelon inventory optimization using reinforcement learning.

We assume that the factory produces a product with a constant cost of z_0 dollars per unit, and the production level at time step t is $a_{0,t}$. Next, there is a factory warehouse with a maximum capacity of c_0 units. The storage cost for one product unit for one time step at the factory center is z_0^S, and the stock level at time t is $q_{0,t}$.

At any time t, the number of units shipped from the factory warehouse to the distribution center j is $a_{j,t}$, and the transportation cost is z_j^T dollars per unit. Note that the transportation cost varies across the distribution warehouses.

Each distribution center j has maximum capacity c_j, storage cost of z_j^S, and stock level at time t equal to $q_{j,t}$. Products are sold to retail partners at price p which is the same across all warehouses, and the demand for time step t at warehouse j is $d_{j,t}$ units. We also assume that the manufacturer is contractually obligated to fulfill all orders placed by retail partners, and if the demand for a certain time step exceeds the corresponding stock level, it results in a penalty of z_j^P dollars per each unfulfilled unit. Unfulfilled demand is carried over between time steps (which corresponds to backordering), and we model it as a negative stock level.

Let us now combine the above assumptions and define the environment in reinforcement learning terms. First, we obtain the following reward function for each time step:

$$
\begin{aligned}
r = p \sum_{j=1}^{w} d_j - z_0 a_0 - \sum_{j=0}^{w} z_j^S \max[q_j, 0] \\
- \sum_{j=1}^{w} z_j^T a_j + \sum_{j=1}^{w} z_j^P \min[q_j, 0]
\end{aligned}
\tag{R9.32}
$$

The first term is revenue, the second relates to production cost, the third is the total storage cost, and the fourth is the transportation cost. The last term represents the penalty cost and enters the equation with a plus sign because stock levels would be already negative in case of unfulfilled demand.

We choose the state vector to include all current stock levels and demand values for all warehouses for k previous steps:

$$
s_t = \left(q_{0,t}, q_{1,t}, \ldots, q_{w,t}, d_{t-1}, \ldots, d_{t-k} \right)
$$

where
$$
d_t = \left(d_{1,t}, \ldots, d_{w,t} \right)
\tag{R9.33}
$$

Note that we assume that the agent observes only past demand values, but not the demand for the current (upcoming) time step. This means that the agent can potentially benefit from learning the demand pattern and embedding the demand prediction capability into the policy. The state update rule will then be as follows:

$$s_{t+1} = \left(\min \left[q_{0,t} + a_0 - \sum_{j=1}^{w} a_j, c_0 \right], \right. \quad \text{(factory stock update)}$$

$$\min \left[q_{1,t} + a_{1,t} - d_{1,t}, c_1 \right], \quad \text{(DC stock updates)}$$

$$\ldots,$$

$$\min \left[q_{w,t} + a_{w,t} - d_{w,t}, c_w \right],$$

$$d_t, \quad \text{(demand history shifts)}$$

$$\ldots,$$

$$\left. d_{t-k+1} \right)$$

$$\text{(R9.34)}$$

In other words, the factory stock is updated by adding the inventory produced at a given time step and subtracting the inventory shipped to the distribution centers, but with a cap of c_0 units. At the distribution centers, the stock is updated by adding replenishment orders and subtracting the demand. Finally, the action vector consists of production and shipping controls:

$$\mathbf{a}_t = \left(a_{0,t}, a_{1,t}, \ldots, a_{w,t} \right) \quad \text{(R9.35)}$$

We instantiate the environment assuming three distribution centers, that is $w = 3$. The overall layout of this small environment and the mapping between the physical entities and their action and state representations are shown in Figure R9.19.

We further assume episodes with 26 time steps (e.g. weeks), and holding and transportation costs that vary significantly across the locations. The demand functions differ across the distribution centers, and each function is defined using a baseline seasonal curve with a random component added on top of it:

$$d_{j,t} = \frac{d_{max}}{2} \left(1 + \sin \left(\frac{4\pi(t + 2j)}{T} \right) \right) + \eta_{j,t} \quad \text{(R9.36)}$$

where $d_{j,t}$ is the demand at distribution center j at time t, and η is a random variable with a uniform distribution. This family of demand functions is visualized in Figure R9.20. For the sake of simplicity, we also assume that fractional amounts of the product can be produced or shipped (alternatively, one can think of it as measuring units in thousands or millions, so that rounding errors are immaterial).

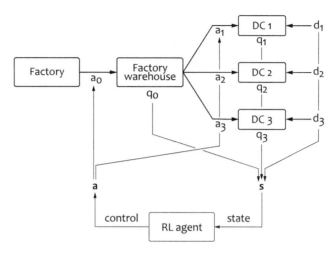

Figure R9.19: Environment instance used for prototyping.

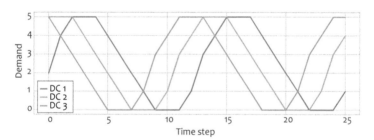

Figure R9.20: Examples of demand realization for one episode.

R9.5.2.2 *Establishing the Baselines*

The inventory flow in the above environment can, in principle, be managed using separate continuous or periodic review policies deployed at the factory warehouse and distribution centers. This approach is not necessarily optimal even if the policy parameters are jointly optimized, but it helps to establish the baseline that can be used to benchmark the reinforcement learning approach.

In the environment with one factory and three distribution centers, we need to optimize four policies in a coordinated way. For the sake of prototyping, let us use continuous review policies, so that we have to jointly optimize four pairs of parameters (s, Q). This is a relatively small parameter space, and we use Bayesian optimization to find the near-optimal point in this eight-dimensional parameter space. The optimization algorithm basically performs multiple simulations and moves toward the profit-maximizing point. An example simulation trace for the final set of parameters and achieved profit is presented in Figure R9.21. This visualization shows how the inventory levels, shipments, production levels, and profits change over time, allowing us to understand the control dynamics.

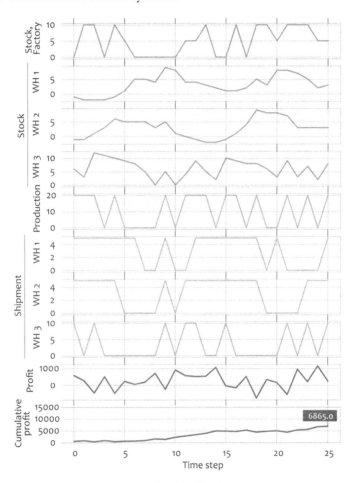

Figure R9.21: Example of (s, Q) policy simulation.

In the environment we have specified, the random component of the demand is relatively small, and it makes more sense to ship products on an as-needed basis rather than to accumulate large safety stocks in the distribution centers. This is visible in Figure R9.21, where the shipment patterns loosely follow the oscillating demand pattern, while stock levels do not develop a pronounced sawtooth pattern.

R9.5.2.3 *Learning the Control Policy Using DDPG*

Our next step is to implement a reinforcement learning-based solution. We have already specified how the environment is represented in terms of the Markov decision process in expressions R9.32, R9.33, and R9.35 for reward, state, and action, respectively. This enables us to plug the environment simulator into standard reinforcement learning algorithms and to train inventory control policies in a relatively straightforward way. The specific choice of the algorithm, however, is influenced by the environment design. We have defined the action vector as a real-valued vector of production and shipment controls, and thus our choice is limited to continuous control algorithms. We choose to use the DDPG algorithm introduced in Section 3.4.6.2. The policy trained by this algorithm significantly outperforms the baseline we established in the previous section, as illustrated in Figure R9.22.

The production and shipment patterns visualized in Figure R9.22 are significantly different from the patterns of the regular continuous review policy in Figure R9.21. One of the most curious facts about this result is that the policy recognizes the fact that it can collect a large number of backorders towards the end of the episode and artificially boost the profits this way.

The above prototype demonstrates the concept of supply chain optimization using reinforcement learning, but the practical application of this idea faces a number of challenges:

- First, reinforcement learning tends to produce irregular policies that can be difficult to interpret as well as to implement, because of constraints associated with logistics, packaging, and contractual aspects.

- Second, such irregular policies tend to be unpredictable and unstable, so that service levels and costs can have very high variance, and the policy can occasionally make completely wrong decisions, with disastrous consequences.

- Third, the dimensionality (or cardinality) of the action space grows with the number of supply chain nodes. Most reinforcement learning algorithms are not designed to handle large action spaces, and this problem is in general very challenging.

The first two issues can be partly mitigated by combining reinforcement learning with parametric policies. For example, a reinforcement

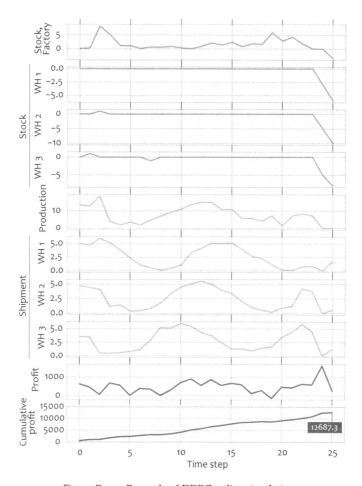

Figure R9.22: Example of DDPG policy simulation.

learning algorithm can be used to manage the parameters of the periodic review policy which, in turn, is used to make low-level ordering decisions. The third problem arises when a single-agent reinforcement learning algorithm is used to control a complex environment such as a multi-echelon chain. The alternative approach is use multiple independent agents or multi-agent algorithms where certain components are shared across the agents. For example, each supply chain node can be controlled by a separate policy. This solution helps to avoid large action spaces, but imposes the problem of agent coordination. For instance, consider a multi-echelon chain where each node is controlled by an independent agent. Ideally, each agent should contribute towards maximizing the global profit, and the reward function can be defined accordingly. This, however, can create a deadlock because the upstream agents (nodes that are closer to the supply side) will only be making losses until the downstream agents (nodes that closer to the client side) learn how to order and use the inventory properly. However, these downstream nodes will not be able to learn until the upstream nodes deliver some inventory. Although coordination problems like that can be alleviated using a number of techniques, the development of stable and practical reinforcement learning solutions for supply chain optimization is generally challenging.

R9.6   VARIATIONS AND EXTENSIONS

In the previous sections, we have developed methods for controlling the inventory flow at individual nodes of a supply chain, as well as controlling groups of nodes in a coordinated way. All of this analysis, however, has been done for a relatively simple environment. We assumed only one item, unlimited shelf life and product lifespan, and a fairly abstract demand model. The simulation methods that we have developed provide enough flexibility to replace these assumptions with more realistic business logic if needed, and we spend this section discussing several common extensions in greater detail.

R9.6.1   *Seasonal and Perishable Items*

The environment models used in this recipe assume that the products purchased from suppliers can remain in the chain for unlimited time before they are delivered to the external clients. In other words, the units purchased just recently are indistinguishable from the units purchased a long time previously. Strictly speaking, this assumption is never true, but it can be a more or less critical issue depending on the ratio between the products' shelf life and supply chain latency. It is clearly an important concern for perishable products with a shelf life ranging from days to months such as foods and beverages sold in supermarkets, meals prepared by catering companies and cafeterias, cosmetics, pharmaceutical drugs, and volatile chemicals. Some products such as apparel and other fashion items might not be perishable, but their lifetime can be strictly limited to one season, and this time can be comparable to the replenishment time. Finally, there are products such as consumer electronics that are neither perishable nor strictly seasonal, but the length of the product's life cycle can be comparable to production and transportation times.

Overstocking of seasonal and replenishable items is associated not only with the holding costs, but with value losses and disposal costs. This can be illustrated with the newsvendor model which is, in fact, one of the oldest supply chain models [Edgeworth, 1888]. The newsvendor model considers a newspaper vendor who needs to decide how many copies of the daily newspaper to procure given that the unsold copies will lose all their value by the end of the day. This problem can be expressed as follows:

$$\text{profit}(q) = (p - c)\min[d, \ q] - (c - s)\max[q - d, \ 0] \qquad \text{(R9.37)}$$

where q is the purchased quantity (on-hand inventory in the beginning of the cycle), p is the unit price, c is the unit procurement cost, d is the demand which is considered to be a random variable, and s is the residual value of each unit. The residual value s can be positive if the inventory retains some value at the end of the cycle, zero, or negative if disposal costs are involved.

All stages of the inventory management process can be adjusted to incorporate value losses and disposal costs. First, these costs can be accounted for at the aggregate planning stage. In particular, the allocation procedure developed in Section R9.3 explicitly assumes the limited life cycle. Second, the profit equation R9.1 can be extended with additional costs and all downstream algebraic optimization solutions and simulation models can be updated accordingly. In particular, the profit function specified by expression R9.37 can be maximized analytically, or multiple values of q can be evaluated using simulations to determine the optimal option assuming a certain demand distribution. Finally, the profit function R9.37 is often maximized not only by choosing the optimal value of q, but also by various manipulations with the price, demand, and residual value. For example, apparel retailers commonly target to sell off the inventory by the end of the season, and switch between regular prices and markdowns to accelerate or decelerate the demand accordingly. In terms of equation R9.37, this means to find a price schedule that minimizes the difference between the stock level q and total demand d by the end of the season. If this difference is greater than zero, the retailer can run a liquidation sale at discounted price s which is also optimized based on the expected demand. We have discussed these categories of problems and corresponding solutions at length in recipe R7 (Price and Promotion Optimization).

More generally, price changes and promotion can be used to not only reduce losses associated with the depreciation of perishable and seasonal items, but also to reduce holding costs and mitigate other supply chain constraints. In many applications, replenishment decisions and pricing decisions complement each other and need to be closely coordinated. For example, it might not be possible to accurately determine the optimal replenishment quantity because of uncertain demand, but the errors might be efficiently corrected using revenue management techniques such as dynamic pricing.

R9.6.2   *Multiple Sales Channels*

The multi-echelon model assumes that one node can have two or more downstream (client) nodes, and thus serve two or more demand streams. In practice, these streams can have different priorities and require different SLAs, so we might need specialized methods for tuning the trade-offs between the SLAs guaranteed to different clients that share the same pool of inventory.

The problem of demand prioritization can be illustrated using the ship from store (SFS) scenario. The SFS capability was implemented by many retailers as a part of their omnichannel strategies to reduce shipment times for online orders and improve the inventory turnover. It is usually implemented by routing of certain online orders to physical stores where store associates collect the ordered items directly from the store's shelves, package them, and ship them to the customers. This means that the store associates compete with regular in-store customers for the inventory, and we generally need to balance the SLAs for online customers and in-store customers. More specifically, the problem usually stems from the fact that the digital commerce system has an accurate real-time view of the inventory on the shelves, so that it can keep accepting orders even after the product is sold out. It can also be the case that the store associates process the orders with a significant delay which also can lead to overselling. This issue is often addressed by setting inventory reservation levels, so that a certain number of units are reserved for in-store customers, and the remaining stock is considered as available-to-promise (ATP) for online customers, as illustrated in Figure R9.23. These reservation levels are assumed to be recomputed on a regular basis.

The SFS use case is very similar to another popular scenario known as buy online pickup in store (BOPUS). The difference is that in the latter case the orders packaged in stores are picked up by customers rather than being shipped to them.

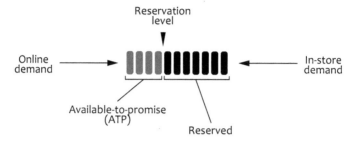

Figure R9.23: Environment model for SFS and BOPUS use cases.

The quality of the reservation algorithm can usually be assessed using the following two metrics:

PICK RATE The ratio between the number of successfully fulfilled items and the total number of ordered items over a certain time interval.

EXPOSURE RATE The ratio between the number of items potentially available for online ordering (the difference between on-hand inventory and true in-store demand) and the actual ATP.

A retailer can balance these two metrics differently depending on their business goals, the cost of fulfillment exceptions and the cost of underexposed inventory. For example, some retailers can redirect SFS orders at a low cost from one store to another in case of exceptions, and can thus accept a low pick rate to achieve high exposure rates. On the other hand, some retailers might be concerned about customer dissatisfaction caused by order fulfillment exceptions, and choose to maintain high pick rates at the expense of exposure rates.

The pick and exposure rates are determined not only by the reservation level, but also by the amount of the safety stock. One can clearly achieve both the near-perfect pick and exposure rates by stocking enough inventory to cover any spikes in online and offline demands combined. Safety stock, however, increases the holding costs and reduces the inventory turnover, so we should assess the efficiency of the reservation algorithm only in the context of a specific replenishment constraint. An example plot that can support such an assessment is presented in Figure R9.24. In this plot, each curve corresponds to a set of possible trade-offs between the pick and exposure rates given a specific combination of two parameters; average on-hand inventory level I^h and reservation algorithm a. An individual point on any curve corresponds to a specific reservation level r, and thus the trade-off between the pick and exposure rates is determined by triplet (I^h, a, r). Assuming that the average inventory level I^h and the reservation algorithm a are fixed, each curve can be viewed as a Pareto frontier, and we can vary the reservation level to achieve appropriate trade-offs between pick and exposure rates. The Pareto frontier achievable at any given inventory level is determined by the demand variance, the accuracy of the forecast, and other properties of the reservation algorithm.

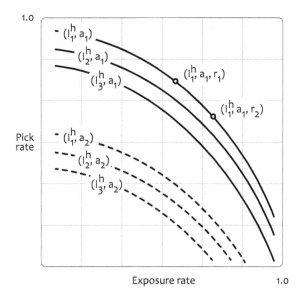

Figure R9.24: Visualization of Pareto frontiers for SFS.

The solid-line and dash-line curves in Figure R9.24 correspond to two different reservation algorithms. The plot suggests that the algorithm that corresponds to the solid-line curves strictly outperforms the algorithm that produces dash-line curves, providing better trade-offs between pick and exposure rates for all inventory levels.

R9.6.3 Multiple Items: Policy Differentiation

In many industries, companies need to manage inventory on a large scale. For instance, the average number of SKUs carried in a supermarket is estimated to be 30,000 and the number of SKUs managed by large manufacturers and retailers can be in the hundreds of thousands. Moreover, inventory is often managed at the regional level so that exactly the same item in two different locations is treated as two different SKUs.

Inventory optimization on a large scale is challenging even with highly automated systems because each item potentially requires investigating unique data issues, building a separate forecast, and performing some troubleshooting. The optimization process can be made more manageable by introducing several categories of items and providing different service levels for each of these categories. This approach is conceptually similar to the product categorizations used in recipe R7 (Price and Promotion Optimization) to differentiate price management and demand forecasting strategies.

One of the most basic approaches to strategy differentiation is known as ABC analysis. This approach is based on the observation that the revenue contribution of SKUs typically has near-exponential distribution as shown in Figure R9.25.

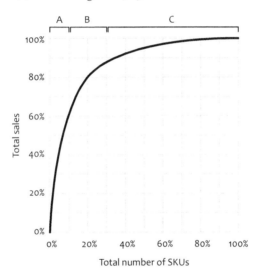

Figure R9.25: ABC inventory categorization.

The items with the highest contribution, commonly referred to as A items, generally require close attention, which assumes a combination of decision automation components with manual reviews. This category can be split further into high-value slow-moving items such as heavy machinery and low-value fast-moving items such as consumer provisions. The next bucket, referred to as B items, can mainly be managed by decision automation systems, and relatively high revenue contribution justifies the investments into the development of advanced optimization models. Finally, the remaining items, known as C items, can be managed using methods geared towards operational costs reduction and simplicity rather than precision. For example, it is common to group similar C items together and manage groups rather than individual SKUs to reduce the total number of entities that need to be tracked. Items A usually constitute about 10% of the total number of SKUs, items B account for about 20%, and the remaining 70% are items C.

R9.6.4 *Multiple Items: Coordinated Replenishment*

In the previous sections of this recipe, we were developing models and methods under the assumption that all SKUs are managed independently, do not share any resources, and do not have any dependencies in terms of costs and logistical constraints. This assumption is impractical in many real-world environments because SKUs often share the same transportation and storage infrastructure, and procurement terms are often negotiated for groups of SKUs. Consequently, inventory management might need to be coordinated across multiple SKUs to achieve the following goals:

REDUCE PURCHASE COSTS Coordinated procurement of multiple SKUs can help to get quantity discounts through consolidation of multiple smaller orders into bigger ones.

REDUCE TRANSPORTATION COSTS Coordination of replenishment times and quantities can help to reduce transportation and shipping costs through better utilization of vehicles and other resources.

REDUCE TRANSACTION COSTS In some scenarios, multiple related SKUs can be grouped together to reduce production setup costs and other per-transaction expenses. For example, a furniture item can include multiple SKUs of different accent colors, and the setup cost can be reduced by grouping such SKUs into a single batch.

The above benefits, however, are often achieved at the expense of a higher average inventory, lower inventory turnover, and more difficult exception handling compared to independent SKU management. Consequently, optimization models for coordinated inventory management generally aim to find the balance between the group costs (including setup, transportation, and discounts) and metrics for individual SKUs including holding costs and service levels.

Coordinated replenishment can be supported at all levels of the inventory management process. In particular, coordination can be implemented using control policies that have special mechanisms for grouping items together. This can be illustrated using the following classic policy, known as a *can-order policy* or (S, c, s) policy, that is basically a multi-item extension of the continuous review policy [Balintfy, 1964]:

> *Assume a group of related items where each item i is associated with three parameters: up-to level S_i, can-order level c_i, and must-order level s_i.*
>
> *If item i's level drops below s_i, place a replenishment order that includes*
>
> - *the number of item i units needed to backfill this item up to level S_i,*
>
> - *for each item j that is currently below its can-order threshold c_j, the number of units needed to backfill this item up to level S_j*

The parameters of the can-order policy can be optimized analytically or using simulations. This policy provides a basic solution for reducing the setup costs, but it is not feasible for solving more sophisticated problems such as unlocking discounts by meeting certain volume conditions. Such scenarios often require custom control processes that solve a mathematical programming problem at each reordering step to determine the best subset of items to be ordered.

R9.7   SUMMARY

- Inventory buffers are needed to connect production and transportation processes with different input and output batch sizes, lead times, and service level agreements.

- Inventory buffers can be reduced and inventory availability can be increased in several different ways including redesign of physical production processes, better scheduling of manufacturing operations, and better algorithms for controlling the levels of inventory in the buffers.

- The inventory management process can involve multiple stages including aggregate planning, allocation, rebalancing, and replenishment.

- The single-echelon inventory optimization problem focuses on controlling an individual inventory node such as a warehouse.

The inventory control policy aims to minimize the operational costs (including holding costs, transactions fees, and backorder penalties) given the target service levels guaranteed to the clients.

- The most common performance metrics for an inventory control policy include cycle service level and fill rate.

- The multi-echelon problem formulation focuses on coordination across multiple inventory nodes such as factories, central warehouses, and distribution centers.

- The main types of control policies include continuous review and periodic review policies.

- The parameters of control policies can be optimized analytically or using simulations. The simulation-based approach provides more flexibility and helps to model complex demand patterns, business rules, and logistical constraints that are difficult to account for in analytical solutions.

- The multi-echelon optimization problem can be expressed in mathematical programming terms provided that special assumptions about the service level guarantees are made. The classic solution that uses this approach is the guaranteed service model (GSM).

- Reinforcement learning can be used to learn control policies for arbitrary single-echelon and multi-echelon environments. The main challenges of this approach include irregularity and instability of the resulting policies.

- Specialized inventory control methods are used for multi-item environments, omnichannel commerce, and perishable products.

Part V

PRODUCTION OPERATIONS

The main focus of the Parts I to IV was on distribution channels and supply management. The third major area of operations is production, which is the process of turning inputs, such as raw materials and human resources, into outputs, which are products and services. From the analytics standpoint, production operations are associated with a wide range of planning and resource optimization tasks, as well as ongoing monitoring and control.

In Part V, we provide recipes for intelligent monitoring of production processes and assets including anomaly detection in IoT sensor data, predictive maintenance, and defect detection using machine vision methods. Although our main focus is on production operations, the same methods can be efficiently applied to a wider range of use cases including transportation, chemical distribution, fleet management, and IT operations.

Recipe

10

ANOMALY DETECTION

Detecting Anomalies and Preventing Failures Based on IoT Metrics

Many modern industrial environments, systems, and machines include IoT sensors that measure physical quantities such as pressure, temperature, levels of liquids, or voltage. These measurements can typically be represented as time series which can be monitored and analyzed with a goal to detect and correct failures or degradations that can potentially result in failures or outages. Examples of such applications include the analysis of vibration sensor data in wind turbines with a goal to prevent bearing failures, monitoring of flows in a petroleum production system, and monitoring of energy consumption patterns in buildings to detect faulty appliances and theft.

In this recipe, we focus on the problem of building intelligent monitoring systems that can automatically analyze sensor data streams, detect abnormal situations, prescribe reactive or preventive actions, and reduce the amount of information that needs to be processed by the operations teams. We discuss how some of these tasks can be accomplished using relatively basic methods, and then demonstrate how more powerful solutions can be created using the representation learning methods introduced in Chapter 2.

We assume that our goal is to monitor a system that consists of multiple components, and, for each component, we collect one or more metrics represented as time series. For example, we can monitor a mechanical system that includes several bearings and attach multiple accelerometers to each bearing in order to measure the vibrations along different axes. We further assume that the components are interrelated in two ways. First, a failure in one component can trigger failures in other components. Second, the overall system health is determined by a combination of component states, so that individual component failures do not necessarily represent a risk for the entire system. In other words, components can fail and be replaced without system downtimes provided that certain requirements regarding the number and types of the functioning components are met.

The raw data collected from the sensors can be enriched by the analysts. From this perspective, we distinguish between the following three scenarios. First, we might have only the raw data that potentially includes segments that correspond to both normal and abnormal situations, but we do not have any ground truth labels or reliable rules that allow us to identify specific segments as normal or abnormal and to differentiate between them. Second, we might have a dataset that consists only of the metrics collected in a normal system state, so that we can be certain that all abnormal observations are removed. Finally, we might have a dataset with metric segments explicitly labeled as normal or abnormal. These labels may be available for individual components, as well as for the entire system. We might also have multiple classes of abnormal situations. For example, bearing failures can be categorized as *inner race damage*, *outer race damage*, and *ball damage*. In practice, the creation of labeled datasets is often challenging because of the rarity of abnormal observations, limited availability of domain experts who can perform labeling, and other factors.

R10.1.1   *Anomaly Monitoring, Scoring, and Detection*

Our goal is to build a system that consumes and analyzes the inputs described above and produces outputs that help to maintain and manage the components under monitoring more efficiently. For brevity, we refer to such a system as an *anomaly detection system*, although it can carry out several different functions, as outlined in Figure R10.1. First, the system can perform various transformations of the input metrics with a goal to reduce the amount of data that needs to be monitored by the operations team, as well as reduce noises and remove irrelevant anomalies that complicate the downstream monitoring processes. The transformed metrics can be monitored using conventional tools such as dashboards and threshold-based alerting rules.

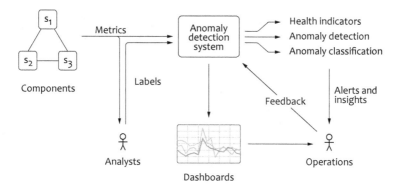

Figure R10.1: The anomaly detection environment.

The second common group of outputs is *health indicators* that can be computed for the entire system under monitoring or individual components or metrics. Each health indicator is a univariate time series that describes the dynamics of the system or component health. Health indicators are typically designed in a way that the health value at any given time can be interpreted as an *anomaly score, failure risk score,* or *remaining useful life estimate.*

The health indicators need to be monitored to detect abnormal situations and to take preventive or corrective actions. Assuming that the indicators properly capture the level of risk and represent it as a numerical score, the monitoring stage is required to manage alerting thresholds and provide the operations teams with relevant information that facilitates the root cause analysis and troubleshooting. We refer to the problem of converting health indicators into decisions (alerts) as *anomaly detection.* The anomaly detection algorithms should optimally balance the costs of false positives (e.g. level of effort associated with alert investigation) and false negatives (e.g. losses associated with failure propagation). We assume that this can be done, in particular, using the feedback on the relevancy of the alerts provided by the operations team. Once the alerts are generated, their operationalization, including root cause analysis and troubleshooting, can be facilitated using granular component-level health indicators and automatic *anomaly classification.*

R10.1.2   *Predictive Maintenance*

The general solution architecture described in the previous section can be used as a template for implementing a wide range of use cases, and each use case requires making multiple design choices regarding monitoring dashboards, health indicators, and alerting algorithms. In this section, we discuss one particularly important group of use cases which is collectively known as *predictive maintenance*, and formulate more specific requirements for it.

Consider the problem of maintaining the system being monitored in working order. The most basic approach to this problem is *reactive maintenance* that assumes that the system runs to failure, and the maintenance operation is performed in response to it. The metrics that describe system health or degradation can be collected, but they are not supposed to influence the decisions with regard to the maintenance time, as illustrated in Figure R10.2. The reactive strategy is typically associated with downtime, and it cannot be applied in environments where failures are not acceptable because of the safety or recovery costs considerations.

The alternative strategy is *preventive maintenance*. This approach aims to minimize the probability of failures by planning and scheduling maintenance of equipment before a problem occurs. One of the main problems in preventive maintenance is the schedule optimization. Maintenance delays can result in failures, but excessively frequent maintenance leads to the loss of *usable time*, as illustrated in Figure R10.2 (b). Preventive maintenance can involve data-driven methods for the schedule optimization, but it does not assume dynamic decision-making based on the current system conditions.

The third strategy is *predictive maintenance* that aims to dynamically optimize maintenance decisions based on the expected system trajectory. The central problem of predictive maintenance is the estimation of the *remaining useful life* (RUL) of the system. This estimate is then used to determine the optimal maintenance timing, as shown in Figure R10.2 (c). We consider the RUL a particular case of a health indicator that is calibrated in time units (instead of the relative risk levels).

We discuss the specialized RUL estimation methods later in this recipe. In real-world predictive maintenance solutions, however, the RUL model is only one of many components, and other general-purpose methods presented in this recipe are also applicable to predictive maintenance tasks.

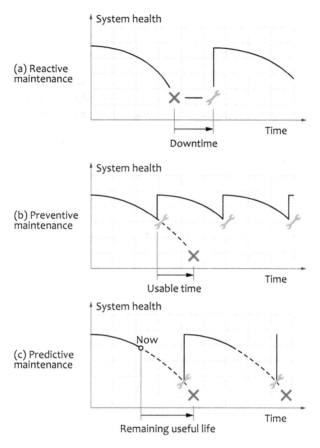

Figure R10.2: Reactive, preventive, and predictive maintenance strategies.

R10.2   SOLUTION OPTIONS

One of the main challenges in the development of anomaly detection solutions is the very high diversity and complexity of production processes and environments which often requires devising a somewhat unique approach for each particular application. In addition to that, the tasks outlined in the previous section, including the creation of informative dashboards and detection of anomalous situations, are relatively open-ended, and one can use a broad range of statistical and machine learning methods to approach them, depending on their specific application.

To deal with these challenges, we first discuss the basic design principles that can be used to correctly transform a domain-specific anomaly detection problem into a machine learning problem that can be solved using standard methods. Next, we discuss how health monitoring and anomaly detection tasks can be solved in the environments where we observe only the normal state of the system and do have access to any labels or feedback data. Finally, we discuss methods that can be applied in environments where labels or feedback data are available. We generally aim to develop a toolkit of methods that can be combined in many different ways to create specific solutions rather than develop a universal template that fits all applications.

R10.3 SYSTEM MODELS

In Chapter 2, we discussed the situation that a stochastic process can initially be observed as a complex and seemingly chaotic set of samples in the space spanned on the observed dimensions, but that this set often lives on a low-dimensional surface embedded into the observed space because the original representation is redundant. We named such surfaces *manifolds*, and introduced several methods, including linear and variational autoencoders, for learning manifold topology models. These methods are relevant for our current discussion because we can attempt to learn a manifold of normal systems states based on the available observations, and detect deviations from these. We refer to a model that approximates the manifold of the normal states as the *model of normality* and refer to samples that deviate from it as *outliers*.

A natural question that can be posed at this point is whether outliers and anomalies refer to the same concept. We have previously stated that anomalies are the deviations from the normal system behavior that represents relevant operational or business risks, while outliers are the deviations from the normal manifold specified using some model. This suggests that outliers can be interpreted as anomalies only if the model of normality correctly represents the physical, operational, or business model.

Let us review a simple example that illustrates the mismatch between the model of normality and the physical constraints of the production process. Consider a terminal at a chemical plant where some liquid product is loaded from a stationary tank to tank cars, as depicted in the top part of Figure R10.3. The loading pipeline includes two meters, one measuring the outflow from the stationary tank side, and another one measuring the inflow on the tank car side. Assuming that the volume of the product passed through each meter is reported at a regular time interval (e.g. every 30 minutes), we can visualize the collected data using a scatter plot, as shown in Figure R10.3 (a). In this example, we assume that the volume can vary significantly depending on the demand, weather, time of the day, and other factors, but the measurements of the two meters should match, otherwise we are likely to have a leak or some other dangerous issue that needs to be urgently investigated.

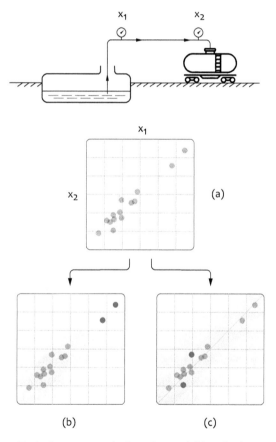

Figure R10.3: Designing an anomaly detection model for a basic setup with two metrics.

It can now be seen that the dataset presented in Figure R10.3 (a), considered in isolation, can be used to build multiple different models of normality, and a valid model can be designed using only the context described above. For example, we can assume that the measurement pairs (x_1, x_2) should follow the bivariate normal distribution, that is

$$(x_1, x_2) \sim N(\boldsymbol{\mu}, \boldsymbol{\Sigma}) \tag{R10.1}$$

where the distribution parameters $\boldsymbol{\mu}$ and $\boldsymbol{\Sigma}$ can be learned from the data. The anomaly score for any specific observation $\mathbf{x} = (x_1, x_2)$ can then be computed as the Mahalanobis distance between $\mathbf{x}$ and the distribution:

$$\text{score}(\mathbf{x}) = \sqrt{(\mathbf{x} - \boldsymbol{\mu})^\mathsf{T} \boldsymbol{\Sigma}^{-1} (\mathbf{x} - \boldsymbol{\mu})} \tag{R10.2}$$

This solution is illustrated in Figure R10.3 (b) where the high-volume samples are incorrectly scored as anomalies. In other words, the manifold model is constructed in a way that the outliers do not correspond to meaningful anomalies.

The alternative solution is to leverage our knowledge about the physical process and, more specifically, the fact that the difference between the measurements on two sides of the pipeline should normally be zero. We can define a new metric $x_0 = x_1 - x_2$, and use a univariate normal distribution model for it:

$$x_0 \sim N(0, \sigma^2) \tag{R10.3}$$

Each observation can then be scored using a one-dimensional Mahalanobis distance for the corresponding x_0, as illustrated in Figure R10.3 (c). This model is aligned with the physical process, and the outliers generally match the anomalies.

Although the example with the loading of tank cars is fairly basic, it demonstrates several important techniques that can be used to pre-process the input metrics, simplify the anomaly detection models, and ensure the correctness of the solution:

COMPUTING INVARIANTS First, it is often beneficial to calculate and analyze *invariant* values instead of the original metrics. The discrepancies between the metrics that should normally match are one commonly used type of invariants. Another common option is the frequency-domain representation of the original metrics obtained using the Fourier transform where we expect the power spectral density or other statistics to stay relatively stable over time. The invariants are typically designed based on the physical laws and various constraints that command the system under monitoring. The invariants usually provide more informative and concise representation of the system state compared to the original metrics.

REDUCING DIMENSIONALITY Second, we can use invariants and other derived metrics to reduce the dimensionality of the input data. In our example, we managed to replace two separate time series with one series of differences.

CANCELLING EXTERNAL FACTORS Finally, we can eliminate the impact of unknown factors using properly constructed derived metrics. In the tank car loading example, the bivariate normal distribution model is inadequate because the total loaded volume can change arbitrarily depending on the unknown external factors such as demand and weather. We worked around this issue by computing a derived value where these factors cancel each other out.

We refer to the model that leverages the knowledge about the physical and business principles and constraints of the monitored system to compute more convenient derived metrics as a *system model*. In the overall architecture of an anomaly detection solution, system models can be viewed as feature engineering blocks that produce appropriate inputs for the downstream models and processes. System models can significantly simplify monitoring, anomaly detection, and predictive maintenance tasks, but the development of such models is not always feasible in complex environments with a large number of metrics. The methods we develop in the next sections do not assume that the input metrics are preprocessed using system models, although preprocessing can improve their performance.

R10.4   MONITORING

The ability to visualize the system metrics and provide the operations teams with dashboards that enable the monitoring and analysis of the data is usually one of the first steps towards the development of a comprehensive anomaly detection solution. This capability does not necessarily involve advanced modeling, but statistical methods can be used to enhance the input metrics and reduce the operational effort. We have already discussed that, in some environments, we can reduce the number of metrics and improve their semantics using system models. In this section, we discuss more advanced methods of metric preprocessing.

One transformation that is commonly used for metric preprocessing is *noise reduction*, also referred to as *anomaly removal*. The goal of this operation is to suppress noises that are considered irrelevant for monitoring purposes. For example, the observed time series can include multiple spikes and missed values because of the sensor connectivity issues which are considered normal, and we might want to filter them out. This problem can be approached using basic smoothing techniques and other heuristics, but we can also approach it from the manifold learning perspective, and build a model that removes the outliers by projecting the observed series on the normal manifold.

We can implement this idea using autoencoders introduced in Section 2.6.2. For the sake of illustration, let us review a toy example that demonstrates how anomalies can be removed from multivariate time series using principal component analysis (PCA) which can be viewed as a particular type of linear autoencoder.

We assume that the input metrics are represented as $m \times p$ matrix $\mathbf{X}$ where m is the number of metrics and p is the number of time steps. A small example of such data is shown in the leftmost column of Figure R10.4 where each metric includes a trend, periodic component, additive noise, and spikes. Such spikes, for example, can be a result of sensor connectivity issues. We perform the standard PCA transformation of this matrix to determine the principal components $\mathbf{v}_1, \ldots, \mathbf{v}_m$, each of which is a t-dimensional vector. In our example, such components are visualized in the middle column of Figure R10.4. In PCA, the components are ordered by the variance they capture, so we can build the model of normality that captures the major patterns in the observed series by selecting top $k < m$ components. We can stack them into $t \times k$ matrix $\mathbf{V}$:

$$\mathbf{V}_k = \text{PCA}_k(\mathbf{X}) = (\mathbf{v}_1, \ldots, \mathbf{v}_k) \tag{R10.4}$$

We can further compute the projection of the input metrics on the principal components as $\mathbf{Z}_k = \mathbf{X}\mathbf{V}_k$, and this projection can be viewed as an embedding of the input series. We can then reconstruct the original series from this embedding as $\hat{\mathbf{X}} = \mathbf{Z}_k\mathbf{V}_k^T$. The result of such a reconstruction for our numerical example and two principal components ($k = 2$) is shown in the rightmost column of Figure R10.4. This example demonstrates how the autoencoding operation helps to remove the undesirable zero-valued outliers highlighted in red in the leftmost column of Figure R10.4 from the observed metrics.

The reference implementation for the noise
reduction example is available at
https://bit.ly/3K7RTwa

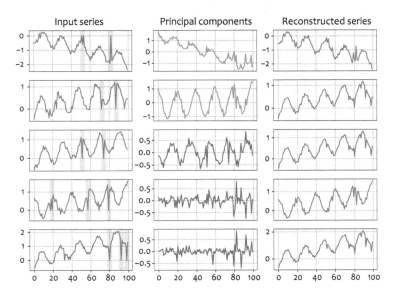

Figure R10.4: Example of noise reduction using a linear autoencoder (PCA).

The second preprocessing operation that is commonly used for the monitoring purposes is *dimensionality reduction*. The purpose of this operation is to reduce the number of metrics that need to be monitored. The ability to solve this problem using statistical methods is important for complex environments where thousands of metrics can be collected. From the machine learning perspective, this problem can be approached from several angles. One option is to use unsupervised methods such as autoencoders to learn a transformation that maps the input metrics to a low-dimensional representation (embedding) that preserves the most important information about the input signals. However, this approach is typically not feasible for monitoring purposes because the dimensions of such a representation are semantically meaningless. In our previous example using PCA, the top two principal components presented in Figure R10.4 preserve enough information to accurately reconstruct the original series, but they do not have any meaning from the domain standpoint.

The alternative solution is to keep the original semantically meaning-ful metrics, but to remove the non-informative series. Assuming that we have ground truth anomaly labels available, this can be done by building a supervised anomaly detection model that predicts such la-bels based on the input metrics, and then ranking the metrics based on their feature importance scores. The metrics that do not have significant predictive power with regard to the anomalies can then be deemed to be non-informative.

The methods described above can be combined in a multistage met-ric preprocessing pipeline as shown in Figure R10.5. Such a pipeline helps to leverage the domain knowledge and labeled data to improve the quality of the dashboards and efficiency of the operations teams.

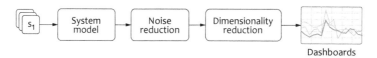

Figure R10.5: Example of a multistage metric preprocessing pipeline.

R10.5 ANOMALY SCORING

The preprocessing methods described in the previous section help to reduce the amount and complexity of the information that needs to be monitored. However, ideally, we want the metrics to be summarized into a single score that can be interpreted as a risk of failure, time to failure, or some other integral indicator of the system or component health. In this section, we discuss how the basic indicators can be cre-ated using unsupervised methods. We refer to such indicators as *health scores* or *anomaly scores*. In the next sections, we discuss how the indica-tors can be used to make anomaly detection decisions and how more informative indicators can be produced using supervised techniques.

R10.5.1 *Basic Models of Normality*

Assuming that we can build a model of normality that describes the expected behavior of the system, the difference between the actual ob-served state and the state predicted by the model can be deemed as a measure of system health. In the most basic cases, we can manu-ally specify the model of normality based on the domain knowledge. Let us illustrate this using a simple example where we leverage the knowledge that the observations can be described using the binomial distribution.

Consider an assembly line that produces electronic components which may have a defect with known probability p. As a part of the quality control process, we regularly sample a batch of n components, test each of them, and count the number of defective items. This number is a random variable that follows the binomial distribution, and which we denote as k. Since the expected number of defective items is np, the probability that the difference between the expected and observed number of defects does not exceed threshold δ can be expressed as follows:

$$p(|k - np| \leqslant \delta) = \sum_{i=np-\delta}^{np+\delta} \binom{n}{i} p^i (1-p)^{n-i} \qquad (R10.5)$$

This expression can be interpreted as a function of δ for fixed n and p. Assuming that we observe a specific value k, the above probability can be evaluated for $\delta = |k - np|$, and the result can be interpreted as a risk score, that is the probability of the assembly line being in an anomalous state. This score is the lowest for $\delta = 0$, and it grows monotonically as δ grows approaching the value of one. Since we perform the quality check on a regular basis, the score values form a time series that can be monitored as an indicator of system health.

R10.5.2   *State Prediction Models*

A more general method for creating models of normality based on the time series data is forecasting. As we discussed in Section 2.4.2, forecasting models are usually designed to predict the future state of the time series based on the previous states (lags) and external features. Provided that the capacity of the model and the number of input lags are limited, the forecast describes the normal behavior of the system, and deviations can be deemed as anomalies.

A high-level design of an anomaly scoring solution that uses the forecasting approach is shown in Figure R10.6. Assuming that we observe a multivariate time series with m metrics, the system state at time t can be described as $m \times p$ matrix X_t where p is the number of lags. This state representation can be preprocessed using a system model ψ to obtain an enhanced representation U_t. We have already discussed that such a representation can be obtained by computing system invariants, and we will discuss more advanced methods in one of the next sections. The future state then can be described as $m \times q$ matrix X_{t+1}

where q is the number of forecasted samples. This matrix can also be preprocessed using the transformation ψ to obtain the representation $\mathbf{U}_{t+1}$. The forecasting model M is then trained based on the normal dataset to predict the future state based on the current state using a standard loss such as the MSE. Finally, the trained model can be used to score the ongoing data. We compute the anomaly score at time t as the difference between the prediction made based on the previous state and actual observation:

$$\text{score}(t) = \left\|\hat{\mathbf{U}}_t - \mathbf{U}_t\right\|^2 \tag{R10.6}$$

Internally, the model can map the system state to embedding $\mathbf{z}_t$ and generate the output prediction $\hat{\mathbf{U}}_{t+1}$ based on it. These embeddings can be captured, and the embedding space can be visualized to assess the separation of anomalous states from the normal manifold, as well as the separation of different classes of anomalies from each other. For instance, we can use the state vector of LSTM models to perform such an analysis.

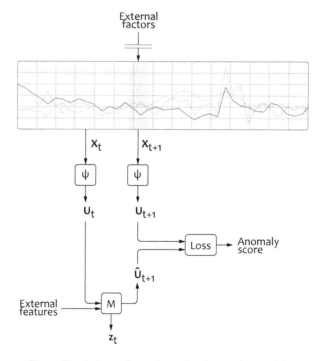

Figure R10.6: Anomaly scoring using forecasting models.

The main limitation of the forecasting-based approach is that the future state has to be predictable based on the previous state and other known contextual variables. This generally requires the system to be isolated from unpredictable external factors. For example, this assumption holds true for many types of rotating machinery such compressors and turbines. If the system is exposed to unknown external factors that impact the future state, the forecasting-based approach might not be applicable. The loading terminal described in Section R10.3 is an example of such a system because the liquid flow is impacted by the tank car traffic which is considered to be random. In such cases, the state prediction approach can be applied only if we manage to develop a system model that cancels out the external factors by computing some kind of invariants. Alternatively, we can collect additional metrics to ensure the completeness of the context which is used to make state predictions [Sezer et al., 2018; Cook et al., 2020]. For example, we might not be able to reliably predict the telemetry metrics for a train until we have a sensor that allows us to differentiate between the train moving on flat ground and ascending an incline in a rural area.

The state prediction approach, however, has important advantages. First, we can use a wide range of off-the-shelf forecasting models which helps to reduce the development effort. Second, the ability to predict the trajectory of the system provides an additional validation of the model correctness. For example, we can deliberately choose to use the forecasting approach to score the health of an isolated rotating machine because its future state *must* be predictable based on the known metrics.

The complete reference implementation of the prototypes for this and next sections is available at https://bit.ly/3uXHpch

We illustrate the state prediction approach using a basic example from the energy domain. We create a synthetic dataset that simulates energy generation data received from smart sensors installed on residential solar panels [Pereira and Silveira, 2018]. This dataset includes several daily patterns such as normal operations, spikes, major failures, cloudy conditions, and snowfalls, as shown in Figure R10.7. The shape of the curves corresponds to the intuitive expectations about the changes in the energy output under various weather conditions.

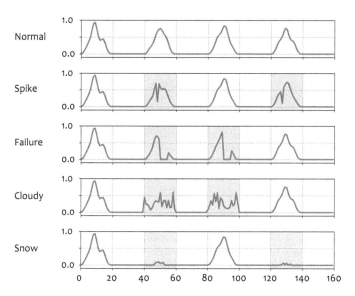

Figure R10.7: Examples of anomalies in solar energy production data.

We build a standard LSTM forecasting model for univariate time series that predicts the energy production level based on a sliding window of 80 time steps. This model is trained using only the normal data, and it is then used to produce the forecast on the test dataset that includes both normal and anomalous instances, as shown in Figure R10.8. Finally, the anomaly score for each time step is computed as the squared forecasting error. This basic solution correctly identifies small anomalies, but fails to properly handle major deviations such as snow conditions.

R10.5.3   *State Manifold Models*

The state prediction approach is not valid for unknown external factors that potentially impact the future state. The alternative solution is to learn the manifold of the current states using an autoencoder model and to evaluate the health score based on the deviation from this manifold. More specifically, we can autoencode the current state with a proper information bottleneck, and evaluate the health score as the state reconstruction error. This design is illustrated in Figure R10.9 where $\mathbf{X}_t$ is the segment of the original multivariate series that represents the state at time t, $\mathbf{U}_t$ is the state representation obtained using

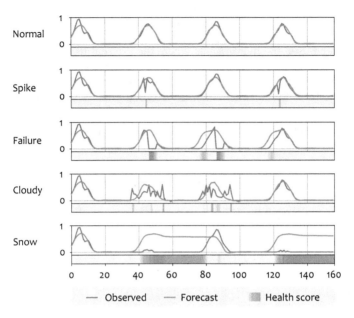

Figure R10.8: Anomaly scoring using an LSTM forecasting model.

preprocessing transformation ψ, M is the autoencoder model, and $\hat{U}_t$ is the reconstruction of the state.

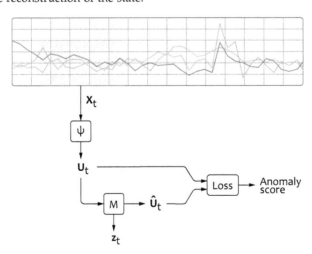

Figure R10.9: Anomaly scoring in time series using autoencoders.

The manifold learning approach requires the future state to be predictable based on the current state and known external features, so it can be used in environments where the external factors are not explicitly observed, but collectively shape a learnable manifold of the observed states. In general, we can use a wide range of autoencoder architectures to implement anomaly scoring. In particular, we can use the linear autoencoder discussed in Section R10.4. This is a relatively basic design, but it can be successfully used in practice for strongly correlated metrics such as web traffic time series [Lakhina et al., 2004].

A more advanced option is variational autoencoders. As discussed in Section 2.6.2.4, variational autoencoders provide a powerful solution for learning regular embedding spaces that are suitable for computing distances between the entities, so we can expect this architecture to be efficient for computing the health scores which are basically the distances between the normal and anomalous states [Pereira and Silveira, 2018].

For the sake of illustration, we implement a basic prototype of the variational autoencoder and evaluate it on the solar energy generation dataset introduced in the previous section. We use a sliding window of 80 time steps as the input vector which we denote as x_t. This input is encoded using a stack of two convolution layers to obtain the distribution parameters μ_t and σ_t, each of which is a two-dimensional vector. The state embedding is then sampled from the normal distribution

$$z_t \sim N(\mu_t, \text{diag}(\sigma_t^2)) \tag{R10.7}$$

and decoded using two upconvolution layers to obtain the reconstruction $\hat{x}_t$. The model is trained on a large number of normal series, and then used to score the test instances as shown in Figure R10.10. At each time step t, the health score is computed as the MSE between the observed state x_t and its reconstruction $\hat{x}_t$.

Variational autoencoding is a probabilistic method that can be conveniently used not only for projecting the observed state on the normal manifold and assessing the distance between the state and projection, but also for assessing the probability of observing a specific state. This capability is essential for anomaly detection, and we continue to discuss this topic in the corresponding section later in this recipe.

R10.5.4   *Metric Preprocessing*

In the previous sections, we assumed that the raw metrics can be transformed using some preprocessing operation to obtain the inputs for

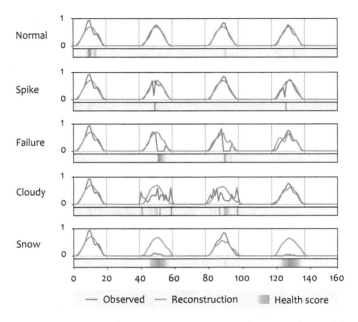

Figure R10.10: Anomaly scoring using a variational autoencoder model.

the state prediction or state manifold models. Such a preprocessing operation can be performed using a hand-crafted system model, but we can also leverage a wide range of methods developed in the signal processing domain and other fields. We review several commonly used transformations in this section.

R10.5.4.1 *Frequency-domain Representations*

Many mechanical and electrical systems include oscillating components, which are the components that perform the repetitive or periodic variation around a central value or between two or more different states. The metrics collected from such systems often represent a mix of multiple oscillations that add up to a complex pattern. For example, an accelerometer attached to a rotating machine can record a superposition of the vibrations produced by a motor shaft and multiple bearings. The individual oscillations might not be distinguishable in the time domain representation, but the frequency domain analysis can help to separate them and reveal patterns that are characteristic for normal and anomalous behaviors. Consequently, the metrics collected in such environments are often preprocessed using short-time Fourier transform

(STFT), wavelet transform (WT), and other frequency-domain methods.

We can illustrate the frequency-domain transformation using our running example with the solar energy generation data, and visualize the result of the STFT for the test samples in Figure R10.11. This figure demonstrates that each type of anomaly has a characteristic pattern in the frequency domain, although the frequency domain representation is not particularly insightful for this type of data.

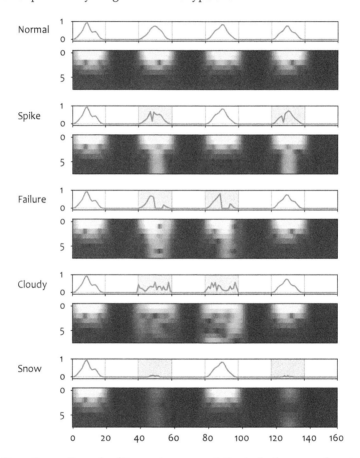

Figure R10.11: Example of time series representation in the frequency domain.

The frequency domain transforms usually increase the dimensionality of the data to capture both the time-related and frequency-related features. For example, the STFT of a one-dimensional signal is a two-dimensional spectrogram, as illustrated in Figure R10.11. This impacts the design of the state prediction and state manifold models, but the adjustments are usually straightforward because the standard RNN and CNN layers are readily applicable to multidimensional inputs [Verstraete et al., 2017]. For example, the LSTM state prediction model introduced in Section R10.5.2 can consume the spectrogram as a sequence of vectors, and the autoencoder developed in Section R10.5.3 can process the spectrogram provided that the one-dimensional convolution layers are replaced by two-dimensional layers.

R10.5.4.2 *Representations for Multivariate Time Series*

The methods described in the previous sections are generally able to process multivariate time series and capture the dependencies between the individual metrics to assess the health status of the entire system. For instance, multivariate time series can be directly consumed by LSTM models and autoencoders with two-dimensional convolutional layers. These general solutions, however, might not be sufficient to properly capture the inter-correlations between the metrics, and specialized features might be engineered to enhance the model inputs.

One possible option is to represent a multivariate time series as a sequence of correlation matrices. Assuming that the input is k-variate time series, we can compute the elements of a $k \times k$ correlation matrix M_t for every time step t as follows:

$$m_{ij,t} = \frac{1}{w} \sum_{\tau=0}^{w} x_{i,t-\tau}\, x_{j,t-\tau} \qquad (R10.8)$$

where x_t are the normalized samples of the input time series, indexes i and j iterate over all pairs of metrics, and w is the length of the correlation window. This layout is illustrated in Figure R10.12. The original multivariate time series can then be represented as a three-dimensional tensor (stack of correlation matrices) in which anomalies can be scored using the forecasting and autoencoding methods [Song et al., 2018; Zhang et al., 2019].

R10.6 ANOMALY DETECTION AND CLASSIFICATION

The anomaly scoring methods developed in the previous sections evaluate the deviations from the normal manifold, and we assumed that the output of this process was a continuous score. This score, however, does not explicitly prescribe when to take an action in response to the degradation in system health, or what action specifically needs

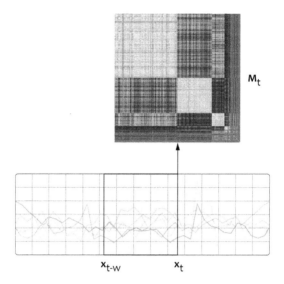

Figure R10.12: Representing multivariate time series using correlation matrices.

to be taken. In this section, we focus on converting anomaly scores into actions and designing advanced scores that facilitate automatic decision-making and operationalization.

R10.6.1   *Thresholding*

In most applications, it is not feasible to track anomaly scores manually, and we need to automatically make a binary decision on whether a given system state is a significant anomaly or not based on a continuous anomaly score. We refer to this problem as *anomaly detection*. The anomaly detection decisions can trigger the creation of alerts or the execution of other actions.

The most basic approach to anomaly detection is *thresholding*. We set a certain numerical threshold, continuously compare the ongoing anomaly scores with it, and flag all samples that exceed the threshold as anomalies. The threshold is typically computed based on the empirical distribution of the anomaly scores for the normal observations. For instance, we can compute the alerting threshold as follows:

$$\text{threshold} = \beta \cdot q_k \tag{R10.9}$$

where β is a scaling parameter, q_k is the k-th percentile of the anomaly scores on normal samples, and k is typically chosen to be high. The scaling parameter β is chosen heuristically or optimized using backtesting on a labeled dataset. The primary objective of this process is to identify the threshold that achieves the optimal balance between the false positive and false negative rates, and this optimization might need to assess not only the detection accuracy, but also the costs associated with the incident investigation and system failures.

R10.6.2 *Reconstruction Probability*

The threshold-based anomaly detection has several limitations. First, this approach requires managing data-specific detection thresholds using various heuristics which makes it prone to misconfigurations. Second, it does not take into account the distribution of the anomaly score on the sample under test; that is the distribution of the state prediction or reconstruction error. We can address these limitations by taking a more rigorous probabilistic approach to anomaly scoring. We start to develop this approach by revisiting the variational autoencoder model created in Section R10.5.2.

As we discussed in Section 2.6.2.4, the standard variational autoencoder model assumes that both the encoder and decoder operations are specified using multivariate normal distributions with independent variables. On the encoder side, this means that the embedding vector $\mathbf{z}$ is drawn from the normal distribution $q(\mathbf{z} \mid \mathbf{x})$ whose parameters are estimated using the encoding network g based on the input $\mathbf{x}$:

$$(\mu_z, \sigma_z) = g(\mathbf{x})$$
$$\mathbf{z} \sim q(\mathbf{z} \mid \mathbf{x}) = q(\mathbf{z} \mid \mu_z, \sigma_z) = N(\mu_z, \operatorname{diag}(\sigma_z^2)) \tag{R10.10}$$

On the decoder side, the reconstruction $\hat{\mathbf{x}}$ is drawn from the isotropic normal distribution $p(\mathbf{x} \mid \mathbf{z})$ with the mean estimated using the decoder network f based on the embedding $\mathbf{z}$ and constant variance:

$$\mu_x = f(\mathbf{z})$$
$$\hat{\mathbf{x}} \sim p(\mathbf{x} \mid \mathbf{z}) = p(\mathbf{x} \mid \mu_x) = N(\mu_x, c \cdot \mathbf{I}) \tag{R10.11}$$

Finally, we estimate the anomaly score as the reconstruction error. This error is an unnormalized proxy for the likelihood of observing a specific input because of the normality assumption:

$$\operatorname{score}(\mathbf{x}) = \|\mathbf{x} - \mu_x\|^2 \propto \mathbb{E}_{\mathbf{z} \sim q}[\log p(\mathbf{x} \mid \mathbf{z})] \tag{R10.12}$$

This perspective on the regular variational autoencoder suggests that we can obtain the *normalized* probability of observing a specific input.

First, we can modify the decoder network to estimate all parameters of the input distribution instead of estimating only the mean. This leads to replacing expression R10.11 with the following:

$$(\mu_x,\ \sigma_x) = f(z)$$
$$\hat{x} \sim p(x \mid z) = p(x \mid \mu_x, \sigma_x) = N(\mu_x,\ diag(\sigma_x^2)) \qquad (R10.13)$$

Second, we can estimate the probability of observing a specific input by sampling multiple embedding values and accurately evaluating the log likelihoods. This leads to the algorithm presented in box R10.1 where the distributions q and p are given by expressions R10.10 and R10.13, respectively. This estimate is known as the *reconstruction probability* [An and Cho, 2015; Pereira and Silveira, 2018].

Algorithm R10.1: Reconstruction probability evaluation

inputs:
    x – input sample at a specific moment of time

parameters:
    L – sampling size
    g and f – trained encoder and decoder functions

$(\mu_z,\ \sigma_z) = g(x)$ *(Embedding distribution parameters)*
for $i = 1, 2, \dots, L$ **do**
    $z \sim q(z \mid \mu_z, \sigma_z)$ *(Embedding sampling)*
    $(\mu_x,\ \sigma_x) = f(z)$ *(Input distribution parameters)*
    $s_i = \log p(x \mid \mu_x, \sigma_x)$ *(Log-likelihood of the input)*
end
$score(x) = \frac{1}{L}\sum_{i=1}^{L} s_i$ *(Reconstruction probability)*

The final anomaly detection decision is made by comparing the reconstruction probability with the threshold. The reconstruction probability approach has several advantages over the deterministic reconstruction error discussed in the previous sections. First, it is a normalized probabilistic measure, and thus the detection threshold can be set in a data-independent way. Second, the reconstruction probability incorporates the variability of the data which helps to improve the expressive power of the anomaly score. For instance, anomalous samples typically have higher variance than the normal samples, and this can drive the corresponding reconstruction probabilities lower. Finally, this approach is flexible enough to support arbitrary parametric distributions instead of the normal distributions we used in this section.

R10.6.3   *Supervised Detection and Classification*

In the previous sections, we focused on unsupervised anomaly scoring and detection methods that do not require ground truth anomaly labels or feedback data to be available. In this section, we discuss the collection and usage of such data.

The creation of labeled datasets for anomaly detection is associated with several challenges. First, it can be difficult or impossible to collect enough anomalous samples to create properly balanced datasets that outline the boundary of the normal manifold. It can be related to both the rarity of anomalous events and unfeasibility to enumerate all possible types of anomalies in advance. This problem can sometimes be alleviated using data augmentation, that is the generation of artificial anomalous instances. This strategy is particularly efficient when it is possible to build a system model that allows one to simulate failures or other anomalous scenarios in accordance with the laws of physics that govern the actual system. The second challenge is the labeling of the collected data. In many applications, the metrics can be properly labeled only by domain experts which makes the process slow and expensive. This problem is often mitigated by creating custom labeling tools with domain-specific features that improve the productivity of the domain experts.

Assuming that the balanced data is collected and labeled, a wide range of architectures can be used to build supervised anomaly detection and classification models. For example, one can use convolutional neural networks to perform the classification of spectrograms introduced in Section R10.5.4.1 to identify specific types of anomalies or failures [Verstraete et al., 2017]. The quality of such models can be evaluated using standard metrics such as accuracy and precision.

The supervised methods can also be used to enhance the unsupervised solutions in the environments where only a limited number of labels can be collected. For example, we might not have labeled historical data available during the development of an anomaly detection system, but, once the system is deployed to production, the operations team can start to provide the feedback on the generated alerts, tagging them as true and false positives. This feedback can be used to create a supervised model that post-processes the anomaly detection decisions made by the unsupervised part of the solution with a goal to suspend false positives.

R10.7   REMAINING USEFUL LIFE PREDICTION

The anomaly scoring, detection, and classification methods discussed in the previous sections can help to evaluate the magnitude of the deviation from the normal manifold and make a decision as to whether a specific deviation needs to be investigated. These capabilities, however, are not sufficient for predictive maintenance purposes where we need to estimate the remaining useful life (RUL) measured in time units. In this section, we develop specialized solutions for this problem.

R10.7.1   *Solution Approach*

For the predictive maintenance setup, we assume the availability of historical run-to-failure data. These data typically consist of multiple *trajectories* each of which represents a multivariate time series that ends with the failure event and, optionally, collection of attributes that characterize the entire trajectory. For example, consider the problem of developing a predictive maintenance model for aircraft jet engines. In this setup, the training dataset can include records for multiple engines where each engine is represented by sensor data and static attributes such as initial wear and manufacturing variation. The sensor data for one engine, that is the engine's trajectory, is a multivariate time series where each variable corresponds to one sensor and each time step corresponds to one operational cycle or time interval. It is essential that each series ends with a failure event, so that the RUL for the i-th trajectory can be calculated at any time t as

$$RUL(i, \ t) = t_i^f - t \qquad\qquad (R10.14)$$

where t_i^f is the time of the failure event for trajectory i. The failure event might correspond to the actual system or component failure or achieving a certain safety condition.

In the above setup, our goal is to predict the RUL value based on a given segment of the trajectory. This is essentially a regression problem, but it can be approached in several different ways. One common strategy is to calculate a single health indicator based on the input metrics, and then estimate the RUL based on it. The health indicator is a univariate time series that is designed to characterize the system degradation over time. For example, we can compute a regular anomaly score using an autoencoder, as described in Section R10.5.3. We can then use this score as a health indicator under the assumption that the metric patterns deviate increasingly from the normal manifold as the system

health degrades [Gugulothu et al., 2017]. The RLU can then be estimated using the second model that maps the health score to time-to-
failure. For example, we can use the nearest neighbors approach and estimate the distribution of the RUL or expected RUL for a given system
by looking up the most similar historical health profiles and averaging
their time-to-failures. This approach is illustrated in Figure R10.13. The
advantage of this strategy is that the health indicator can be designed,
visualized, and analyzed separately from the RUL estimation.

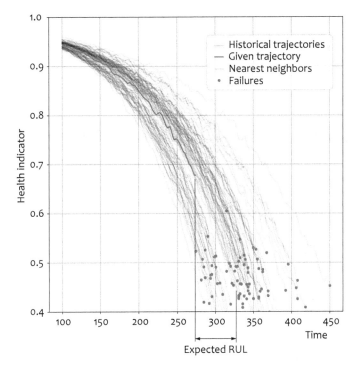

Figure R10.13: RUL estimation using the nearest neighbor search based on the
health indicator.

The alternative strategy is to build a regression model that predicts
the RUL directly based on the input metrics. In the next section, we
examine this approach in more detail and develop a prototype that
estimates the RUL using a convolutional network [Li et al., 2018].

R10.7.2 *Prototype*

The complete reference implementation for this section is available at https://bit.ly/3uRciPI

We start with a subset of the Turbofan Engine Degradation Simulation dataset that includes 100 run-to-failure trajectories for turbofan engines. Each trajectory is a multivariate time series that includes numerical measurements from 26 sensors and 3 additional real-valued variables that characterize the operational settings. Each time step in the series corresponds to one operational cycle.

Turbofan Engine Degradation Simulation Dataset

The Turbofan Engine Degradation Simulation dataset was developed at the NASA Ames Research Center in 2008 [Saxena et al., 2008]. It consists of multiple multivariate time series each of which represents a run-to-failure trajectory of one engine obtained using a physics-based simulation model. All engines are assumed to be of the same type, but the dataset includes four different groups of trajectories for four different operational modes and degradation scenarios. Each group includes from 100 to 250 train and test trajectories.

We preprocess the original dataset to remove the metrics that are known to be non-informative for the RUL prediction purposes, which leaves us with 15 metrics. Examples of such metrics for one of the engines are shown in Figure R10.14. These plots suggest that the system health degradation typically manifests itself through exponential growth or decline of individual metrics.

The design of the RUL prediction model is shown in Figure R10.15. We start by cutting the preprocessed multivariate time series into segments of 30 time steps each using a sliding time window, as shown in the lower part of the figure. For each segment, we assign a training label equal to the number of time steps between the latest sample of the segment and failure event; this value corresponds to the RUL defined by expression R10.14. We also limit the maximum label value, so that all system states with the RUL of more than 150 operational cycles are

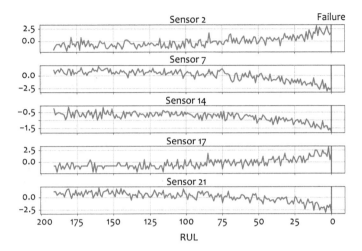

Figure R10.14: A subset of normalized metrics for one of the trajectories (engines) from the Turbofan Engine Degradation Simulation dataset.

considered healthy. The resulting RUL curve computed according to this logic is shown in the upper part of the figure.

The model is designed to predict the RUL value based on one input segment. The model represents a small stack of one-dimensional convolution layers (temporal convolutions) followed by two dense layers that produce the final RUL estimate, as shown the middle of Figure R10.15. The model is trained to minimize the regular MSE loss, and can then be used to estimate the RUL curve for a given segment of a trajectory. An example of the predicted RUL curve for one of the engines in the test dataset is shown in Figure R10.16.

The prototype described above demonstrates one particular way of predicting the RUL based directly on the input time series. In practice, we would normally need to customize both the network architecture and loss function. From the architecture perspective, we can use a variety of components with sequential inputs including convolutional and recurrent networks, as well as transformers. The loss function is often chosen to be asymmetrical to account for the difference between the underestimation and overestimation costs. Underestimation of the RUL translates into the unused equipment resource, while overestimation results in failures and downtimes [Li et al., 2018].

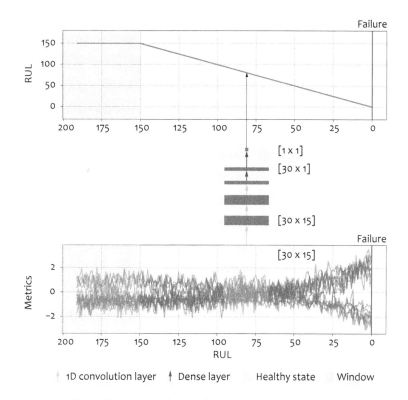

Figure R10.15: The design of the RUL prediction model.

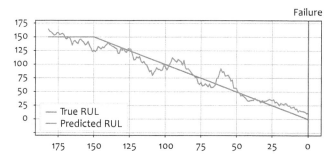

Figure R10.16: The predicted and ground truth RUL curves for one of the engines in the test dataset.

R10.8   SUMMARY

- Anomaly detection in IoT metrics generally requires developing data visualization capabilities, health indicators, and decision-making components for anomaly detection and classification.

- Health indicators are the measures of deviation from the manifold of the normal states. System health can be measured using abstract scores, normalized probabilities of observing a specific deviation, or semantically meaningful units such as the remaining useful life in days. Health indicators measured in time units are important in applications that require preventive actions to be determined.

- Generic statistical methods can detect outliers in the raw data, but these outliers do not necessarily relate to defects, failures, and other events of interest (anomalies). The input metrics might need to be preprocessed using a system model to ensure that statistical outliers can be interpreted as meaningful anomalies.

- Monitoring is a challenging problem in most IoT environments because of the large number of devices, sensors, and metrics. The efficiency of monitoring can be improved using noise removal and dimensionality reduction techniques.

- In environments where only the normal observations are available, we can use time series forecasting and autoencoding methods to score the deviations from the normal manifold.

- The original time series are not necessarily the optimal input representations for forecasting and autoencoding models. It is common to preprocess the input metrics using frequency-domain and correlation analysis methods.

- Anomaly scores can be converted to actionable decisions such as alerts using thresholding. The thresholds are usually data-dependent for distance-based scores and data-independent for normalized scores obtained using probabilistic methods.

- Anomaly detection and classification can be performed using regular supervised methods in environments where labeled anomaly events or feedback data are available. In particular, regression models with sequential inputs can be used to predict the remaining useful life of a system and its components.

Recipe

11.

VISUAL QUALITY CONTROL

Identifying Production Defects Using Computer Vision

Production yield and quality are the main performance metrics for most manufacturing companies. Quality issues can incur significant financial and operational losses resulting from reworked parts, reduced yield, shortened service life of the final product, safety risk, reputation damages, post-sale recalls, and warranty claims. The ability to mitigate these risks is an important enterprise capability, and companies usually include multiple quality control steps in their manufacturing processes to identify defects and discard defective parts.

Manufacturers use a wide range of quality control methods including electromagnetic and ultrasonic testing, X-ray scanning, spectroscopy, and visual inspections. Visual inspection, that is an inspection of an asset's appearance in the visual spectrum made using the naked eye, microscopic device, or photographic image is one of the most basic, but also the most versatile techniques. It is used in many industries including automotive, electronics, semiconductor, and general-purpose manufacturing to inspect paint surfaces, welding seams, semiconductor wafers, printed circuit boards, fabrics, and packaging.

Traditional visual inspection is a highly manual process that can be expensive, time-consuming, and prone to errors and inconsistencies related to variations in the operator's perception and experience. Computer vision methods can solve many of these challenges and help to create fully automated, consistent, and accurate quality control solutions. In this recipe, we discuss the details of the visual inspection problem and develop several methods for the detection of defects.

R11.1 BUSINESS PROBLEM

We consider the case of a manufacturing process that produces discrete objects or a continuous flow of material that can be photographed. The captured images can then be analyzed to detect defects such as spots, holes, and scratches. The outputs of the defect detection system can be integrated with the manufacturing machines to automatically remove defective parts, stop certain processes, or perform other actions. In the next sections, we discuss a high-level architecture of the defect detection solution, typical properties of the input images, and solution objectives.

R11.1.1 *Environment*

The conceptual architecture of the defect detection solution is presented in Figure R11.1. We utilize cameras or sensors that produce images of the objects that need to be inspected. This requires some synchronization between the production and image-capturing processes, so that the objects are regularly photographed at specific stages of production. For example, images might be captured at the end of the object coating operation, but not when the operation is in progress. The synchronization can be precisely done by using coordinating signals, or various computer vision methods that can detect the right moments for capturing static images from continuous video streams.

The captured images often need to be preprocessed to detect the objects of interest in the image, separate them from the background, and to normalize the object orientation and scale. In many environments, the preprocessing is a challenging problem that requires involving multiple computer vision methods. In this recipe, we consider the synchronization and preprocessing tasks to be out of scope and assume that the input images have been properly captured and prepared for the defect detection stage.

The captured images are often consolidated and preprocessed on edge servers that are collocated with the production equipment and then forwarded to the centralized analytics system where the data are further prepared for modeling. We assume that the captured images

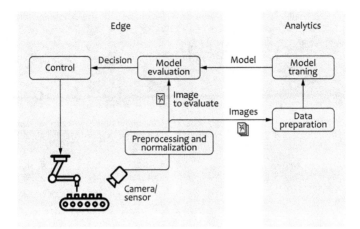

Figure R11.1: Conceptual architecture of the defect detection solution and its integrations.

are labeled as normal and defective at the preparation step and, optionally, defect type labels and defect location labels (bounding boxes or masks) can be created.

The prepared data are used to train the defect detection model, and this model is typically deployed on the edge devices collocated with the cameras to perform the evaluation of the incoming images in near real time. The results of the evaluation, such as anomaly scores and binary decisions, are fed into services that control the production flow and maintenance operations.

R11.1.2 *Data*

The examples of images that can be produced by industrial cameras installed on manufacturing machines are provided in Figure R11.2. In the figure, each row corresponds to a separate manufacturing process, the leftmost column contains examples of nondefective outputs, and the other three columns contain examples of defective outputs. In this particular dataset, defective items are identified by labels stating the type of defect, such as bent, cut, or hole, but we do not assume that such labels are necessarily available.

Datasets used for the development of defect detection algorithms typically exhibit two main characteristics of anomaly detection problems which we discussed in recipe R10 (Anomaly Detection). First, de-

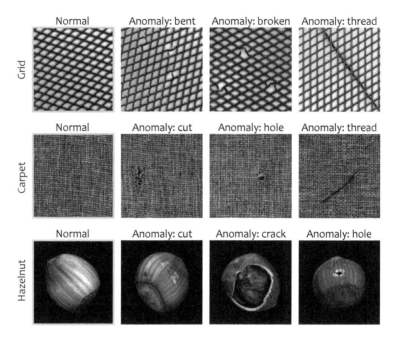

Figure R11.2: Examples of defective and nondefective instances from the MVTec AD dataset [Bergmann et al., 2019].

fects are usually quite rare events, so it can be challenging to collect a representative set of defective instances. At the same time, collecting a large number of nondefective instances is a much more straightforward task. Consequently, we commonly need to deal with highly imbalanced datasets. Second, it is usually challenging to unambiguously specify or enumerate all possible defect types and appearances. We can sometimes define a reasonably comprehensive categorization of the previously observed defects and collect image examples for each category, but it is seldom possible to guarantee that all future instances will follow the same patterns.

R11.1.3 *Objectives*

Our primary objective is to build a model that can discriminate between defective and nondefective samples. We usually want such a model to produce a continuous defect likelihood score for a given image that can be thresholded to make the final binary decision (defect or no defect). This approach enables us to manage the trade-off between false positives and false negatives, and to set the threshold value based on operational needs, risks, and cost considerations. Consequently, it is common to evaluate the quality of the defect detection model using a receiver operating characteristic curve, or ROC curve, as illustrated in Figure R11.3. Each point on the ROC curve corresponds to a specific decision threshold value and false positive rate achieved at this threshold, and the entire curve characterizes the Pareto frontier achievable by the model. The area under the curve (AUC) is a metric that helps to summarize the model performance in a single number and to compare different models.

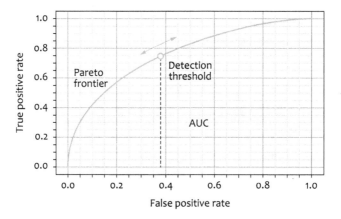

Figure R11.3: Evaluating the performance of the defect detection model using a ROC curve.

The second common objective is to localize the defect in the image. This can be accomplished by building a model that produces a bounding box or pixel-level segmentation mask, similar to what we did in recipe R5 (Visual Search) in the context of visual search tasks. Bounding boxes and segmentation masks can help to operationalize the outputs of the defect detection system, facilitating the analysis and troubleshooting of the issues. Assuming that we have ground truth bounding boxes or pixel-level segmentation masks, the quality of segmentation can be evaluated using the intersection over union (IoU) metric defined in expression R5.3.

R11.2   SOLUTION OPTIONS

The problem of defect detection requires estimating the manifold of nondefective images, so that all images outside of the boundaries of this manifold can be deemed to be defective. In this section, we discuss how a model of the normal (nondefective) manifold can be learned using supervised and unsupervised methods, and how such models can be used to assess images under test. We will also discuss how transfer learning can be used to extract image features and to create representations that help to learn manifolds more efficiently.

R11.2.1 *Supervised Defect Classification Models*

In principle, the problem of defect detection can be solved by training a regular image classification model on a dataset with labeled defective and nondefective instances. However, this requires the creation of a dataset that contains enough samples of both classes to explicitly outline the boundaries of the normal manifold. Creating such a dataset can be challenging for several reasons:

- First, all possible defect types are usually not known in advance, making it difficult to cover the boundaries of the normal manifold in the training dataset.

- Second, the scrap rates might be too low to produce enough defective instances for training deep learning-based image classification models.

- Finally, image labeling often requires deep domain knowledge and experience, so it can be done only by domain experts, which makes the process expensive and slow.

Despite of these challenges, supervised defect defection is a very common approach in practice, and companies invest heavily in creating appropriate training datasets and advanced tools that improve the labeling efficiency. The above problems can also be mitigated using data augmentation methods, that is by artificially generating defective samples from the normal samples, as shown in Figure R11.4. This approach enables us to create a balanced training dataset and fit a supervised model even if defective instances are not available. On the other hand, this solution is not particularly efficient because we have to explicitly generate a cloud of defective instances around the normal manifold solely to ascribe the problem to the supervised form. As we discuss in the next sections, we can fit a manifold model directly on the normal samples, bypassing the data generation.

Figure R11.4: Defective samples generated for data augmentation.

R11.2.2 *Anomaly Detection Models*

The problem of defect detection can be approached as the problem of learning the model of normality which can be used to identify instances that are significantly different from the norm. These instances can then be interpreted as anomalies (defects). Since the model of normality aims to approximate the distribution of the nondefective images, we can attempt to fit it using exclusively nondefective instances without demarcating the boundaries of the nondefective manifold with defective samples, as we discussed in the previous section.

One of the most usual ways of creating a model of normality is to train an autoencoder that maps the input image to a low-dimensional embedding and then reconstructs the input based on the limited information contained in the embedding vector. Assuming that $\mathbf{x}$ is a $w \times h$ input image with k channels, $\mathbf{z}$ is the d-dimensional embedding vector, and $\hat{\mathbf{x}}$ is the reconstructed image, the transformation performed by the autoencoder can be expressed as follows:

$$\mathbf{z} = E(\mathbf{x})$$
$$\hat{\mathbf{x}} = D(\mathbf{z})$$
(R11.1)

where $E : h \times w \times k \rightarrow d$ and $D : d \rightarrow h \times w \times k$ are the encoder and decoder functions, respectively. As we discussed in Section 2.6.2, the dimensionality of the embedding vector controls the capacity of the model, and we can capture the curvature of the normal manifold in smaller or greater detail by varying the size of the embedding vector.

The training process optimizes the parameters of the autoencoder model based on the loss function $L(\mathbf{x}, \hat{\mathbf{x}})$ that evaluates the difference between the input and reconstructed images, as shown in Figure R11.5 (a). Once the model is trained, a test image can be assessed by computing its reconstruction which basically represents the closest point on the normal manifold, and then computing the loss function for the input and reconstructed images, as shown in Figure R11.5 (b).

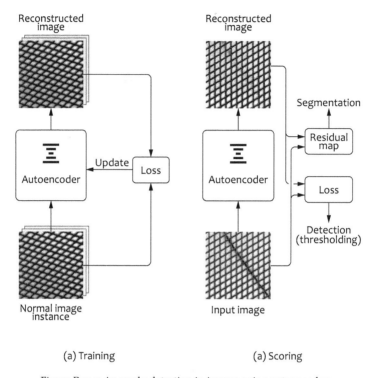

(a) Training   (a) Scoring

Figure R11.5: Anomaly detection in images using autoencoders.

The loss function is usually computed by averaging the pixel-level differences between the images. However, the pixel-level difference matrix $R(\mathbf{x}, \hat{\mathbf{x}})$, referred to a *residual map*, is also commonly used to analyze the location of the defect and thus create a segmentation mask. The loss function and residual maps can be computed in several different ways, and these design choices significantly influence the accuracy of the defect detection, as well as the quality and usefulness of the segmentation maps. In the next section, we discuss the design of the autoencoder model, residual maps, and loss functions in more detail.

R11.2.2.1 *Model Architecture*

Autoencoders for anomaly detection in images can use standard convolutional architectures with contracting and expanding subnetworks. Let us consider one commonly used architecture presented in Figure R11.6 as an example [Bergmann et al., 2018]. This model assumes a 128×128 input single-channel (grayscale) image. This input is processed by a stack of convolution layers that gradually decrease the size of the feature maps from the original 128×128 down to 8×8 and, at the same time, increase the number of channels. The size of the feature maps is controlled using strides, and no pooling layers are used. The output of this stack is processed by an additional convolution layer with 100 filters and a linear activation function to produce a 100-dimensional embedding vector. This vector is then expanded back to 128×128×1 output using a stack of upconvolution layers that basically represent the reversed version of the contracting stack. Similar to the contracting path, the expanding path also controls the size of the feature maps using strides.

Conceptually, the specification presented in Figure R11.6 is sufficient to train the model and score test images provided that we define an appropriate loss function. In practice, we might need to extend this design with additional pre- and post-processing components to support images of different sizes and levels of detail. We discuss this topic later in the solution prototype section.

R11.2.2.2   *Structural Similarity*

The autoencoder is trained to reconstruct the input image as accurately as its capacity allows, and this process is guided by the loss function. The most straightforward choice for the loss function is the mean squared error (MSE):

$$\text{MSE}(\mathbf{x},\, \hat{\mathbf{x}}) = \sum_{i=1}^{h} \sum_{j=1}^{w} \left(x_{ij} - \hat{x}_{ij} \right)^2 \tag{R11.2}$$

and the corresponding residual map is a matrix of pixel-wise distances:

$$r_{ij} = \left(x_{ij} - \hat{x}_{ij} \right)^2 \tag{R11.3}$$

The MSE loss is a simple and computationally efficient measure that works reasonably well for our purposes, but it has disadvantages as well. The main problem with MSE is its sensitivity to common reconstruction artifacts such as small image shifts or blurring that are generally irrelevant for the defect detection purposes and should be ignored. This issue stems from the fact that SME is a sum of per-pixel distances which are computed independently, so that cross-pixel correlations typical for reconstruction artifacts cannot be detected and properly accounted for. This suggests that we can create a more robust model by using a loss function that assesses the distance between image patches rather than individual pixels.

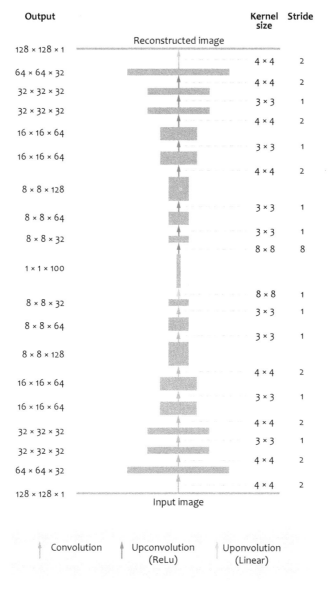

Figure R11.6: Example architecture of the autoencoder for anomaly detection in images.

One commonly used distance measure that satisfies the above requirement is *structural similarity* (SSIM). This measure was originally introduced in the context of image processing problems to assess the quality of images in a way consistent with human perception which also has low sensitivity to minor shifts, blurs, and other transformations alike [Wang et al., 2004]. The SSIM score is defined for a pair of $k \times k$ image patches $\mathbf{a}$ and $\mathbf{b}$ as a product of three terms called luminance $l(\mathbf{a}, \mathbf{b})$, contrast $c(\mathbf{a}, \mathbf{b})$, and structure $s(\mathbf{a}, \mathbf{b})$:

$$SSIM(\mathbf{a}, \mathbf{b}) = l(\mathbf{a}, \mathbf{b})^{\alpha} c(\mathbf{a}, \mathbf{b})^{\beta} s(\mathbf{a}, \mathbf{b})^{\gamma} \tag{R11.4}$$

where α, β, and γ are the term weights that are usually set to 1. The luminance component is the normalized difference between mean intensities μ_a and μ_b of the patches:

$$l(\mathbf{a}, \mathbf{b}) = \frac{2\mu_a \mu_b + c_1}{\mu_a^2 + \mu_b^2 + c_1} \tag{R11.5}$$

where c_1 is a small constant added for numerical stability. In a similar vein, the contrast component is the difference between patch variances σ_a and σ_b:

$$c(\mathbf{a}, \mathbf{b}) = \frac{2\sigma_a \sigma_b + c_2}{\sigma_a^2 + \sigma_b^2 + c_2} \tag{R11.6}$$

Finally, the structure component is evaluated based on the covariance σ_{ab} of two patches:

$$s(\mathbf{a}, \mathbf{b}) = \frac{2\sigma_{ab} + c_3}{2\sigma_a \sigma_b + c_3} \tag{R11.7}$$

The SSIM residual map for the entire image $\mathbf{x}$ and its reconstruction $\hat{\mathbf{x}}$ is computed by sliding a $k \times k$ window over the image and evaluating expression R11.4 at each pixel. The overall SSIM loss can then be obtained as the sum of all elements of the residual map.

The difference between MSE and SSIM losses is illustrated by the example in Figure R11.7. We take an image of a fabric patch with a hole, prepare its reconstruction where the hole is mainly removed, and also shift this reconstructed version by two pixels. The MSE residual map has a lot of background noise created by the shift that almost masks the location of the defect, but the SSIM map is more robust and clearly highlights the defect. The component-level breakdown presented in the lower part of Figure R11.7 also indicates that, in this particular example, the contrast term makes the largest contribution to the residual map.

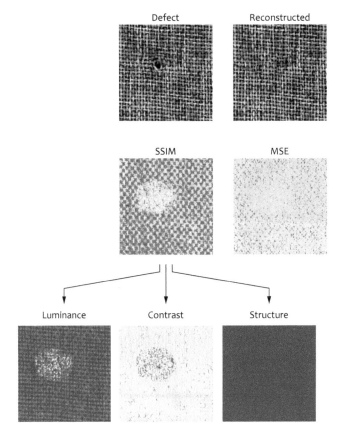

Figure R11.7: Comparison of SSIM and MSE residual maps for the same pair of images. SSIM is computed using 11×11 patches.

R11.2.3   *Anomaly Detection with Transfer Learning*

The autoencoder-based solution developed in the previous section assumes that the model is trained from scratch based on nondefective images, and the encoding part of the network learns how to extract meaningful feature maps which can be further condensed into the embedding vector. This approach is not necessarily optimal because, as we discussed in recipe R5 (Visual Search), high-quality feature maps can typically be extracted using pretrained computer vision networks which sharply reduces the amount of data needed for training. In this section, we explore how pretrained models can be used in anomaly detection applications to efficiently extract image features and reduce the overall complexity of the solution.

To understand how transfer learning can help with the anomaly detection task, let us assume that we have a pretrained network that produces a high-quality image representation which we can flatten into a d-dimensional feature vector. In principle, we can create a decoding network that reconstructs the input image based on this vector and train it using the SSIM loss function, in the same way as we train the complete autoencoder model. This solution produces the same outputs as the autoencoder trained from scratch, including the residual maps that can be used for defect segmentation, but it achieves lower complexity and higher data efficiency. On the other hand, the decoder network can still require a considerable amount of data and computational resources to be trained. The alternative solution is to leverage the fact that the image is already converted to a representation where the normal manifold is better separated than in the original image space. We can then build a relatively simple model of normality that can be used to score the test images just as we did with the basic defect classification models in Section R11.2.1.

One possible solution is to approximate the normal manifold with a multivariate Gaussian distribution [Rippel et al., 2021]. Assuming that images are represented by d-dimensional feature vectors, the probability density of the normal manifold can be specified as

$$p_{\mu,\Sigma}(x) = \frac{1}{\sqrt{(2\pi)^d \det(\Sigma)}} \exp\left(-\frac{1}{2}(x-\mu)^{\mathsf{T}}\Sigma^{-1}(x-\mu)\right) \quad \text{(R11.8)}$$

where μ is the d-dimensional mean vector and Σ is the d × d covariance matrix. Assuming that we have a training set with n nondefective images, and these images are transformed into feature vectors $x_1, \ldots, x_n$ by the pretrained network, the distribution parameters can be estimated as follows:

$$\hat{\mu} = \frac{1}{n}\sum_{i=1}^{n} x_i$$

$$\hat{\Sigma} = \frac{1}{n-1}\sum_{i=1}^{n}(x_i - \hat{\mu})(x_i - \hat{\mu})^{\mathsf{T}} \quad \text{(R11.9)}$$

Once the manifold model is fitted, the anomaly score of a given image represented by feature vector x can be evaluated as the distance between the point x and the distribution. The standard measure of the

distance between a point and distribution is the Mahalanobis distance
defined as follows:

$$M_{\mu, \, \Sigma}(\mathbf{x}) = \sqrt{(\mathbf{x} - \mathbf{\mu})^{\mathsf{T}} \Sigma^{-1} (\mathbf{x} - \mathbf{\mu})} \qquad (\text{R11.10})$$

The Mahalanobis distance is basically a generalization of the idea of
measuring how many standard deviations the point is from the mean
of the distribution. We can evaluate this measure for any test image
provided that parameters μ and Σ were estimated based on the training
set as described above.

The anomaly scoring method described above relies on the assumption that we have a model for mapping images to a proper feature
space. This mapping can be done by capturing feature maps produced
by intermediate layers of a generic image classification model pretrained on a standard dataset such as ImageNet.

To illustrate this approach, let us consider one specific design
which is based on the EfficientNet-B0 model[1] [Rippel et al., 2021].
The EfficientNet-B0 network includes nine major blocks, and we can
capture the output of each block and compute nine feature vectors
by averaging each output across spatial dimensions, as shown in Figure R11.8. Consequently, each of nine feature vectors $x_1, \ldots, x_9$ has
as many dimensions as channels in the output of the corresponding
block. We compute these vectors for each image in the training set, and
then independently fit nine Gaussian models according to expressions
R11.8 and R11.9.

A test image $\mathbf{x}$ is then scored by computing and summing nine Mahalanobis distances for each of its feature vectors:

$$\text{score}(\mathbf{x}) = \sum_{i=1}^{9} M_{\mu_i, \, \Sigma_i}(\mathbf{x}_i) \qquad (\text{R11.11})$$

The above solution leverages the pretrained feature extraction
networks to simplify the model of normality, reduce the training
complexity, and improve the accuracy. These properties can give the
EfficientNet-B0 solution an advantage over the autoencoder-based
methods in applications that do not require defect segmentation.
However, the advantages of pretrained computer vision models
should be carefully assessed for each particular application. Industrial
images are fundamentally different from the standard image datasets

---

1 See recipe R5 (Visual Search) for more details about the EfficientNet models.

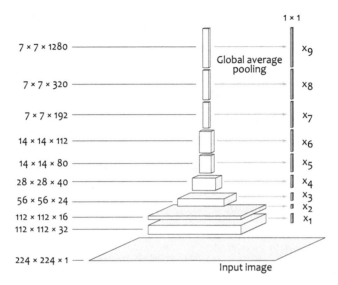

1 × 1

7 × 7 × 1280

Global average
pooling

x_9

7 × 7 × 320

x_8

7 × 7 × 192

x_7

14 × 14 × 112

x_6

14 × 14 × 80

x_5

28 × 28 × 40

x_4

56 × 56 × 24

x_3
x_2

112 × 112 × 16

x_1

112 × 112 × 32

224 × 224 × 1

Input image

Figure R11.8: Feature extraction for anomaly detection using EfficientNet-B0.

such as ImageNet used for pretraining, and the gains delivered by pretraining can be small or negligible.

R11.3   PROTOTYPE

The complete reference implementation for this section is available at https://bit.ly/35I4Fm5

In this section, we build a prototype of an anomaly detection solution based on the autoencoder architecture described in Section R11.2.2.1 and SSIM loss measure. For training and evaluation, we use the MVTec dataset which we previewed in Figure R11.2 at the beginning of this recipe.

> **MVTec AD Dataset**
>
> MVTec Anomaly Detection (AD) is a dataset for benchmarking visual quality control methods [Bergmann et al., 2019]. The dataset contains 15 categories of industrial objects and textures such as *grid, carpet,* and *screw,* and each category includes nondefective and defective instances. The dataset contains more than 5000 images.

One of the practical challenges that we need to address in our prototype is a relatively small number of images for individual object categories. Most categories contain around 200-300 nondefective instances which might not be sufficient for training a high-capacity autoencoder. At the same time, the images have a relatively high resolution, and the size of anomalies in defective instances can be small compared to the image size. This also represents a challenge because we can lose important details if we simply resize all images to match the relatively small input shape (128×128 pixels) of the autoencoder network.

These two problems can be alleviated by cutting large images into smaller patches and processing these patches independently [Bergmann et al., 2018]. First, we create the training dataset by sampling patches with random offsets from the available nondefective images, as shown in Figure R11.9. This technique allows us to augment the original dataset and create an arbitrary number of training samples for each category. We choose to sample 10,000 patches per category, and then train autoencoders independently for each category using the SSIM loss function.

We then use the trained autoencoders to reconstruct test images and compute the residual maps. Since the autoencoders are trained on patches, we have to cut each input image into patches, reconstruct each patch separately, and assemble these reconstructions into the final output image. Although we can use nonoverlapping patches, this approach is not optimal because reconstructed artifacts tend to create seams in the final image. A better solution is to sample overlapping patches with a fixed or random stride and sum their reconstructions into the final image, as shown in Figure R11.10.

We use this process to analyze defective images from several categories as shown in Figure R11.11. The left-hand column contains the input (defective) images, the middle column visualizes the reconstructions produced by the autoencoders, and the right-hand column contains the SSIM maps for input and reconstructed images. The SSIM

Input images   Training dataset

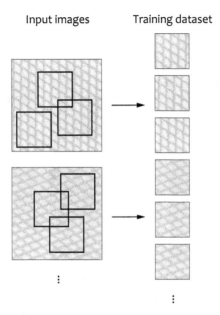

Figure R11.9: Sampling training patches from the input dataset.

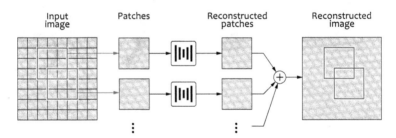

Figure R11.10: Reconstructing a large image patch by patch.

maps highlight the location of defects in all three categories, although the autoencoding process does not necessarily remove the defects perfectly, and reconstructed images might contain defect-like features.

R11.4   VARIATIONS AND EXTENSIONS

The methods developed in the previous sections aim at learning the model of normality based on nondefective images and using it to evaluate the likelihood of a test image being defective. We discussed both

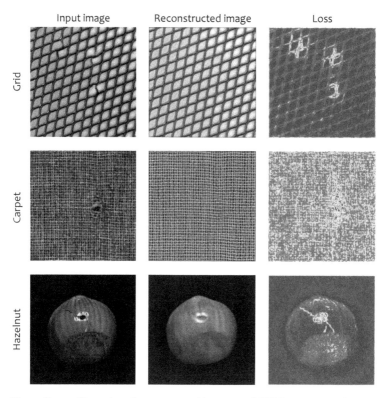

Figure R11.11: Examples of reconstructed images and SSIM maps created using the prototype.

unsupervised methods that can learn based exclusively on nondefective images and classification methods that can incorporate a basic supervision signal if it is available. In many visual inspection applications, however, we have access to more detailed and comprehensive ground truth information. This can be leveraged to produce more accurate results or deal with complex environments where regular anomaly detection methods cannot be applied. In this section, we briefly discuss two examples that illustrate the extended usage of ground truth data.

The first use case we consider is the verification of printed circuit boards (PCBs). In this scenario, it is usually possible to precisely compare test images of newly produced PCBs with a reference image, referred to as a template, and detect defects based on the pixel-wise difference. The verification procedure can include the following steps:

1. The test and reference images are first aligned to ensure rotation, scale, and translation invariance of the input images. This can be done using interest point detection algorithms or models that identify matching points in the test and reference images and then performing any necessary geometric transformations.

2. The residual map for the aligned test and reference images is computed, and defect locations are identified based on the clusters of large residual values.

The second example is planogram verification which is an important use case for retailers and manufacturers of consumer packaged goods. In this scenario, the ground truth is a planogram which specifies how items should be placed on shelves, and test images are often captured on smartphone cameras by merchandisers in stores. The key challenges in planogram verification are the low quality of test images that can be taken from different angles, in changeable lighting conditions, and with high variability in item appearance including rotated and fallen packages, items at the back of shelves, and different products with similar package designs. The planogram verification flow can include the following steps:

1. Bounding boxes or segmentation masks for individual items are estimated using object detection or instance segmentation models.

2. Image patches with individual items are cut out, and items are identified using classification models.

3. The sequences of identified items are compared with the planogram and discrepancies are reported.

These two use cases demonstrate that visual quality control can be implemented using very different techniques depending on the quality of the input images, the number of objects that need to be analyzed, and the availability of ground truth data. Consequently, one often needs to combine multiple models and algorithms to build an end-to-end solution, and unsupervised anomaly detection is only one of the tools we can use.

R11.5   SUMMARY

- Automated visual inspection is an important enterprise capability that can be used across multiple stages of the manufacturing process to control the quality, prevent losses, and reduce risks.

- Visual quality control can be performed using image classification models that discriminate between defective and nondefective instances. Collecting a sufficiently large number of defective samples can be a challenge in many manufacturing environments.

- The alternative approach is to learn a model of normality using only nondefective instances. The model of normality approximates the distribution (manifold) of nondefective images.

- The model of normality can be created using an autoencoder network that is trained to reconstruct the input image based on the embedding vector of a limited size. The difference between the input and reconstructed images can be used to identify defect location and compute an integral anomaly score.

- The choice of the loss function is an important aspect of the autoencoder design. In many applications, structural similarity (SSIM) produces better results than generic loss measures such as mean squared error.

- The model of normality can be constructed based on features produced by pretrained image classification models. This can help to reduce the number of instances needed for training and simplify the design of the model.

BIBLIOGRAPHY

A. Agarwal. Multi-echelon supply chain inventory optimization: An industrial perspective. 2014.

A. Ahmed, N. Shervashidze, S. Narayanamurthy, V. Josifovski, and A. J. Smola. Distributed large-scale natural graph factorization. In *Proceedings of the 22nd International Conference on World Wide Web*, WWW '13, pages 37–48, New York, NY, USA, 2013. Association for Computing Machinery.

J. An and S. Cho. Variational autoencoder based anomaly detection using reconstruction probability. volume 2, pages 1–18, 2015.

S. Arora and D. Warrier. Decoding fashion contexts using word embeddings. In *KDD Workshop on Machine learning meets fashion*, 2016.

D. Bahdanau, K. Cho, and Y. Bengio. Neural machine translation by jointly learning to align and translate. *arXiv preprint arXiv:1409.0473*, 2014.

L. Baldassini and J. A. R. Serrano. client2vec: Towards systematic baselines for banking applications. 2018.

J. L. Balintfy. On a basic class of multi-item inventory problems. *Management science*, 10(2):287–297, 1964.

J. Barbour. Learning node embedding in transaction networks. 2020.

O. Barkan and N. Koenigstein. Item2vec: neural item embedding for collaborative filtering. In *2016 IEEE 26th International Workshop on Machine Learning for Signal Processing (MLSP)*, pages 1–6. IEEE, 2016.

Y. Bengio, P. Simard, and P. Frasconi. Learning long-term dependencies with gradient descent is difficult. *IEEE Transactions on Neural Networks and Learning Systems*, 5(2):157–166, 1994. ISSN 1045-9227.

P. Bergmann, S. Löwe, M. Fauser, D. Sattlegger, and C. Steger. Improving unsupervised defect segmentation by applying structural similarity to autoencoders. *arXiv preprint arXiv:1807.02011*, 2018.

P. Bergmann, M. Fauser, D. Sattlegger, and C. Steger. MVTec AD–a comprehensive real-world dataset for unsupervised anomaly detection. In *Proceedings of the IEEE/CVF Conference on Computer Vision and Pattern Recognition*, pages 9592–9600, 2019.

L. Bernardi, T. Mavridis, and P. Estevez. 150 successful machine learning models: 6 lessons learned at Booking.Com. KDD19. Association for Computing Machinery, 2019.

N. Bloom, M. Floetotto, N. Jaimovich, I. Saporta-Eksten, and S. J. Terry. Really uncertain business cycles. *Econometrica*, 86(3):1031–1065, 2018.

S. Cao, W. Lu, and Q. Xu. GraRep: Learning graph representations with global structural information. In *Proceedings of the 24th ACM International on Conference on Information and Knowledge Management*, CIKM '15, pages 891–900, New York, NY, USA, 2015. Association for Computing Machinery.

R. Caruana. Multitask learning. *Machine learning*, 28(1):41–75, 1997.

A. Cavallo. More Amazon effects: online competition and pricing behaviors. Technical report, National Bureau of Economic Research, 2018.

N. V. Chawla, K. W. Bowyer, L. O. Hall, and W. P. Kegelmeyer. SMOTE: Synthetic minority over-sampling technique. *Journal of Artificial Intelligence Research*, 16(1):321–357, jun 2002.

Q. Chen, H. Zhao, W. Li, P. Huang, and W. Ou. Behavior sequence transformer for e-commerce recommendation in Alibaba. In *Proceedings of the 1st International Workshop on Deep Learning Practice for High-Dimensional Sparse Data*, DLP-KDD '19, New York, NY, USA, 2019. Association for Computing Machinery.

W. C. Cheung, D. Simchi-Levi, and H. Wang. Dynamic pricing and demand learning with limited price experimentation. *Operations Research*, 65(6):1722–1731, 2017.

W. Chu, L. Li, L. Reyzin, and R. Schapire. Contextual bandits with linear payoff functions. In *Proceedings of the Fourteenth International Conference on Artificial Intelligence and Statistics*, volume 15 of *Proceedings of Machine Learning Research*, pages 208–214. JMLR Workshop and Conference Proceedings, 2011.

A. A. Cook, G. Misirli, and Z. Fan. Anomaly detection for iot time-series data: A survey. *IEEE Internet of Things Journal*, 7(7):6481–6494, 2020.

P. Covington, J. Adams, and E. Sargin. Deep neural networks for YouTube recommendations. In *Proceedings of the 10th ACM Conference on Recommender Systems*, New York, NY, USA, 2016.

J. Deng, W. Dong, R. Socher, L.-J. Li, K. Li, and L. Fei-Fei. Imagenet: A large-scale hierarchical image database. In *2009 IEEE conference on computer vision and pattern recognition*, pages 248–255. Ieee, 2009.

J. Deng, J. Guo, N. Xue, and S. Zafeiriou. ArcFace: Additive angular margin loss for deep face recognition. In *2019 IEEE/CVF Conference on Computer Vision and Pattern Recognition (CVPR)*, pages 4685–4694, 2019.

A. Dosovitskiy, L. Beyer, A. Kolesnikov, D. Weissenborn, X. Zhai, T. Unterthiner, M. Dehghani, M. Minderer, G. Heigold, S. Gelly, et al. An image is worth 16x16 words: Transformers for image recognition at scale. *arXiv preprint arXiv:2010.11929*, 2020.

F. Y. Edgeworth. The mathematical theory of banking. *Journal of the Royal Statistical Society*, 51(1):113–127, 1888.

C. Eksombatchai, P. Jindal, J. Z. Liu, Y. Liu, R. Sharma, C. Sugnet, M. Ulrich, and J. Leskovec. Pixie: A system for recommending 3+ billion items to 200+ million users in real-time. In *Proceedings of the 2018 world wide web conference*, pages 1775–1784, 2018.

D. Ernst, P. Geurts, and L. Wehenkel. Tree-based batch mode reinforcement learning. *Journal of Machine Learning Research*, 6:503–556, 2005.

A. S. Eruguz, E. Sahin, Z. Jemai, and Y. Dallery. A comprehensive survey of guaranteed-service models for multi-echelon inventory optimization. *International Journal of Production Economics*, 172:110–125, 2016. ISSN 0925-5273.

K. Ferreira, B. Lee, and D. Simchi-levi. Analytics for an online retailer: Demand forecasting and price optimization. *Manufacturing and Service Operations Management*, 18, 11 2015.

K. J. Ferreira, D. Simchi-Levi, and H. Wang. Online network revenue management using Thompson sampling. *Operations research*, 66(6): 1586–1602, 2018.

R. Ganti, M. Sustik, Q. Tran, and B. Seaman. Thompson sampling for dynamic pricing. *arXiv preprint arXiv:1802.03050*, 2018.

L. A. Gatys, A. S. Ecker, and M. Bethge. Image style transfer using convolutional neural networks. In *Proceedings of the IEEE Conference on Computer Vision and Pattern Recognition (CVPR)*, June 2016.

J. Gauci, E. Conti, Y. Liang, K. Virochsiri, Y. He, Z. Kaden, V. Narayanan, X. Ye, Z. Chen, and S. Fujimoto. Horizon: Facebook's open source applied reinforcement learning platform, 2019.

K. Greff, R. K. Srivastava, J. Koutnik, B. R. Steunebrink, and J. Schmidhuber. LSTM: A search space odyssey. *IEEE Transactions on Neural Networks and Learning Systems*, 28(10):2222–2232, 2017. ISSN 2162-2388.

A. Grigoriev. Clothing dataset. https://github.com/alexeygrigorev/clothing-dataset, 2020.

A. Grover and J. Leskovec. node2vec: Scalable feature learning for networks. In *Proceedings of the 22nd ACM SIGKDD international conference on Knowledge discovery and data mining*, pages 855–864, 2016.

S. Gu, T. Lillicrap, I. Sutskever, and S. Levine. Continuous deep Q-learning with model-based acceleration, 2016.

N. Gugulothu, V. TV, P. Malhotra, L. Vig, P. Agarwal, and G. Shroff. Predicting remaining useful life using time series embeddings based on recurrent neural networks. In *Proceedings of the 2nd ML for PHM Workshop at SIGKDD 2017, Halifax, Canada*, 2017.

S. Guo and M. Fraser. *Propensity Score Analysis*. SAGE, 2015.

W. L. Hamilton, R. Ying, and J. Leskovec. Representation learning on graphs: Methods and applications. *IEEE Data Eng. Bull.*, 40(3):52–74, 2017.

F. M. Harper and J. A. Konstan. The MovieLens datasets: History and context. *ACM Trans. Interact. Intell. Syst.*, 5(4), dec 2015. ISSN 2160-6455.

F. W. Harris. How many parts to make at once. *Factory, the Magazine of Management*, 10(2):135–136, 1913.

X. He, T. Chen, M.-Y. Kan, and X. Chen. Trirank: Review-aware explainable recommendation by modeling aspects. In *Proceedings of the 24th ACM International on Conference on Information and Knowledge Management*, pages 1661–1670, 2015.

M. Hessel, J. Modayil, H. van Hasselt, T. Schaul, G. Ostrovski, W. Dabney, D. Horgan, B. Piot, M. Azar, and D. Silver. Rainbow: Combining improvements in deep reinforcement learning, 2017.

B. Hidasi, A. Karatzoglou, L. Baltrunas, and D. Tikk. Session-based recommendations with recurrent neural networks. *arXiv preprint arXiv:1511.06939*, 2015.

S. Hochreiter and J. Schmidhuber. Long short-term memory, 1995.

S. Hochreiter and J. Schmidhuber. Long short-term memory. *Neural Computation*, 9:1735–1780, 1997.

J. Hsu. A quantitative approach to product market fit. 2019.

S. Humair, J. Ruark, B. Tomlin, and S. Willems. Incorporating stochastic lead times into the guaranteed service model of safety stock optimization. *Interfaces*, 43:421–434, 09 2013.

V. Isaev. Identifying screws, a practical case study for visual search, 2019.

W.-C. Kang and J. J. McAuley. Self-attentive sequential recommendation. pages 197–206. IEEE Computer Society, 2018.

L. Kemmer, H. von Kleist, D. de Rochebouët, N. Tziortziotis, and J. Read. Reinforcement learning for supply chain optimization. In *European Workshop on Reinforcement Learning*, volume 14, 2018.

D. P. Kingma and M. Welling. Auto-encoding variational bayes. In *2nd International Conference on Learning Representations, ICLR 2014, Banff, AB, Canada, April 14-16, 2014, Conference Track Proceedings*, 2014.

Y. Koren, R. Bell, and C. Volinsky. Matrix factorization techniques for recommender systems. *Computer*, 42(8):30–37, 2009.

A. Lakhina, M. Crovella, and C. Diot. Diagnosing network-wide traffic anomalies. *ACM SIGCOMM computer communication review*, 34(4): 219–230, 2004.

Y. Lan, Y. Zhu, J. Guo, S. Niu, and X. Cheng. Position-aware ListMLE: A sequential learning process for ranking. UAI'14, pages 449–458, Arlington, Virginia, USA, 2014. AUAI Press.

T. Lang and M. Rettenmeier. Understanding consumer behavior with recurrent neural networks. In *Workshop on Machine Learning Methods for Recommender Systems*, 2017.

Y. LeCun et al. Generalization and network design strategies. *Connectionism in perspective*, 19:143–155, 1989.

L. Li, W. Chu, J. Langford, and R. E. Schapire. A contextual-bandit approach to personalized news article recommendation. *Proceedings of the 19th international conference on World wide web*, 2010.

X. Li, Q. Ding, and J.-Q. Sun. Remaining useful life estimation in prognostics using deep convolution neural networks. *Reliability Engineering and System Safety*, 172:1–11, 2018.

T. P. Lillicrap, J. J. Hunt, A. Pritzel, N. Heess, T. Erez, Y. Tassa, D. Silver, and D. Wierstra. Continuous control with deep reinforcement learning, 2015.

B. Lim, S. O. Arik, N. Loeff, and T. Pfister. Temporal fusion transformers for interpretable multi-horizon time series forecasting. *International Journal of Forecasting*, 37(4):1748–1764, 2021.

Q. Liu, Y. Zeng, R. Mokhosi, and H. Zhang. STAMP: Short-term attention/memory priority model for session-based recommendation. In *Proceedings of the 24th ACM SIGKDD International Conference on Knowledge Discovery and Data Mining*, KDD '18, pages 1831–1839, New York, NY, USA, 2018. Association for Computing Machinery.

T. Liu, A. W. Moore, A. G. Gray, and K. Yang. An investigation of practical approximate nearest neighbor algorithms. In *NIPS*, volume 12, 2004.

Z. Liu, Y. Lin, Y. Cao, H. Hu, Y. Wei, Z. Zhang, S. Lin, and B. Guo. Swin transformer: Hierarchical vision transformer using shifted windows. In *Proceedings of the IEEE/CVF International Conference on Computer Vision*, pages 10012–10022, 2021.

Z. Liu, H. Mao, C.-Y. Wu, C. Feichtenhofer, T. Darrell, and S. Xie. A convnet for the 2020s. *arXiv preprint arXiv:2201.03545*, 2022.

T. Mikolov, K. Chen, G. Corrado, and J. Dean. Efficient estimation of word representations in vector space, 2013a.

T. Mikolov, I. Sutskever, K. Chen, G. S. Corrado, and J. Dean. Distributed representations of words and phrases and their compositionality. *Advances in neural information processing systems*, 26, 2013b.

S. Mistry. Transformer-based real-time recommendation at Scribd. 2021.

V. Mnih, K. Kavukcuoglu, D. Silver, A. A. Rusu, J. Veness, M. G. Bellemare, A. Graves, M. Riedmiller, A. K. Fidjeland, G. Ostrovski, et al. Human-level control through deep reinforcement learning. *nature*, 518(7540):529–533, 2015.

A. Oroojlooyjadid, M. Nazari, L. Snyder, and M. Takáč. A deep Q-network for the beer game: A deep reinforcement learning algorithm to solve inventory optimization problems. *arXiv preprint arXiv:1708.05924*, 2017.

L. Page, S. Brin, R. Motwani, and T. Winograd. The PageRank citation ranking: Bringing order to the web. Technical Report 1999-66, Stanford InfoLab, November 1999.

N. Pakhomova. Detecting and correcting e-commerce catalog misattribution with image and text classification using Google TensorFlow, 2017.

J. Pereira and M. Silveira. Unsupervised anomaly detection in energy time series data using variational recurrent autoencoders with attention. In *2018 17th IEEE International Conference on Machine Learning and Applications (ICMLA)*, pages 1275–1282, 2018.

V.-T. Phi, L. Chen, and Y. Hirate. Distributed representation based recommender systems in e-commerce. In *DEIM Forum*, 2016.

M. Riedmiller. Neural fitted Q iteration–first experiences with a data efficient neural reinforcement learning method. In *European Conference on Machine Learning*, pages 317–328. Springer, 2005.

O. Rippel, P. Mertens, and D. Merhof. Modeling the distribution of normal data in pre-trained deep features for anomaly detection. In *2020 25th International Conference on Pattern Recognition (ICPR)*, pages 6726–6733, 2021.

O. Ronneberger, P. Fischer, and T. Brox. U-Net: Convolutional networks for biomedical image segmentation. *Medical Image Computing and Computer-Assisted Intervention - MICCAI 2015*, 2015.

P. R. Rosenbaum and D. B. Rubin. The central role of the propensity score in observational studies for causal effects. *Biometrika*, 70(1): 41–55, 04 1983.

A. Ruggiero and J. Haedt. Evaluating the impact of pricing actions to drive further actions. In *The ROI of Pricing: Measuring the Impact and Making the Business Case*, 2014.

D. E. Rumelhart, G. E. Hinton, and R. J. Williams. Learning representations by back-propagating errors. *Nature*, 323(6088):533–536, 1986.

J. Salch. Unconstraining passenger demand using the EM algorithm. In *Proceedings of the INFORMS Conference*, 1997.

A. Saxena, K. Goebel, D. Simon, and N. Eklund. Damage propagation modeling for aircraft engine run-to-failure simulation. In *2008 International Conference on Prognostics and Health Management*, pages 1–9, 2008.

F. Scarselli, M. Gori, A. C. Tsoi, M. Hagenbuchner, and G. Monfardini. The graph neural network model. *IEEE Transactions on Neural Networks*, 20(1):61–80, 2009.

F. Schroff, D. Kalenichenko, and J. Philbin. FaceNet: A unified embedding for face recognition and clustering. In *2015 IEEE Conference on Computer Vision and Pattern Recognition (CVPR)*, pages 815–823, 2015.

M. Schultz and T. Joachims. Learning a distance metric from relative comparisons. In S. Thrun, L. Saul, and B. Schölkopf, editors, *Advances in Neural Information Processing Systems*, volume 16. MIT Press, 2004.

I. Seleznev, I. Irkhin, and V. Kantor. Automated extraction of rider's attributes based on taxi mobile application activity logs. 2018.

O. B. Sezer, E. Dogdu, and A. M. Ozbayoglu. Context-aware computing, learning, and big data in internet of things: A survey. *IEEE Internet of Things Journal*, 5(1):1–27, 2018.

R. H. Shumway and D. S. Stoffer. *Time Series Analysis and Its Applications*. Springer International Publishing, 2017.

D. Silver, G. Lever, N. Heess, T. Degris, D. Wierstra, and M. Riedmiller. Deterministic policy gradient algorithms. In *Proceedings of the 31st International Conference on Machine Learning*, pages 387–395, 2014.

E. Silver, D. Pyke, and D. Thomas. *Inventory and Production Management in Supply Chains*. CRC Press, forth edition, 2016.

H. Simon and M. Fassnacht. *Price Management: Strategy, Analysis, Decision, Implementation*. Springer International Publishing, 2018.

K. Simonyan and A. Zisserman. Very deep convolutional networks for large-scale image recognition, 2014.

K. F. Simpson. In-process inventories. *Operations Research*, 6(6):863–873, 1958.

J. Sokolowsky. Starbucks turns to technology to brew up a more personal connection with its customers. 2019.

D. Song, N. Xia, W. Cheng, H. Chen, and D. Tao. Deep r-th root of rank supervised joint binary embedding for multivariate time series retrieval. In *Proceedings of the 24th ACM SIGKDD International Conference on Knowledge Discovery and Data Mining*, KDD '18, pages 1129–2238, New York, NY, USA, 2018. Association for Computing Machinery.

S. Stiebellehner, J. Wang, and S. Yuan. Learning continuous user representations through hybrid filtering with doc2vec. *arXiv preprint arXiv:1801.00215*, 2017.

F. Sun, J. Liu, J. Wu, C. Pei, X. Lin, W. Ou, and P. Jiang. BERT4Rec: Sequential recommendation with bidirectional encoder representations from transformer. CIKM '19, pages 1441–1450, New York, NY, USA, 2019. Association for Computing Machinery.

M. Syntetos, J. Boylan, and J. Croston. On the categorization of demand patterns. *Journal of the Operational Research Society*, 56, 05 2005.

K. Talluri and G. van Ryzin. *The Theory and Practice of Revenue Management*. Kluwer Academic Publishers, Norwell, MA, USA, 2004.

M. Tan and Q. Le. EfficientNet: Rethinking model scaling for convolutional neural networks. In *Proceedings of the 36th International Conference on Machine Learning*, volume 97 of *Proceedings of Machine Learning Research*, pages 6105–6114. PMLR, 09–15 Jun 2019.

L. Tang and H. Liu. Relational learning via latent social dimensions. In *Proceedings of the 15th ACM SIGKDD International Conference on Knowledge Discovery and Data Mining*, KDD '09, pages 817–826. Association for Computing Machinery, 2009.

J. Teo. Can a neural network perform PCA?, 2020.

G. Theocharous, P. S. Thomas, and M. Ghavamzadeh. Personalized ad recommendation systems for life-time value optimization with guarantees. IJCAI 15, pages 1806–1812. AAAI Press, 2015.

I. Tomek. Two modifications of CNN. *IEEE Transactions on Systems, Man, and Cybernetics*, 7(2):679–772, 1976.

R. van den Berg, T. N. Kipf, and M. Welling. Graph convolutional matrix completion. *CoRR*, 2017.

A. Vaswani, N. Shazeer, N. Parmar, J. Uszkoreit, L. Jones, A. N. Gomez, Ł. Kaiser, and I. Polosukhin. Attention is all you need. *Advances in neural information processing systems*, 30, 2017.

D. Verstraete, A. Ferrada, E. L. Droguett, V. Meruane, and M. Modarres. Deep learning enabled fault diagnosis using time-frequency image analysis of rolling element bearings. *Shock and Vibration*, 2017: 5067651, Oct 2017.

E. Wang. How we use AutoML, multi-task learning and multi-tower models for Pinterest ads. 2020.

H. Wang, Y. Wang, Z. Zhou, X. Ji, D. Gong, J. Zhou, Z. Li, and W. Liu. CosFace: Large margin cosine loss for deep face recognition. In *2018 IEEE/CVF Conference on Computer Vision and Pattern Recognition*, pages 5265–5274, 2018.

R. Wang, B. Fu, G. Fu, and M. Wang. Deep & cross network for ad click predictions. In *Proceedings of the ADKDD'17*, pages 1–7. 2017.

Y.-A. Wang and Y.-N. Chen. What do position embeddings learn? an empirical study of pre-trained language model positional encoding. *arXiv preprint arXiv:2010.04903*, 2020.

Z. Wang, A. C. Bovik, H. R. Sheikh, and E. P. Simoncelli. Image quality assessment: From error visibility to structural similarity. *Trans. Img. Proc.*, 13(4):600–612, 2004. ISSN 1057-7149.

K. Q. Weinberger, J. Blitzer, and L. Saul. Distance metric learning for large margin nearest neighbor classification. In Y. Weiss, B. Schölkopf, and J. Platt, editors, *Advances in Neural Information Processing Systems*, volume 18. MIT Press, 2006.

R. J. Williams. Simple statistical gradient-following algorithms for connectionist reinforcement learning. In *Machine Learning*, pages 229–256, 1992.

R. H. Wilson. *A scientific routine for stock control*. Harvard Business Review, 1934.

C.-Y. Wu, A. Ahmed, A. Beutel, A. J. Smola, and H. Jing. Recurrent recommender networks. In *Proceedings of the Tenth ACM International Conference on Web Search and Data Mining*, WSDM '17, pages 495–503, New York, NY, USA, 2017. Association for Computing Machinery.

N. Wu, B. Green, X. Ben, and S. O'Banion. Deep transformer models for time series forecasting: The influenza prevalence case. 2020.

S. Wu, Y. Tang, Y. Zhu, L. Wang, X. Xie, and T. Tan. Session-based recommendation with graph neural networks. *Proceedings of the AAAI Conference on Artificial Intelligence*, 33(01):346–353, 2019.

H. Xiao, K. Rasul, and R. Vollgraf. Fashion-MNIST: a novel image dataset for benchmarking machine learning algorithms, 2017.

C. Yang, X. Shi, L. Jie, and J. Han. I know you'll be back: Interpretable new user clustering and churn prediction on a mobile social application. pages 914–922, 2018.

W. Yang, P. Luo, and L. Lin. Clothing co-parsing by joint image segmentation and labeling. In *2014 IEEE Conference on Computer Vision and Pattern Recognition (CVPR)*. IEEE, 2013.

Z. Yang, M. Ding, C. Zhou, H. Yang, J. Zhou, and J. Tang. *Understanding Negative Sampling in Graph Representation Learning*, pages 1666–1676. Association for Computing Machinery, New York, NY, USA, 2020.

R. Ying, R. He, K. Chen, P. Eksombatchai, W. L. Hamilton, and J. Leskovec. Graph convolutional neural networks for web-scale recommender systems. In *Proceedings of the 24th ACM SIGKDD International Conference on Knowledge Discovery and Data Mining*, pages 974–983, 2018.

J. Yosinski, J. Clune, Y. Bengio, and H. Lipson. How transferable are features in deep neural networks? *Advances in neural information processing systems*, 27, 2014.

C. Zhang, D. Song, Y. Chen, X. Feng, C. Lumezanu, W. Cheng, J. Ni, B. Zong, H. Chen, and N. V. Chawla. A deep neural network for unsupervised anomaly detection and diagnosis in multivariate time series data. In *The Thirty-Third AAAI Conference on Artificial Intelligence, AAAI 2019*, pages 1409–1416. AAAI Press, 2019.

K. Zolna and B. Romanski. User2vec: user modeling using LSTM networks. 2016.

CPSIA information can be obtained
at www.ICGtesting.com
Printed in the USA
BVHW051414050423
661662BV00002B/4